Introduction to Wood Building Technology

A guide to building and inspecting wood construcion.

Canadian
Wood
Council

Conseil
canadien
du bois

ISBN 0-921628-46-3

1.5M97-09

Illustrations:
RJS ID Inc., Ottawa, ON

Accurate Design & Communication Inc.,
Nepean, ON

Book design and production:
Eton Systems, Ottawa, ON

Printing:
Tri-Graphic Printing Ltd., Ottawa, ON

40.—
MAR 99

Preface

The Canadian Wood Council (CWC) is the national federation of forest products associations responsible for the development and dissemination of technical information about the use of wood products in construction.

This publication, *Introduction to Wood Building Technology,* is a summary in revised format of information found in the Datafiles published by CWC. It complements the following major CWC publications and design tools which have been developed expressly for engineers, architects, building code officials, builders, developers, and for students and professors:

• *Wood Design Manual 1995*

• *WoodWorks® Design Software*

• *Wood Highway Bridges*

• *Permanent Wood Foundations*

• *Introduction to Design in Wood*

• *Wood Reference Handbook*

• *Fire Safety Design in Buildings*

The information in *Wood Building Technology* is based on the latest information available from the *National Building Code of Canada (1995)* and from CSA Standard O86.1 (1994). Every effort has been made to ensure the accuracy of the information in this book. However, it remains the responsibility of the designer to apply the information according to sound technical principles.

CWC acknowledges the contribution of the following firms in the development of the book:

• Quaile Engineering Limited

• Randal Brown and Associates Ltd.
  Chapter 9

Kelly R. McCloskey
President

July, 1997

Environmental Benefits of Building with Wood

In a recent survey of building specifiers, the majority perceived wood to be the most environmentally friendly building material. This is due mainly to the renewability of wood, the low energy consumption required for production and the low levels of pollutant emission during manufacture compared to other major building materials.

In recent years, environmental considerations have acquired more importance in the specification of materials. Technical and economic aspects of building materials are still the primary considerations for specifiers, but increasingly, they are considering the environmental effects when selecting appropriate building materials for their designs. Architects, engineers and designers require accurate information to assess the true environmental consequences of the materials they specify.

The environmental impacts of various building materials have been examined by a Canadian Research Alliance using the internationally accepted method called life-cycle analysis (LCA). The Alliance consists of researchers from the wood, steel and concrete industries as well as university groups and consultants.

LCA evaluates the direct and indirect environmental effects associated with a product, process or activity. It quantifies energy and material usage and environmental releases at each stage of a products life-cycle including resource extraction, manufacturing, construction, service and post-use disposal. One product of this five-year life-cycle project is a computer model, Athena™, that facilitates comparative evaluation of the environmental effect of building assemblies.

In addition to those familiar qualities that have made wood such a dominant material in North America, the LCA methodology confirms wood products to be a wise choice for designers from an environmental standpoint. The reasons for this are explained below.

Resource Extraction

The environmental effects of resource extraction are the most difficult to quantify because of the variability of extraction methods and the variability in the ecology of different sites.

The study made the following observations. There are three dimensions to the extraction process: extensiveness, intensiveness, and duration. All extraction creates significant ecological impacts. Mining extractions are more intensive and endure longer than forest extractions. Forest extractions are more extensive in terms of land area affected.

Of all the phases of the life-cycle, extraction is the most subjective. The ecological impacts of forest cutting can differ by several orders of magnitude from best practice to worst practice. Similarly, the differences between the worst practices and the best practices of each extractive industry may well be greater than the differences between those industries. This does not offer a definitive conclusion, but highlights the importance of Canada's leadership in practising sustainable forestry.

Manufacturing

During the manufacturing stage raw resources are converted into usable products. The manufacturing stage is the most easily quantifiable stage as all the processes are under human control, and the stage where the environmental advantage of using wood is most apparent.

Wood requires much less energy to manufacture and causes much less air and water pollution than steel or concrete. The Athena™ model was used to compare the environmental effects of a 4 620m^2, three storey office building with wood, steel or concrete structure. The results showed the steel design used twice the energy, produced 1.5 times more carbon dioxide, produced 120 times more water pollution than the wood structure. The concrete structure used 1.5 times the energy, produced 1.8 times more carbon dioxide and generated 1.9 times more water pollution than the wood structure.

The wood structure, by requiring much less energy to manufacture, reduces the use of fossil fuels. Fossil fuels are non-renewable and their use is linked to global warming, thinning of the ozone layer, and acid rain.

Construction

The construction stage includes on-site construction as well as transportation of the materials from local plants or suppliers. The major impacts at the construction stage are caused by the energy used for transportation and construction equipment and the solid waste generated during construction. Comparison of building materials in this life-cycle phase showed no major differences in energy use, or solid waste for the wood and steel buildings. The concrete building used twice as much energy and generated twice the waste of either the wood or steel options. The wood option used many types of engineered wood products which eliminated much of the job site waste.

Service

The service phase of the life-cycle is the period when the material performs its function as part of the structure.

Framing materials do not present environmental impacts when they are in service since they consume neither energy nor resources. However, the choice of building materials can significantly affect the energy requirements for heating and cooling. When compared with steel, wood is a much better thermal insulator. Thus, wood-frame structures consume far less energy for heating and cooling than steel-frame structures for the same quantity of insulation.

Post-Use Disposal

The last stage of the life-cycle, post-use disposal, is difficult to assess because it takes place far in the future – at the end of the useful life of the product.

Steel is better established as a recyclable material with facilities in place. The wood recycling industry in Canada is still in its infancy but is expanding rapidly. Several large centres in Canada now have wood recycling facilities that use wood scrap to produce products such as horticultural mulch or wood chips for hardboard. Recycling is a return to the manufacturing stage, and as wood recycling increases, the environmental advantage of wood during this stage will be apparent. Where wood recycling facilities are not available, wood products are biodegradable and return to the earth and ultimately are renewed through new growth.

Conclusion

In spite of scientific analyses that demonstrate many environmental advantages for wood building materials, the public still has concerns about wood. This is due in part to the highly visible effects of wood resource extraction. To address these concerns the Canadian Forest Industry, in addition to adopting enhanced forest management techniques, is actively supporting the development of Sustainable Forestry Certification Standards by the Canadian Standards Association (CSA). Certification assures consumers that the products they buy are made from wood that comes from an environmentally sound and sustainable forestry operation.

The preceding information forms the basis for responsible choices by specifiers – choices which are not always easy or straightforward. Some products are simply better suited for particular applications. Specifying a product that comes from a renewable resource, that is energy conserving in manufacture and use, and that can be easily recycled or reused, minimizes the environmental impact and makes sustainable development an achievable goal. Wood is an extraordinary material that offers these environmental advantages.

Table of Contents

Introduction

1.1 General Information

The *Wood Building Technology* book is a guide to the construction of wood buildings. It provides practical information for both the designer, the one responsible for the quality and completeness of the design, and the site inspector, the person responsible for ensuring the intent of the design is achieved in the finished product. The book is based on the construction requirements given in the *1995 National Building Code of Canada (NBCC)* and the Canadian Standards Association (CSA) Standard *CSA O86.1(1994), Engineering Design in Wood (Limit states design).*

The book is intended to assist students and design professionals to plan and construct a range of types of buildings, both residential and commercial, which meet their clients needs of economy, durability, adherence to fire and other code requirements, and, where specifically requested, to provide the unique appearance qualities unique to wood.

Wood is a simple material in that most people have used it to construct some type of feature to enhance their living or working environment. However, being a naturally occurring material, it is a somewhat complex material from an engineering standpoint.

The purpose of this book is to combine those aspects of wood which make it easy to use with an understanding of those properties which make it complex, to optimize the use of this marvelous building material. Careful use of our wood resources is particularly important given the demand for forest resources, and the mutual goal of manufacturers, designers, builders and clients to be concerned with the stewardship of our forest lands.

The book covers a range of topics, from structure to thermal insulation, acoustics, and fire protection. Some chapter subjects, such as post and beam construction, are of course unique to wood construction while others, such as thermal insulation, although pertinent to wood construction, will provide the reader understanding of a subject which can be used to advantage in buildings where wood is not the main structural material.

Like all building materials, wood is not always used correctly. Therefore information is provided on common deficiencies and remedial measures which can be taken to eliminate a serviceability problem for both new and existing construction.

Chapter 2 describes the typical wood structural products used in the construction of wood buildings and it includes a description of each product, its availability and how to verify its quality. It describes the correct storage and handling and general care of wood products and outlines some common defects that can occur when these materials are not cared for adequately.

Chapter 3 describes wood-frame construction techniques as they apply to both Parts 4 and 9 of the *National Building Code of Canada (NBCC).* Common problems that occur in wood-frame buildings are also described in this chapter.

Chapter 4 describes post and beam construction.

Chapter 5 describes the *NBCC* requirements for stairs and guards and gives some recommended connection and construction details.

Chapter 6 describes the *NBCC* requirements for thermal insulation including typical RSI values for some common wood assemblies.

Chapter 7 provides information on building envelopes with extensive coverage of vapour barriers, air barriers, the rain screen principle and wood claddings.

Chapter 8 discusses the sound control requirements for buildings and gives sound ratings for typical wood assemblies.

Chapter 9 gives information on fire protection details specific to wood buildings including fire stopping and sprinkler protection.

Chapter 10 provides information about windows and doors from the standpoint of energy conservation, sealing and moisture control.

Chapter 11 provides suggestions for the inspection of new construction with an emphasis on catching deficiencies before they become costly to repair, cross-referenced to other parts of the book.

Chapter 12 describes the inspection, evaluation and repair of wood buildings which have been in service for long periods of time.

At the end of the book, an information sources section gives the names of the many associations and agencies that can provide technical assistance on a range of subjects ranging from product quality and availability to structural design issues.

References

1. *Canadian Wood-Frame House Construction,* Canada Mortgage and Housing Corporation, Ottawa, ON, 1997

2. *Fire Safety Design in Buildings,* Canadian Wood Council, Ottawa, ON, 1996

3. *Wood Design Manual,* Canadian Wood Council, Ottawa, ON, 1995

4. *Wood Reference Handbook,* Canadian Wood Council, Ottawa, ON, 1995

1.2   **Contemporary Wood Buildings**

Because wood is strong, economical, available, and easy to work, it is the structural material of choice for residential construction in North America. Many countries are reviewing and adapting North American residential construction methods to meet local housing needs.

But the suitability of wood as a structural building material does not end with residential construction. Wood is also being used successfully for larger commercial buildings.

The photograph above shows a stunning example of wood used as both a structural and finishing element in a residential building. The following pages include photographs depicting a range of budgets and building types, both residential and commercial.

Single-Family Residential

Multi-unit Residential

Medical

Mercantile

Offices

Schools

Religious

Industrial

Recreational

Wood Building Products

2

Canadian dimension lumber is a strong, light-weight, and versatile material for both residential and commercial building construction.

Visually graded lumber, in this case No.2 and Better Structural Joists and Planks, is assessed for a number of characteristics such as knot size and location.

Dimension lumber is used for frame construction and is also further manufactured into engineered products such as light frame trusses.

Fingerjoined studs and rafters are visually graded and mechanically tested and are assigned the same engineering values as corresponding visually graded lumber.

Machine Stress Rated (MSR) lumber is assigned engineering values on the basis of mechanical evaluation.

Sawn timber is used in post and beam construction.

Glulam is made by laminating carefully selected lam-stock pieces using exterior grade glues.

Laminated make-up of glulam allows large members and curved shapes.

Metal plate connected light frame trusses can be made in many shapes.

Heavy trusses can be made from sawn timber, PSL, or, in this case, glulam.

Parallel strand lumber (PSL) is a manufactured-wood material with high engineering values.

PSL columns and glulam beams form the structure of this office building.

Laminated veneer lumber (LVL) is made into long members by laminating wood veneers.

LVL is often used for headers, lintels, and beams.

Wood I-joists
are made from
several types of
lumber and
panel products.

Wood I-joists,
most often used
for floor assem-
blies, are
framed into wall
assemblies for
a high wind load
application.

The penetration
and retention of
preservatives in
pressure
treated lumber
can be
increased by
incising.

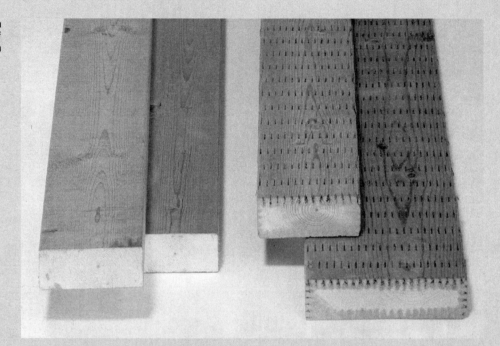

Preservative
treated wood is
used where
ground contact
or wet service
conditions exist.

Plywood *(top)* and OSB *(bottom)* are the common panel sheathing products used for residential and commercial construction.

Plank decking is most often used in combination with beams and purlins.

Dry lumber products are wrapped for shipping and should be kept as dry as possible during storage and installation.

Nylon slings or ropes should be used for handling wood products.

Factory applied wrap should be left in place as long as possible during storage and installation as in the case of these glulam frames.

2.1   General Information

Wood is a natural building material which has amazing versatility. Wood fibre can be used in its natural form as in the case of lumber, or it can be broken down and then be reconstituted into large structural members as in the case of glulam or parallel strand lumber (PSL). In either case, wood products have a high strength to weight ratio, and few would argue that any other building materials compare to wood in terms of its beauty of texture and pattern.

Because wood occurs naturally, there is variability in wood fibre properties dependent upon factors such as rate of growth, growing conditions, species, and moisture content. A basic understanding of the unique properties of wood is necessary so that wood products can be used by the designer to maximum potential.

There are many wood products used for building construction for both main structural members such as beams, joists, and columns, and for secondary structural members such as sheathing and decking.

The products for main structural members range from the standard sawn wood products such as dimension lumber, to enhanced sawn wood products such as machine stress-rated (MSR) lumber, to reconstituted wood products such as parallel strand lumber (PSL). For secondary structural elements, plank decking, board sheathing, plywood and oriented strand board (OSB) panels are available.

Whether a wood product is solid lumber or manufactured from a gluing process, an understanding of the mechanism of moisture movement in wood fibre is imperative to the proper specification and installation of wood products.

This chapter provides basic information about moisture and about the structural wood building products available:

2.2 Basic Properties

2.3 Main Structural Members

2.4 Sheathing and Decking

2.5 Storage and Handling

2.6 Preservative Treatment

2

Wood Building Products

2.2   **Basic Properties**

Introduction

Like all building materials, wood has unique properties. In some cases these properties are favourable, and in other cases they are not. Steel, for example, is subject to oxidation and concrete to deterioration from freeze-thaw cycles. Despite these properties, steel and concrete are structural materials of importance. By understanding the nature of materials, designers are able to maximize the positive attributes of and minimize the negative properties. This applies to wood as well.

Hygroscopicity (the ability to absorb moisture) is the major property of wood which requires understanding so that its negative effect on the long term performance of wood products can be made inconsequential.

During the life of a tree, moisture moves up the tree through the outer living portion of the trunk transporting nutrients. When a tree is transformed into a building material, the transportation network in the structure of the wood remains, and therefore moisture continues to be lost or gained depending on the environmental conditions to which the wood is subjected.

Moisture affects wood products in two ways. First, change in moisture content causes dimensional change (shrinkage and swelling). Secondly, when combined with other necessary conditions, moisture leads to deterioration of wood by decay.

Dimensional Change

Wood shrinks when it dries, and swells when it becomes wet. The extent to which dimensional changes occur depends on the species and the orientation of the wood fibres.

When wood dries from its green condition, little or no shrinkage occurs until the moisture content falls below the fibre saturation level. At this level, all free moisture has been released from the cell cavities, leaving only the cell walls saturated. The moisture content at which this condition is reached varies, but averages 30% (based on the ratio of the weight of water to the oven-dried weight of wood) for Canadian softwoods. As the cell walls continue to release moisture, the wood shrinks almost in direct proportion to its moisture loss (Figure 2.1).

The moisture level of the wood will eventually reach equilibrium with that of the surrounding air, and will continue to adjust

2

Wood Building Products

Figure 2.1
Anisotropic shrinkage of wood

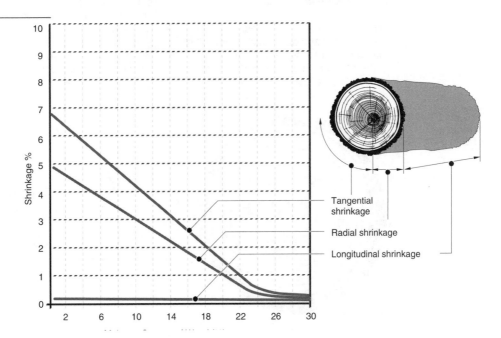

Tangential shrinkage

Radial shrinkage

Longitudinal shrinkage

to changing conditions by gaining or losing moisture.

Lumber which has been air dried or kiln dried to lumber grading standards will have a moisture content of 19% or less. Using dried lumber reduces the amount of shrinkage that will occur in drying to the equilibrium moisture content.

Due to the cellular structure of wood, it does not shrink or expand equally in each direction. Generally, wood shrinks very little along the grain (longitudinally), while the shrinkage across the grain can be quite large. In addition, shrinkage along the growth rings (tangentially) is generally larger than the shrinkage across the growth rings (radially) (Figure 2.2).

The difference in shrinkage between the radial and tangential directions can cause lumber to warp. Badly warped pieces of lumber are unsuitable for use as framing members.

Warping may occur as lumber dries during storage. The use of S-Dry lumber will reduce warpage since it has been surfaced after drying to a moisture content of 19% or less. Warping can also be reduced by restraining the wood while drying takes place.

Checking occurs when lumber is rapidly dried. The surface dries quickly, while the core remains at a higher moisture content for some time. As a result the surface attempts to shrink, but is restrained by the core.

This restraint causes tensile stresses at the surface, which if large enough, can pull the fibres apart thereby creating a check.

Splits are through checks that generally occur at the end of wood members. When a wood member dries, moisture is lost very rapidly from the end of the member. At mid-length, however, the wood is still at a higher moisture content. This difference in moisture content creates tensile stresses at the end of the member. When the stresses exceed the strength of the wood, a split is formed.

Sawn timbers are susceptible to checking and splitting since they are dressed green. Furthermore, due to their large size, the core dries slowly and the tensile stresses at the surface and the ends can be large.

The cutting and reorientation of wood fibre for the manufacture of glued wood products such as plywood obviously disrupt the routes for moisture movement, but the ability to gain and lose moisture remains.

The possibility and severity of splitting and checking can be reduced by prohibiting wood from drying rapidly. This may be done by keeping wood out of direct sunlight and away from any artificial heat sources. In addition, the ends may be coated with an end sealer that retards moisture loss.

The actions required to minimize the possibility of dimension change and deterioration are as follows:

Figure 2.2
Shrinkage effects

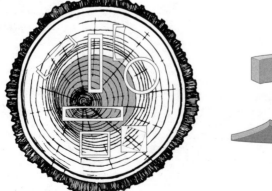

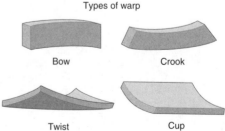

Types of warp

Bow   Crook

Twist   Cup

- detail to provide overhang protection for exposed wood, protect end grain from direct exposure to water, or provide flashing or pressure treatment protection

- specify wood products which are as close as possible in moisture content to the expected equilibrium moisture content of the end use

- through site inspection, ensure that the investment made in purchasing dry wood products is protected by proper storage and handling, and by enclosure of the building as quickly as possible

- where it is necessary to account for shrinkage (as in the case of a multi-storey building to be faced with brick veneer) follow the procedures in the following sections

Deterioration
Wood is an organic material and is subject to deterioration by decay. Decay is a naturally occurring process in the forest whereby fallen wood is broken down into organic matter which in turn nourishes new growth. It is, of course, a process which must be avoided when wood is used as a building material.

For decay to proceed, four conditions must all exist. Elimination of any one arrests decay and the decay can not become active until all four conditions are once again satisfied. The conditions are as follows:

- Fungi must have oxygen to flourish. For buildings, the exclusion of oxygen is not controllable, and therefore the control of decay comes from controlling the other conditions.

- Temperatures in the 20-30°C (68-87°F) are optimum for fungi. At low temperature, fungi activity slows or stops. This means that fungi activity for exposed applications reduces in winter. However, summer temperatures offer ample opportunity for fungi activity, as do the normal temperatures for indoor applications. For this reason, temperature control, like oxygen control, is not usually feasible.

- Enough moisture must be present for fungi to be active. Fungi cannot infest or be active when the moisture content in wood is below 20%. Therefore construction details should keep wood products from direct exposure to water where intermittent drying is not possible.

- The wood food supply must be available. The food supply can be made unavailable by pressure treating with chemicals which are not conducive to fungi, or using species such as cedar which have some natural resistance to decay.

Moisture Content Determination
The moisture content of lumber may be determined by laboratory methods by oven drying samples, or by measuring with electrical meters.

With the oven drying method, the wood samples to be assessed for moisture content are weighed and then dried in an oven until all moisture has been removed. After drying, the samples are weighed again, and the moisture content (MC) is calculated as follows:

$$MC\% = \frac{\text{initial weight} - \text{oven dry weight}}{\text{oven dry weight}} \times 100$$

(The procedures and details of this method are outlined in American Society for Testing Materials [ASTM] Standard D4442).

In many instances, the oven dry method is impractical due to the time required to complete the testing. For this reason, several types of electrical meters have been developed. Although less precise than the oven drying method, moisture meters provide instantaneous readings, are easy to use and are not destructive. This makes them well suited to industrial and field applications.

Several different types of meters are available which measure the electrical resistance, dielectric or radio frequency power loss properties of wood. Those which measure the relationship between moisture

content and electrical resistance (resistance type) are most common. They
consist of a meter and an electrode with
pins. Two pin electrodes are usually used,
but four or eight pins are available for
special applications such as measuring the
moisture content of thin veneer. Pins can
be purchased in a variety of lengths and
they can be insulated or uninsulated.

Uninsulated pins record the highest moisture content along the depth of penetration
of the electrodes, whereas insulated pins
measure the moisture content present in
the wood at the tip (uninsulated) of the
electrodes.

ASTM D4444 recommends that, for dimension lumber and decking, the pins be
driven into the board to a depth equal to
1/5 to 1/4 of the thickness. Since the resistivity of wood differs with the grain orientation, the pins must be driven parallel to the
grain. The reading area must be at least
500mm (20") from the board ends, near
mid-width, and be free of defects such as
knots, splits, resin pockets and decay.

The electrical resistance of wood varies
with both temperature and species.
Resistivity decreases directly with increasing temperature, and is affected by the
presence of electrolytes and moisture
gradients over the depths penetrated by
the electrodes. If temperature or species
differ from the factory calibration of the
instrument, appropriate correction factors
must be applied to the meter reading.

Most of the newer meters have the species
correction applied automatically when the
appropriate species group setting is
chosen on the meter, while some meters
can automatically correct for both species
and temperature. Where correction factors
are required, the tables should be supplied
by the manufacturer with each moisture
meter. It is important to note that resistance type meters are only reliable
between 6% and 30% moisture content.

Effects of Wood Shrinkage in Buildings

Wood shrinks (or swells) tangentially and
radially, and longitudinally. Tangential
shrinkage (concentric to the growth rings)
is approximately twice the radial shrinkage
(perpendicular to the growth rings).
Shrinkage values for individual specimens
of the same species can vary considerably,
and therefore values based on averages
may be somewhat misleading.

For example, the maximum tangential
shrinkage of spruce from the fibre saturation level (30%) to the oven-dried state
(0%) is 7 to 8%, while the radial shrinkage
is about 4%. The longitudinal shrinkage for
most species over this moisture range is
only 0.1 to 0.2%.

This small value is usually ignored in
design, sometimes with unfortunate consequences. Greater longitudinal shrinkage
can occur if the wood is badly cross-
grained or contains juvenile (coming from
trees that grew rapidly during their early
years) or compression wood (wood
subjected to unusual compression stresses
during its growth).

Plywood has shrinkage characteristics
similar to lumber in the longitudinal direction. This stability is due to the much higher
modulus of elasticity of wood with the grain
than across the grain. Alternating the direction of the grain in adjacent plies, therefore,
stabilizes the plywood in both directions.

Oriented strandboard (OSB) benefits from
a similar stabilizing effect because the individual wafers are arranged in plies of grain
orientation.

The heartwood of freshly sawn lumber
contains 30 to 100% moisture, depending
on the species. The moisture content of the
sapwood is usually much higher, from 100
to 200%. When exposed to air, lumber
dries fairly rapidly in warm weather to the
fibre saturation level. It then dries at a
decreasing rate until it is in equilibrium with
the surrounding air. The rate of drying
slows as the air temperature drops.

Equilibrium moisture contents for wood stored under cover during the summer in most inland areas of Canada vary from 11 to 12% , while in the coastal areas they range from 14 to 16%. At these levels, about half to two-thirds of the total potential shrinkage will have occurred.

The closer the moisture content of wood is to the equilibrium moisture content for a given application, the more shrinkage related problems can be avoided.

For this reason, the *National Building Code of Canada (NBCC)* and most provincial building codes specify that the moisture content of framing lumber must not exceed 19% at the time of installation so that a good portion of the potential dimensional change will have already taken place.

Wood in heated buildings can be subjected to a wide range of humidity levels over an annual cycle. Winter humidity levels may reach as low as 20 to 30% in houses, and may be even lower in other occupancies such as offices that generate little or no moisture. During the summer, humidity levels may reach 60 to 70% or more. These differences cause the equilibrium moisture content of wood to vary from season to season.

Effect of Shrinkage on Fasteners

Any shrinkage of the wood along the embedded length of metal fasteners causes their heads to rise above the wood surface while forcing the tips slightly deeper into the wood. The initial and final moisture contents of the wood, and the depth of fastener penetration, are the principal factors in determining the amount of outward moment, but subsequent seasonal cycles of moisture content changes can add to the initial movement.

Nails with annular grooves are generally affected less by shrinkage than plain shank nails because they require less penetration to achieve the same withdrawal resistance. Screw fasteners, which require even less penetration, are affected least.

Wood shrinkage can cause nail popping in drywall finishes. As the fasteners are eased out of the wood, a space is created between the drywall and its supports. Subsequent pressure on the drywall causes the fastener heads to push through the drywall.

Shrinkage produces similar effects when fasteners in the subflooring or underlayment are covered by thin materials such as vinyl. The raised fastener heads may show on the finished floor as a pattern of tiny bumps. This problem can be reduced by recessing the fastener heads into the wood before the flooring is laid.

Other Shrinkage Effects

Since the greater shrinkage occurs across the grain, wood-strip flooring is particularly vulnerable to the effects of shrinkage and swelling. Thus, when flooring is installed, its moisture content should be as close as possible to the level it will attain in service.

Flooring used below ground level may be subjected to humidity that will raise its equilibrium moisture level significantly above its kiln-dried level. To avoid buckling, the flooring should be stored in a location that will allow it to reach the higher moisture level before it is laid. A clearance of 10 to 12mm (3/8" to 1/2") around the floor perimeter should be provided to allow for swelling.

Although conventional wood framing is reasonably able to tolerate the effects of shrinkage, using unseasoned lumber can invite problems, particularly if construction proceeds rapidly and the lumber is enclosed before much of the potential shrinkage has occurred. This prevents corrective action being taken, such as using shims to compensate for the shrinkage effects. Differential shrinkage commonly occurs around windows and doors where the lintels shrink away from the supporting jack studs. It may also occur where metal joist hangers support unseasoned wood joists around floor openings.

The manufacturing process for plywood and OSB results in a final moisture content of about 4%, which is considerably below its moisture content in use. Accordingly, before it is installed, it should be allowed to reach a moisture content level close to that expected

2

Wood Building Products

in service. If OSB or plywood is used in locations subject to high moisture levels, such as wall and roof sheathing, a gap should be left between the sheets to reduce the possibility of buckling due to expansion.

Truss Uplift

An occasional effect of wood shrinkage is the upward bowing of wood trusses in winter. This could cause cracks between the partitions and the ceiling of up to 20mm (3/4") in severe cases. Truss uplift is primarily caused by the differential longitudinal movement of the upper and lower chord members.

Air in a well-ventilated attic space contains approximately the same amount of moisture as the outside air. In winter the relative humidity of the outside air is fairly high; consequently, the top chords and web members will absorb moisture until equilibrium is reached with the surrounding air. The higher moisture content causes the top chords to lengthen.

The lower chords, however, experience a different phenomenon. Since in modern houses the lower chords are often covered with up to 300mm (12") of insulation, their average temperature in winter is closer to the indoor temperature. This causes the air space in the insulation adjacent to the wood to have a lower relative humidity than the air adjacent to the top chords. As a result, the air spaces adjacent to the bottom chords absorb moisture from the wood until an equilibrium moisture level is reached.

The moisture content in the lower chords may decrease to less than 10% during the coldest winter months, and cause the chords to shorten. As the lower chords shrink and the top chords expand, the peaks of the trusses are forced upward. This forces web members attached near the peaks to pull the lower chords upward, which, in turn, causes cracks between the ceiling and the partitions. If the chord members contain compression or juvenile wood, the amount of movement can be significantly increased.

Using unseasoned lumber may be a significant factor in truss uplift problems, particularly when the ceiling is installed before the moisture level of the trusses has been reduced to a reasonable level. Tests on roof trusses containing unseasoned juvenile wood have demonstrated that either upward or downward movement can occur as the wood dries, depending on whether the juvenile wood is located in the upper or lower chords.

A number of factors can influence the degree of uplift:

• Roof slope: The lower the slope, the greater the amount of arching for the same difference in moisture content between the upper and lower chords.

• Amount of insulation: The more insulation there is, the greater the difference in moisture content between the upper and lower chords will be. Differential shrinkage resulting from the lower moisture content of the partition framing in winter, compared with the exterior wall framing, can also contribute to the separation of the ceiling membrane from the partition.

Thermal contraction, in the winter months, of the top chord relative to the bottom chord, is insufficient to counteract arching caused by moisture changes. The weight of the roof assembly and the snow load, in some cases, only partially counteract truss uplift.

Even if seasoned lumber is used, roof truss uplift may not be avoidable without changing the present system of construction so that the top and bottom chords are exposed to the same environmental conditions. Because of the costs and adjustments this would entail, it is more practical to allow the wood truss to bow upwards without causing damage to the interior finish.

This can be achieved by eliminating ceiling fasteners within 300mm (12") of the partitions, and by coupling the ceiling to the partitions at their juncture so that the trusses can move upward without breaking the joint between the partition and ceiling. The ceiling membrane can be coupled to the partition by special clips or corner beads nailed to the tops of the partitions so that the ceiling membrane is forced to flex, rather than tear away from the partition, as the truss moves upward.

If floating corners have not been provided, damage at the partition can be masked by installing cove mouldings fastened to the ceiling supports only. This permits the moulding to slide up and down the wall with the seasonal movement of the trusses. It may be necessary to seal cracks with tape before installing the moulding or the suspended ceiling, to prevent air leakage into the attic if the vapour barrier has been damaged by the arching effect.

Shrinkage in Multistorey Wood-frame Buildings

Wood frame buildings up to four storeys in height are permitted in Canada. For high wood buildings, shrinkage of the wood frame may be an important consideration in the design of the structures, particularly if brick veneer is used.

In such cases, it is important to evaluate the shrinkage of a building's wood frame in four major areas:

- where nonuniform shrinkage may occur

- where metal connections are used to support large solid sawn timber or glued-laminated timber

- where shrinkage could cause distress in the finish material

- where shrinkage could cause distress in plumbing, electrical and mechanical systems

Calculating Wood Shrinkage

The shrinkage of a wood member can be estimated using the equation:

$S = D \times M \times c$

where:

S   is shrinkage (mm)

D   is actual dressed dimension (mm) (thickness or width)

M   is percent of moisture change

c   is shrinkage coefficient

The total shrinkage of the wood frame in a high frame building can be calculated by summing the shrinkage of the wood members making up the wall, plates, and joists.

Shrinkage coefficients for both radial (across the growth rings) and tangential (parallel to the growth rings) directions have been determined for individual species. Because lumber is often sold as a mixture of species and grain orientations, an approximation is recommended whereby a shrinkage coefficient of 0.002 per 1% change in moisture content for multistorey wood frame shrinkage calculations can be assumed.

To determine the percent moisture change, assumptions must be made regarding the initial and final moisture contents of the lumber. The initial moisture content depends largely on what type of lumber is specified. For the purpose of the shrinkage calculation, an initial moisture content of 19% is used based on the *NBCC* requirement for lumber to be 19% moisture content or less at the time of installation. The final in-service moisture content of protected framing members is usually between 8 and 12% in most structures.

The main shrinkage, because of grain orientation, occurs in the plates and header joists (longitudinal shrinkage in the wall studs which is negligible). For a four-storey wall using S-Dry lumber and consisting of three 38 x 235mm (2" x 10" nom.) header joists and twelve 38 x 89mm (2" x 4" nom.) plates (three per floor), and a predicted final moisture content of 10%, shrinkage (in metric units) is calculated as follows:

$$S = D \times M \times c$$
$$= (\,[3 \times 235] + [12 \times 38]\,) \times (19 - 10) \times 0.002$$
$$= 20.9mm$$

Shrinkage of the wall studs is generally neglected because of its negligible effect (using a c value of 0.00004 for shrinkage longitudinally for 3m high walls, $S = 3000 \times 9 \times 0.00004 = 1.1mm$).

Detailing for Shrinkage

Shrinkage should be taken into consideration where wood framing is combined with materials not subject to dimensional change as in the case of a masonry block elevator shaft in a wood frame building. If the floor joists are supported by a wood frame wall on one end and by the masonry block on the other, differential movement between ends of the joists may occur.

This condition may require framing the wood floor so it is entirely independent of the block wall, or framing the joists to the block wall after the wood famed walls and joists reach equilibrium.

The detailing of metal connections to prevent distress due to wood shrinkage is most critical in large wood member connections such as heavy timber framing or glulam framing. Improperly designed connections can restrain shrinkage and cause splitting. An example is the beam to column connection. The preferred method of connecting these members is with a seat or saddle connection rather than with a metal angle with a column of bolts (Section 4.4).

To avoid problems in finish materials such as gypsum wallboard, siding, and sheathing, avoid continuous vertical runs which can result in buckling at each floor level. Expansion joints or slip-type architectural details are typically used at each floor level. When detailing panel sheathing, particularly shear walls, the panels should not extend across the floor joist framing. Breaking the panels at the floor levels may require the use of metal connectors to transfer forces between the panel above and below the floor levels.

Of all the problems involving shrinkage in multistorey buildings, detailing to accommodate the differential movement between the wood and exterior brick veneer may be the most difficult. Procedures exist for calculating the differential movement between wood framing and exterior brick veneer. The difficulty lies in anticipating realistic shrinkage and expansion and in architectural detailing to accommodate this movement. (Building codes do not allow masonry veneer to be supported by wood, so the option of using shelf angles to support the brick in conjunction with an expansion joint at each floor level is not possible.)

2.3 Main Structural Members

Introduction

This section provides information on the types of wood products available which are commonly used for main structural members such as beams, columns, joists, rafters, and studs.

Dimension Lumber

Dimension lumber is solid sawn wood that is less than 89mm (4" nom.) thick. Canadian lumber is manufactured in accordance with CSA Standard 0141 *Softwood Lumber* and marketed under four species combinations (Table 2.1). While it is possible to obtain any species combination, the S-P-F group is by far the most widely used in Canada.

Table 2.2 shows typical sizes and grades of lumber used for studs, joists, rafters and purlins. Other sizes and grades are available, but are less common. Typically, Stud grade is used for wall framing and No.2 and Better for joists, rafters, and purlins. The maximum length of lumber that may be obtained is about 7.3m (24').

Lumber grades are established by a visual examination of the material in accordance with the National Lumber Grades Authority *Standard Grading Rules for Canadian Lumber*. These rules provide a list of the permitted characteristics within each grade. Some of the characteristics that affect the strength and stiffness of lumber are as follows:

- size and location of knots

- slope of grain

- amount of wane

- size of shakes, splits, and checks

Other characteristics are limited by the grading rules for appearance reasons. Some of these include sap and heart stain, torn grain and planer skips.

Once a piece of lumber has been fully evaluated, a grade stamp is applied to one face (Figure 2.3). This stamp contains the following information about the piece of lumber:

- grading agency identification

- species group

- mill identification

- moisture content at time of surfacing

- grade

2

Wood Building Products

Table 2.1 **Commercial species combinations of lumber**	Species combination	Abbreviation	Species included in combination
	Douglas Fir-Larch	D.Fir-L	Douglas fir Western larch
	Hem-Fir	Hem-Fir	Pacific coast hemlock Amabilis fir
	Spruce-Pine-Fir	S-P-F	Spruce (all species except coast sitka spruce) Jack pine Lodgepole pine Balsam fir Alpine fir
	Northern Species	Northern	Western red cedar Red pine Ponderosa pine Western white pine Eastern white pine Trembling aspen Largetooth aspen Balsam poplar Any other Canadian species graded in accordance with the NLGA rules

Air-dried or kiln-dried lumber is readily available in the 38mm (2" nom.) thickness. Material that has been dried to a moisture content of 19% or less before surfacing (planing or dressing) is classified as S-Dry (surfaced dry). Lumber that is surfaced at a higher moisture content is referred to as S-Grn (surfaced green). Generally, 64mm (3" nom.) and 89mm (4" nom.) thick lumber is readily available as S-Grn only.

Lumber is commonly marketed by its nominal size in inches, which means the actual size rounded up to the nearest inch. For instance 38 x 89mm (1-1/2" x 3-1/2") material is referred to as 2 x 4 lumber (Table 2.3). In this publication, the imperial size for lumber is designated 2" x 4" nom. to indicate that the size is nominal and not actual. S-Grn lumber is produced slightly larger than S-Dry lumber to allow for shrinkage as it dries. After drying, S-Grn lumber should be the same size as S-Dry material.

Lumber Properties

Prior to the mid-1980s, the properties of dimension lumber were determined from small clear samples. Certain inconsistencies resulted, and in response, a testing program was instituted to determine lumber properties based on destructive testing of full size dimension lumber specimens (timber was not tested).

The Lumber Properties Program was conducted across North America with the goal of verifying lumber grading correlation from mill to mill, from region to region, and between Canada and the United States.

Figure 2.3
Typical Canadian lumber grade stamp

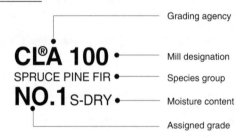

CL®A 100	Grading agency / Mill designation
SPRUCE PINE FIR	Species group
NO.1 S-DRY	Moisture content / Assigned grade

Table 2.2
Typical structural lumber sizes, grades, and moisture content

Use	Common sizes mm	in. (nom.)	Visual grades	Moisture content
Wall studs	38 x 89 38 x 140 38 x 184	2 x 4 2 x 6 2 x 8	Stud	S-Dry or S-Grn
Joists, rafters, and built-up beams	38 x 184 to 38 x 286	2 x 8 to 2 x 12	Select Structural No.1 No.2 No.3	S-Dry or S-Grn
Purlins	64 x 184 to 89 x 286	3 x 8 to 4 x 12	Select Structural No.1 No.2 No.3	S-Grn only

The scientific data resulting from the program showed:

- close correlation in the strength properties of visually graded No.1 and No.2 dimension lumber

- good correlation in the application of grading rules from mill to mill and from region to region

- a decrease in relative strength as size increases (that is, a size effect. For example, the unit bending strength for a 38 x 89mm [2" x 4" nom.] is greater than for a 38 x 114mm [2" x 6" nom.].).

- an adjustment of the strength properties by species group

Both CSA O86 and the *NBCC* have adopted the results from the Lumber Properties Program.

Quality Assurance
Part 9 of the *NBCC* requires that all framing lumber be marked with a grade stamp and be dried to a moisture content of 19% or less prior to installation. The use of dry material also helps to reduce the amount of nail pops and floor squeaks that tend to occur when green lumber is used. Where lumber is not grade stamped, the grade and moisture content should be verified by a grading agency.

Machine Stress Rated (MSR) Lumber
Machine stress rated (MSR) lumber is dimensional lumber that has been graded by mechanical stress rating equipment and manufactured in conformance with the National Lumber Grades Authority (NLGA) *Special Product Standard 2 (SPS-2)*. Under this evaluation method, each piece of lumber is visually inspected prior to testing. Then it is passed through

2

Wood Building Products

Table 2.3 **Dimension lumber sizes**	Nominal size in.	Surfaced green (S-Grn) size in.	Surfaced dry (S-Dry) size in.	Metric size mm
	2 x 2	1-9/16 x 1-9/16	1-1/2 x 1-1/2	38 x 38
	3	2-9/16	2-1/2	64
	4	3-9/16	3-1/2	89
	6	5-5/8	5-1/2	140
	8	7-1/2	7-1/4	184
	10	9-1/2	9-1/4	235
	12	11-1/2	11-1/4	286
	3 x 3	2-9/16 x 2-9/16	2-1/2 x 2-1/2	64 x 64
	4	3-9/16	3-1/2	89
	6	5-5/8	5-1/2	140
	8	7-1/2	7-1/4	184
	10	9-1/2	9-1/4	235
	12	11-1/2	11-1/4	286
	4 x 4	3-9/16 x 3-9/16	3-1/2 x 3-1/2	89 x 89
	6	5-5/8	5-1/2	140
	8	7-1/2	7-1/4	184
	10	9-1/2	9-1/4	235
	12	11-1/2	11-1/4	286

Notes:
1. 38mm (2") lumber is readily available as S-Dry.
2. S-Dry lumber is surfaced at a moisture content of 19% or less.
3. After drying, S-Grn lumber sizes will be approximately the same as S-Dry lumber.
4. Tabulated metric sizes are equivalent to imperial S-Dry sizes, rounded to the nearest millimetre.

the mechanical evaluation equipment and the stiffness is measured and recorded every 150mm (6") along each member. Since stiffness is correlated to strength, the lumber can be grouped into stress grades that have higher strength and stiffness than visually graded lumber.

As for visual grading, MSR evaluation is a continuous process. In a mill operation, the evaluation equipment can process up to 365m (1000') of lumber per minute. This includes evaluating the stiffness and applying a grade stamp to the lumber.

The grade stamp on MSR lumber is similar to that found on visually graded lumber. The grade stamp identifies the material as machine rated along with the stress grade, the grading agency, the mill, the species group, and the moisture content at the time of surfacing.

MSR lumber is commonly used in long span prefabricated trusses and for chords of wood I-joists. It is generally available in 38 x 89 (2" x 4" nom.) to 38 x 184mm

(2" x 8" nom.) lumber only. A number of grades have been developed; some of the most readily available are the following:

- 1650F_b - 1.5E

- 1800F_b - 1.6E

- 2100F_b - 1.8E

- 2400F_b - 2.0E

These grade designations were developed for working stress design and they refer to the allowable bending stress and modulus of elasticity of the material. For instance, 1650F_b - 1.5E means that the allowable bending stress is 1650 psi and the modulus of elasticity is 1.5 million psi. For Limit States Design (LSD), the corresponding values are 23.9 MPa and 10300 MPa, respectively.

Fingerjoined Lumber
Fingerjoined lumber is dimension lumber into which finger profiles have been machined and then joined together by end

Figure 2.4
Fingerjoined lumber

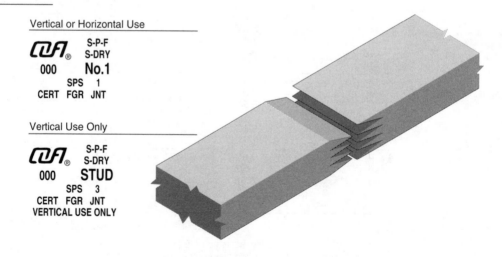

Vertical or Horizontal Use

CQfi®   S-P-F
              S-DRY
000   No.1
              SPS   1
CERT FGR JNT

Vertical Use Only

CQfi®   S-P-F
              S-DRY
000   STUD
              SPS   3
CERT FGR JNT
VERTICAL USE ONLY

gluing (Figure 2.4) to make long length pieces of lumber. This process can result in the production of joists and rafters in lengths of 12m (40') or more.

Canadian fingerjoined lumber is manufactured in conformance with the National Lumber Grades Authority (NLGA) *Special Product Standard 1 (SPS-1)* or *Special Product Standard 3 (SPS-3)*.

Bending members made from fingerjoined lumber are produced to the requirements of *SPS-1*. They are considered to have the same engineering properties as non-fingerjoined lumber and therefore they can be used interchangeably with continuous length lumber of the same grade. Members intended for use in a vertical position (wall studs) are manufactured in accordance with *SPS-3*.

Fingerjoined lumber is assessed for visual grade and is subject to daily quality control testing. The grade stamps for fingerjoined lumber contain similar information to the stamps appearing on dimension lumber, but in addition they indicate whether the fingerjoint is certified for vertical or horizontal use, and the product standard to which it has been manufactured (Figure 2.4).

Sawn Timber

Sawn timber refers to posts and beams with a minimum thickness of 140mm (6" nom.). Timbers are manufactured in accordance with CSA Standard 0141 *Softwood Lumber* and marketed under four species combinations (Table 2.1). Large timbers are generally available in the D.Fir-L and Hem-Fir combinations with smaller sizes available in all species groupings.

The typical sizes and grades of timber used for structural applications are shown in Table 2.4. Sizes up to 394 x 394mm (16" x 16" nom.) may be obtained for D.Fir-L and Hem-Fir species combinations; however, S-P-F and Northern species are generally available in sizes up to 241 x 241mm (10" x 10" nom.) only. Timbers can be obtained in lengths up to 9.1m (30') but availability of large sizes and long lengths should always be checked with suppliers before specifying.

Grading is based on visual examination of the timber in accordance with the National Lumber Grades Authority *Standard Grading Rules for Canadian Lumber.* The most readily available grades are No.1 and No.2, but Select Structural may be ordered.

Table 2.4
Typical sizes and grades of sawn timber for structural applications

| Use | Common sizes | | Visual grade |
	mm	in. nom.	
Posts (square sections)	140 x 140 to 394 x 394	6 x 6 to 16 x 16	Select Structural No.1 No.2
Beams (rectangular sections)	140 x 241 to 292 x 394	6 x 10 to 12 x 16	Select Structural No.1 No.2

Notes:
1. Availability of large sizes should be checked with suppliers.
2. S-P-F and Northern species groups may not be available in sizes larger than 241 x 241mm (10" x 10" nom.).
3. All material is available as S-Grn only.

Sawn timbers are generally surfaced green since their large size makes air or kiln drying impractical. As a result, sawn timbers will shrink as they dry after installation. Checking and splitting may also occur; however, these defects are cause for concern only if they exceed the limits set out in the NLGA grading rules. Standard metric and imperial sizes for timber are shown in Table 2.5.

Materials available from lumber yard stock are usually sawn to order from large timbers and should be regraded after cutting. In addition, the original grade stamp is often removed during resawing and cutting. Therefore, verification of the grade should be obtained in writing from the supplier, or a qualified grading agency should be retained to check the supplied material.

Glulam

Glulam is an engineered wood product manufactured by gluing together lumber laminations with a waterproof adhesive. Glulam is manufactured to meet CSA Standard O122 *Structural Glued-Laminated Timber*, and the manufacturers of glulam must be certified in accordance with CSA Standard O177 *Qualification Code for Manufacturers of Structural Glued-Laminated Timber*.

In the manufacture of glulam, lumber laminations are visually and mechanically sorted for strength and stiffness into lamstock grades. The lamstock must be dried to a moisture content of between 7 and 15% before laminating so that little shrinkage or checking will occur after glulam is installed in a typical structure.

The laminations are glued under pressure using a phenol- resorcinol-formaldehyde adhesive that is fully waterproof.

Glulam is produced using two groups of species: Douglas Fir-Larch and Spruce-Pine (Table 2.6). Hem-Fir species may also be used, but it is not readily available. The standard widths and depths of glulam are shown in Table 2.7; however, some manufacturers may use different sizes. The depth of glulam is a function of the number

Table 2.5
Typical sizes and grades of sawn timber

Nominal size in.	Surfaced green (S-Grn) size in.		Metric size mm
6 x 6	5-1/2 x	5-1/2	140 x 140
8		7-1/2	191
10		9-1/2	241
12		11-1/2	292
14		13-1/2	343
16		15-1/2	394
8 x 8	7-1/2 x	7-1/2	191 x 191
10		9-1/2	241
12		11-1/2	292
14		13-1/2	343
16		15-1/2	394
10 x 10	9-1/2 x	9-1/2	241 x 241
12		11-1/2	292
14		13-1/2	343
16		15-1/2	394
12 x 12	11-1/2 x	11-1/2	292 x 292
14		13-1/2	343
16		15-1/2	394

Notes:
1. Timbers are always surfaced green.
2. Tabulated metric sizes are equivalent to imperial dimensions.

of laminations multiplied by the lamination thickness. For economy, 38mm (2" nom.) laminations are used wherever possible, but 19mm (3/4" nom.) laminations are also used where greater degrees of curvature are required.

Glulam is commonly used in post and beam structures. It can also be curved and tapered to create pitched tapered beams and a variety of arch shapes (refer to Section 4.2). It is also used to build long span trusses.

Glulam is usually custom made, but timber suppliers also stock beams and columns in a number of standard sizes for fast delivery. The suppliers also have prefabricated connection hardware for the stock glulam sizes.

Glulam beams may be cambered. This means that they may be produced with a slight upward bow so that the amount of deflection under service loads is reduced. A typical camber is 2 to 4mm per metre (1/8" per 10') of length.

Generally glulam receives a coat of protective sealer before shipping. It is also wrapped for protection during shipping and erection. This wrapping should be left on as long as possible, ideally until the structure has been enclosed.

Grades of Glulam

There are two classifications or grade categories for glulam:

* stress grade

* appearance grade

Stress grades define the strength of the material. Glulam is available in a number of stress grades depending on the type of member required (Table 2.6). Stress grades are developed by locating higher quality lamstock in high stress areas. For continuous beams, the high strength laminations are placed near the top and bottom to provide the greatest strength and stiffness. For columns and tension members the laminations are more equally distributed.

The stress grade designations were developed for working stress design and they refer to the allowable stress of the material. For instance 20f means an allowable bending stress of 2000 psi. The letter E indicates that mechanical sorting or E-rating has been used to grade the laminations. The lower case letters indicate the use of the grade as follows: f is for flexural (bending) members, c is for compression members, and t is for tension members.

The difference between the f-E grade and the f-EX grade is that the f-E grade has high strength laminations on the bottom only, while the f-EX has them on each face. Therefore, the f-E grade is used for single span beams where little reverse bending can occur. The EX grade is used for two-span beams or cantilevered beams that experience reverse bending and require high strength material on both faces. The top sides of f-E beams should be marked so that they may be installed correctly.

After a glulam member is fabricated, it is difficult to determine the stress grade since the faces of the laminations are hidden.

2

Wood Building Products

Table 2.6 **Glulam species and stress grades**	Species combination	Stress grades		
		Beams	Columns	Tension members
	Douglas Fir-Larch	20f-E 20f-EX 24f-E 24f-EX	16c-E	18t-E
	Spruce-Pine	20f-E 20f-EX	12c-E	14t-E

Note: Glulam may also be manufactured with Hem-Fir species.

Therefore, the manufacturer must provide the purchaser with a certificate confirming that the material has been manufactured to the specified grades and standards.

Glulam is available in the following appearance grades:

• Industrial

• Commercial

• Quality

The appearance grade defines the amount of patching and finishing work done to the exposed surfaces after laminating (Table 2.8). Quality grade provides the greatest degree of finishing and is intended for applications where appearance is important. Industrial grade has the least amount of finishing.

The patching and finishing work carried out after laminating does not affect the strength of stiffness of glulam. As a result, any combination of stress and appearance grades is possible.

Table 2.7 **Standard glulam sizes**	Width		Depth range [1]	
	mm	in.	mm	in.
	80	3	114 to 570	4-1/2 to 22-1/2
	130	5	152 to 950	6 to 37-1/2
	175	6-7/8	190 to 1254	7-1/2 to 49-1/2
	215	8-1/2	266 to 1596	10-1/2 to 62-3/4
	265	10-1/4	342 to 1976	13-1/2 to 77-3/4
	315	12-1/4	380 to 2128	15 to 83-3/4
	365	14-1/4	380 to 2128	15 to 83-3/4

Note:
1. Intermediate depths are multiples of the lamination thickness, which is 38mm (1-1/2" nom.) except for some curved members that require 19mm (3/4" nom.) laminations.

Table 2.8 **Glulam appearance grades**	Grade	Description
	Industrial Grade	Intended for use where appearance is not primary concern such as in industrial buildings; laminating stock may contain natural characteristics allowed for specified stress grade; sides planed to specified dimensions but occasional misses and rough spots allowed; may have broken knots, knot holes, torn grain, checks, wane and other irregularities on surface.
	Commercial Grade	Intended for painted or flat-gloss varnished surfaces; laminating stock may contain natural characteristics allowed for specified stress grade; sides planed to specified dimensions and all squeezed-out glue removed from surface; knot holes, loose knots, voids, wane or pitch pockets are not replaced by wood inserts or filler on exposed surface.
	Quality Grade	Intended for high-gloss transparent or polished surfaces, displays natural beauty of wood for best aesthetic appeal; laminating stock may contain natural characteristics allowed for specified stress grade; sides planed to specified dimensions and all squeezed-out glue removed from surface; may have tight knots, firm heart stain and medium sap stain on sides; slightly broken or split knots, slivers, torn grain or checks on surface filled; loose knots, knot holes, wane and pitch pockets removed and replaced with non-shrinking filler or with wood inserts matching wood grain and colour; face laminations free of natural characteristics requiring replacement; faces and sides sanded smooth.

Structural Composite Lumber (SCL)

There are two structural composite lumber (SCL) products available:

*   laminated veneer lumber (LVL)

*   parallel strand lumber (PSL)

Laminated veneer lumber is manufactured by gluing veneers together to produce a lumber product. The grain direction of each veneer is oriented parallel to the length of the piece.

Parallel strand lumber consists of strands of veneers that are glued together with the strands oriented along the length of the piece. Both LVL and PSL products are manufactured using exterior waterproof adhesives.

Structural composite lumber is a high strength product that is widely used for beams, headers, and columns in light frame or post and beam construction. Typically, SCL has three times the bending strength of a standard grade of lumber. It is also about 30% stiffer.

SCL is produced at a low moisture content so that very little shrinkage will occur after installation. SCL will also be free of checks or splits.

SCL materials are proprietary products and each has its own unique set of design properties. Currently there is no CSA standard for the manufacture of SCL products, so the products and quality control of the materials are the responsibility of the manufacturer. The manufacturer's literature contains allowable load tables for their product along with installation recommendations. Most manufacturers will also size the beams for a project and provide layout drawings. These drawings should be sealed by a professional engineer.

SCL is produced in a number of standard sizes (Tables 2.9, 2.10). Some products are available in a number of thicknesses while others are available in the 45mm thickness only. The 45mm laminations may be nailed or bolted together to form built-up beams. Generally SCL is available in lengths up to about 20m (60'). The manufacturers name or product identification and the stress grade is marked on the material at various intervals, but due to end cutting, it may not be present on every piece.

2

Wood Building Products

Table 2.9 **Typical depths of laminated veneer lumber (LVL)**	Depth mm	in.
	241	9-1/2
	302	11-7/8
	356	14
	406	16
	476	18-3/4

Notes:
1. Available in a thickness of 45mm (1-3/4"). Wider members may be built-up by nailing or bolting two or more plies together.
2. Refer to manufacturer's literature for specific bearing capacity.

Table 2.10 **Typical dimensions of parallel strand lumber (PSL)**	Member type	Size (b x d) mm	in.
	Beams	45 x 241	1-3/4 x 9-1/2
		292	11-1/2
		318	12-1/2
		356	14
		89 x 241	3-1/2 x 9-1/2
		292	11-1/2
		318	12-1/2
		356	14
		406	16
		457	18
		133 x 241	5-1/4 x 9-1/2
		292	11-1/2
		318	12-1/2
		356	14
		406	16
		457	18
		178 x 241	7 x 9-1/2
		292	11-1/2
		318	12-1/2
		356	14
		406	16
		457	18
	Columns	89 x 89	3-1/2 x 3-1/2
		133	5-1/4
		178	7
		133 x 133	5-1/4 x 5-1/4
		178	7
		178 x 178	7 x 7

Light Frame Trusses

Light frame trusses are prefabricated by connecting 38mm (2" nom.) dimension lumber together with metal truss plates. Truss plates are produced by punching light gauge galvanized steel so that teeth protrude from one side (Figure 2.5). The teeth are pressed into the faces of the truss members at each joint to connect the truss framework.

Truss plates must conform to the requirements of the 1994 Limit States Design (LSD) edition of CSA Standard O86.1, *Engineering Design in Wood*. Truss plates are proprietary products and must be approved by the Canadian Centre for Materials in Construction (CCMC). In order to obtain approval, the plates are tested in accordance with CSA Standard S347-M1980 *Method of Test for Evaluation of Truss Plates Used in Lumber Joints*.

Trusses are generally engineered by the truss plate manufacturer on behalf of the truss fabricator. The design procedures are consistent with Part 4 and Part 9 of the *NBCC*. Members of the Truss Plate Institute of Canada (TPIC) also use the design criteria outlined in their publication titled *Truss Design Procedures and Specifications for Light Metal Plate-Connected Wood Trusses, Limit States Design (1996)*.

For each project, the truss fabricator will provide layout and design drawings for each truss. These drawings must be sealed by a professional engineer. Samples of typical drawings along with a description of the information contained on them is provided in Section 3.3.

Light frame trusses may be manufactured to suit any roof profile. Truss shape and size is limited only by manufacturing capabilities, shipping limitations and handling considerations. Some of the most common trusses are shown in Figure 2.6. The arrangement of the webs is generally determined by the fabricator at the detailed design stage and is not included in the figure. Many of these shapes can be designed for single or multiple span applications. Cantilevers and overhangs can also be provided at one or both ends. Flat trusses may be designed for bottom chord bearing or top chord bearing where the supporting beam is to be hidden.

2

Wood Building Products

Figure 2.5
Typical truss plate

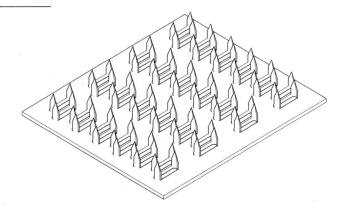

Figure 2.6 **Truss shapes**		Triangular	These trusses may be simple span, multiple bearing, or cantilevered. Where the truss height exceeds approximately 3m (10'), a piggyback system (see below) may be needed due to transportation restrictions.
		Mono	This shape may be simple span, multiple span, or cantilevered. Top chord bearing is possible.
		Inverted	The inverted truss is used to provide a vaulted ceiling along a portion of the span.
		Cut-off (Bobtail, Stubend)	This shape may be used where a triangular truss will not fit.
		Dual Slope	This truss provides an asymmetric roof slope.
		Ridge Truss	The ridge truss provides a stepped roof appearance.
		Piggyback	The piggyback truss is a combination of a gable end truss on top of a hip truss, which can be transported in two sections. It is used when a single triangular truss is too large to transport.

Figure 2.6 *(cont'd)*
**Truss
shapes**

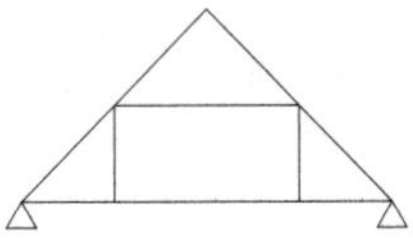

	Attic	The attic truss provides useable area within the roof space.
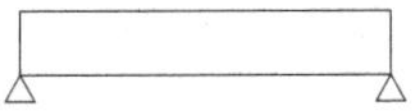	Flat	The flat truss is used in roofs or floors. It may be designed as top or bottom chord bearing, or for simple or multiple spans. It may also be cantilevered at one or both ends.
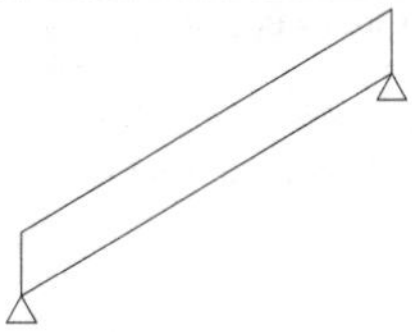	Sloping Flat	This shape is used to create a vaulted ceiling. It may be top or bottom chord bearing.
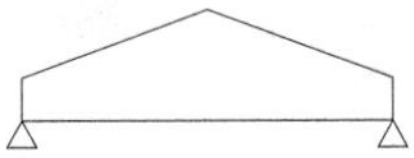	Sloping Chord Flat	This shape is used to provide positive drainage to both sides of the building.
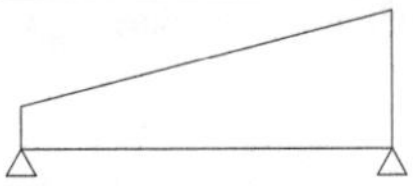	Mono Flat	The mono flat truss provides positive drainage to one side only.
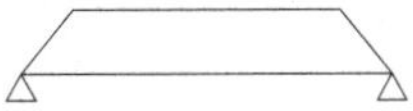	Hip	This shape is used to create hip roofs.
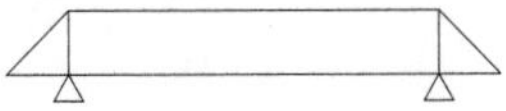	Mansard	This truss is used to create a mansard roof profile.

2

Wood Building Products

Figure 2.6 *(cont'd)* **Truss shapes**		Cathedral	The cathedral truss provides a vaulted ceiling along one portion of the span.
		Vaulted	This truss is a variation of the cathedral shape.
		Scissor	The scissor truss is used to create a vaulted ceiling along the entire span. The slope of the bottom chord is usually equal to 1/2 of the slope of the top chord. Large scissor trusses are often shipped in two pieces and field spliced.
		Half Scissor	The half scissor truss provides a single-sloped vaulted ceiling.
		Gambrel	This truss is used to create a gambrel or barn-shaped roof profile.

Wood I-Joists

Wood I-joists are made by gluing solid sawn lumber (usually MSR) or LVL flanges to a plywood or oriented strandboard web using a waterproof adhesive to produce a dimensionally stable lightweight member with known engineering properties. Because high strength material is used which can be spliced into long lengths, wood I-joists are capable of spanning further than conventional sawn wood joists. They are also dimensionally stable since the materials are dried prior to manufacture.

Wood I-joists are available in a number of standard sizes (Table 2.11) and in lengths up to 20m (60'). Most suppliers also stock standard joist hangers and other prefabricated connection hardware specially designed for use with wood I-joists.

Wood I-joists are proprietary products. Each manufacturer uses a different combination of web and flange materials and a different connection between the web and the flanges. As a result, each manufacturer produces a joist with unique strength and stiffness characteristics.

Manufacturers' literature contains allowable load tables and span tables similar to those found in the *NBCC* for lumber joists. Their literature also contains recommended installation procedures. Most suppliers will provide layout drawings for a particular job showing the required size and location of joists and installation details. These drawings should be sealed by a professional engineer.

Wood I-joists for cathedral ceilings can be obtained with predrilled ventilation holes. Some manufacturers provide prepunched knock-out holes in the webs that facilitate the installation of electrical services. Holes may also be cut in the webs of floor joists for the installation of electrical wiring or ductwork, but field cutting of wood I-joist webs should be made only in strict accordance with the manufacturer's recommendations. Cutting of the flange is not permitted.

The uniform stiffness, strength, and light weight of these prefabricated structural products makes them well suited for longer span joist and rafter applications for both residential and commercial construction.

The I shape of these products gives a high strength to weight ratio. For example, wood I-joists 241mm (9-1/2") deep and 8 m (25') long weigh between 23 and 32 kg (50 and 70 lbs.), depending on the flange size, which means that they can be installed manually.

2

Wood Building Products

Table 2.11 **Typical depths of prefabricated wood I-joists**	Depth	
	mm	in.
	241	9-1/2
	292	11-1/2
	302	11-7/8
	318	12-1/2
	356	14
	406	16
	457	18
	508	20

Note:
1. Refer to manufacturer's literature for widths and specific load bearing capacity.

2.4 Sheathing and Decking

Introduction

This section describes those sheathing and decking wood products that are used as integral structural elements. They transfer the loads to the main structural members while providing, as a system, rigidity to the entire structure. They also play the important role of constituting the nailing surface for the attachment of the building envelope.

Sheathing

Sheathing is manufactured from a wide variety of wood-based materials. Plywood, oriented strandboard (OSB) and waferboard are the most common panel products for structural roof, wall and floor sheathing. In the past, 19mm (3/4" nom.) sawn lumber boards were common, but they are rarely used today. Fibreboard and synthetic insulating panels are also used as wall sheathing in houses.

2

Wood Building Products

Table 2.12
Available plywood grades

Sanded grades	Manufacturing Standard
Good Two Sides (G2S)	DFP
Good One Side (G1S)	DFP
Solid Two Sides (S2S)	CSP
Solid One Side (S1S)	CSP
Numerous sanded grades	Poplar

Unsanded Grades	Manufacturing Standard
Select Tight Face (SEL TF)	DFP or CSP
Select (SELECT)	DFP or CSP
Sheathing (SHG)	DFP or CSP
Select Sheathing (SEL/SHTG)	Poplar
Standard Sheathing (STD/SHTG)	Poplar

Overlaid Grades	Manufacturing Standard
High Density Overlaid (HDO)	DFP, CSP, or Poplar
Medium Density Overlaid (MDO)	DFP, CSP, or Poplar

(specify one or two sides)

Table 2.13
Typical plywood sizes[1] nominal thickness[2]

Sheathing and selected grades mm	Sanded grades mm
7.5	6.0
9.5	8.0
12.5[3]	11.0
15.5[4]	14.0
18.5[4]	17.0[4]
20.5[4]	19.0[4]
22.5[4]	21.0[4]
25.5[4]	24.0[4]
28.5[4]	27.0[4]
31.5[4]	30.0[4]

Notes:
1. Nominal panel sizes of 1220 x 2440 mm (4' x 8') or cut to size.
   Larger panel sizes up to 1250 x 2500 mm are availabe on special order.
2. All thicknesses are metric. Some, but not all, thicknesses approximate imperial dimensions, namely: 6mm (1/4"), 9.5 mm (3/8"), 12.5 mm (1/2"), 15.5 mm (5/8"), 19 mm (3/4"), 22.5 mm (7/8"), 25.5 mm (1"), 28.5 mm (1-1/8"), and 31.5 mm (1-1/4").
3. Available as square edge or with **COFI** ROOF T&G edge.
4. Available as square edge or with **COFI** FLOOR T&G edge.

Plywood

Plywood panels are built-up from sheets of veneer that are glued together. The bond and wood quality, species, thickness, and orientation of the plies determine the performance of the panel. Plywood intended for Canadian construction and industrial applications have minimum requirements covered in the following CSA Standards:

- CSA Standard O121, *Douglas Fir Plywood,*
- CSA Standard O151, *Canadian Softwood Plywood,*
- CSA Standard O153, *Poplar Plywood.*

Typically, the grain direction and thickness of the veneers is balanced about the panel centreline. A number of sanded, unsanded, and overlaid grades are specified in these Standards, and are summarized in Table 2.12.

Unsanded sheathing grade plywood is commonly used for construction sheathing and structural applications. These plywood grades specify adhesive and veneer quality requirements that result in an "Exterior Bond" that is unaffected by exposure to extreme conditions of moisture and temperature. Typical plywood sizes are shown in Table 2.13.

These metric panel thicknesses are similar to the imperial sizes, which have been established through experience and traditional usage. The length and width of panels are typically used for supporting members spaced at 305 mm (12"), 406 mm (16"), 488 mm (19.2") or 610 mm (24").

Tongue and groove plywood (T & G) is often used for floor sheathing. It has a factory machined tongue along one of the long edges and a groove along the other. When T & G plywood is installed, the tongue from one panel is interlocked with the groove in the adjacent panel. This system eliminates the need for blocking the edges from below and provides effective load transfer between adjacent panels.

Figure 2.7
Typical panel marks for Canadian plywood

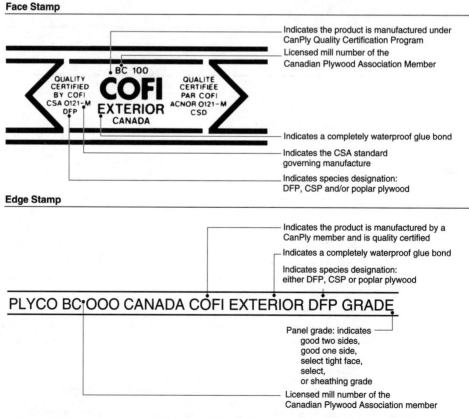

Face Stamp

Indicates the product is manufactured under CanPly Quality Certification Program

Licensed mill number of the Canadian Plywood Association Member

Indicates a completely waterproof glue bond

Indicates the CSA standard governing manufacture

Indicates species designation: DFP, CSP and/or poplar plywood

Edge Stamp

Indicates the product is manufactured by a CanPly member and is quality certified

Indicates a completely waterproof glue bond

Indicates species designation: either DFP, CSP or poplar plywood

PLYCO BC OOO CANADA COFI EXTERIOR DFP GRADE

Panel grade: indicates
good two sides,
good one side,
select tight face,
select,
or sheathing grade

Licensed mill number of the Canadian Plywood Association member

Depending on appearance requirement, either a face stamp or edge stamp is used.
Where a face stamp is used, the grade designation is shown separately on the edge stamp.

All plywood products are marked with a grade stamp that indicates the CSA standard to which it is produced. (Figure 2.7).

Oriented Strandboard (OSB) and Waferboard

OSB and waferboard are structural mat-formed panels made from thin, short aspen wafers or strands that are bonded together with a waterproof adhesive under heat and pressure.

The wafers from which waferboard is manufactured are randomly oriented making the strength properties along both the width and length identical.

OSB is similar to waferboard, but the strands are narrower and oriented in the long direction of the panel in the outer layers. This gives the panel added strength and stiffness in the long direction.

OSB is the new generation of structural panel made from strands. The manufacture of waferboard, that is panels with randomly distributed wafers, is on the decline. At the time of printing this book, only one Canadian mill was still manufacturing waferboard as compared to several mills which have changed over to OSB manufacture.

OSB and waferboard panels are manufactured in both imperial and metric sizes and are either square-edged or tongue-and-grooved on the long edges for panels 15mm (19/32") or thicker. The sizes shown in Table 2.14 are most common.

Both products must conform to CSA Standard O437, *OSB and Waferboard.* This general product standard contains three designations: O-1 and O-2 indicate an oriented panel as in OSB; R-1 indicates a random alignment of the strands as in waferboard.

Another standard that applies to OSB and waferboard, as well as to plywood, is a performance standard: CSA O325, *Construction Sheathing.* This standard sets the perfomance ratings (Table 2.15) for specific end uses such as floor, roof and wall sheathing in light-frame construction. It is refenced in Part 9 of the *NBCC,* and provides an alternative way of specifying products for these applications without referencing product standards.

Figure 2.8 shows the typical panel marks for OSB and waferboard.

Panels meeting CSA O437 shall be marked with:
1. The manufacturers name or mill number
2. The designation CSA O437
3. The words Exterior Bond or EXT. BOND
4. The appropriate grade mark R-1, O-1, O-2
5. The nominal thickness in mm
6. The direction of orientation if O-1 or O-2 grade
7. THIS SIDE DOWN on the back of T and G panels

Panels made for export are marked MADE IN CANADA. The sructural Board Association (SBA) logo may also appear on the panel.

2

Wood Building Products

Figure 2.8
Panel marks for graded OSB and waferboard

CSA O437 Panel
MANUFACTURER'S LOGO
MILL 000
CSA O347.0
EXTERIOR BOND
R-1 or O-1 or O-2
12.5 mm
MADE IN
CANADA

CSA O325 Panel
CONSTRUCTION SHEATHING
EXTERIOR BOND
MILL 000
CSA O325.0
IR24/2F16
12.5 mm
CERTIFICATION
AGENCY

Panels meeting CSA O325 will include in addition the following marks:
1. The designations CSA O325
2. The panel mark denoting the span rating and end use
3. The nominal thickness
4. The certfication agency logo

Note: All panels that do not meet the requirements of CSA O437 or CSA O325 will be marked "REJECT – ALL OTHER MARKS VOID". This mark will be placed adjacent to the original grade if the panel has been previously marked. CSA standard states that reject cannot be used for building construction.

Table 2.14
CSA O437 sizes for OSB and waferboard

| Imperial thickness (in.) | Metric thicknesses for the following grades (mm) | | |
	O-2	O-1	R-1
1/4	6.00	6.35	6.35
5/16	7.50	7.90	7.90
3/8	9.50	9.50	9.50
7/16	11.0	11.1	11.1
15/32	12.0		
1/2	12.5	12.7	12.7
19/32	15.0		
5/8	15.5	15.9	15.9
23/32	18.0		
3/4	18.5	19.0	19.0
7/8	22.5		
1-1/8	28.5		

Note:
   Panel sizes are 4' × 8' (1220 × 2440 mm) or cut to size.
   Larger sizes up to 8' × 24' (2440 × 7320 mm) are available on special order.

Table 2.15
CSA O325 performance marks

| Assumed end use | | Spacing in inches (mm) | | | | | |
		16 (400)	20 (500)	24 (600)	32 (800)	40 (1000)	48 (1200)
Subflooring	(1F)	1F16	1F20	1F24	1F32	– [3]	1F48
Subflooring used with a panel-type undelay	(2F)	2F16	2F20	2F24	– [3]	– [3]	– [3]
Roof sheathing used without edge support	(1R)	1R16	1R20	1R24	1R32	1R40	1R48
Roof sheathing used with edge support	(2R)	2R16	2R20	2R24	2R32	2R40	2R48
Wall sheathing	(W)	W16	W20	W24	– [3]	– [3]	– [3]

Notes:
1. Panel marks consist of an end use mark followed by the appropriate span mark.
2. Multiple panel marks may be used on panels qualified for more than one end use, e.g., 1R24/2F16 or 2R48/2F24/1F24.
3. Not covered by this Standard.

Table 2.16 **CSA O452 Design-rated OSB**	Product type	Design rating grade	Nominal thickness (mm)
	1 (STANDARD)	A	9.5
	2 (PLUS)	B	to
		C	28.5
	3 (PROPRIETARY)	–	unspecified

Note:
Structural properties (strength and stiffness) are given for bending, axial (tension and compression) and shear (in-plane and through-the-thickness). Values are listed for forces applied parallel and perpendicular to major axis (or length) of the panel.

2

Wood Building Products

OBS can be manufactured specifically for engineered design applications, in accordance with CSA standard O452, *Design Rated OSB* (Table 2.16). This standard contains certification and grade-marking requirements for three types of design-rated OSB panels:

- Type 1 (STANDARD):
  Products consisting of three different rating grades (A, B or C), with design values listed in CSAO86.1
- Type 2 (PLUS):
  Products exceeding Type 1 rating grade levels by 10% or more (noted on grade mark).
- Type 3 (PROPRIETARY):
  products for which a certification organization certifies specified design capacities, different from STANDARD or PLUS capacities.

Designers should ensure the availability of design-rated OSB before specifying.

Plank Decking

Plank decking is sawn lumber that is milled into a tongue and groove profile (Figure 2.9). Decking is produced in three thicknesses: 38, 64 and 89mm (2", 3" and 4" nom.). The 38mm (2" nom.) thickness has a single tongue and groove while the thicker sizes have a double tongue and groove. The 64

and 89mm (2" and 3" nom.) decking also have 6mm (1/4") diameter holes predrilled through the centre of the piece at 760mm (30") spacing so that each piece may be nailed to the adjacent one with deck spikes.

Decking is generally available in the following species:

- Douglas fir
- Pacific coast hemlock
- Various spruce-pine-fir species combinations
- Western red cedar

It is available in two grades: Select and Commercial. Select grade has a higher quality appearance than Commercial grade and is also stronger and stiffer. Verification of the grade, since plank decking is not grade marked, should be obtained in writing from the supplier or a qualified grading agency should be retained to check the supplied material.

Plank decking is most readily available in random lengths of 1.8 to 6.1m (6' to 20') and longer. Decking may be ordered in specific lengths, but designers should expect limited availability and extra costs. It is usual to specify that at least 90% of the decking be 3.0m (10') and longer, and between 10 to 50% be 4.9m (16') and longer.

Figure 2.9
Plank decking

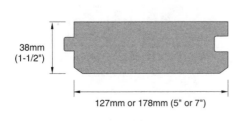

38mm (1-1/2")

127mm or 178mm (5" or 7")

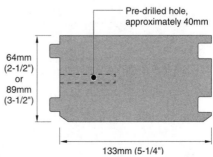

Pre-drilled hole, approximately 40mm

64mm (2-1/2") or 89mm (3-1/2")

133mm (5-1/4")

Decking should always be kiln or air dried to an average moisture content of no greater than 15% (maximum 19%). This will reduce shrinkage after installation. Excessive shrinkage due to the use of green decking will result in the loosening of the tongue and groove joint, which is unsightly and structurally unacceptable.

Information on plank decking installation is provided in Section 4.6

2.5   Storage and Handling

Introduction

Like all building materials, wood products represent an investment which should be treated carefully during the transportation, storage and installation stages to ensure good long term performance.

Deterioration in Storage

Wood is a durable and resilient material, but it can deteriorate unless stored and handled with a reasonable amount of care. Poor storage and handling practices could result in the following defects:

- decay

- sapstain

- weathering

- shrinkage defects such as warping, splitting and checking

Decay
Decay, as explained previously, occurs when wood is attacked by wood destroying fungi. During storage, wood products should be kept under cover. Decay is not usually a likelihood for the short term storage typical of most building projects but it could be a problem for prolonged storage.

Sapstain
Sapstain is a dark blue or black discoloura-tion of the sapwood (live wood near the bark) caused by certain types of fungi. Unlike wood-destroying fungi, sapstain fungi do not digest the wood substance and as a result they do not generally reduce the strength of wood. However, where the appearance of wood is impor-tant, special care should be taken to avoid formation of sapstain.

Sapstain fungi only attack wood with a high moisture content. Therefore, it may be prevented by covering stored wood prod-ucts and by keeping them off the ground. In addition, green lumber and timber should be stacked with stickers between each layer to provide ventilation and promote drying. Green wood may also be surface treated with an anti-sapstain chem-ical such as sodium penta (tetra) chlorophenate.

Weathering
If wood is left unprotected in the outdoors its surface will undergo a series of physical and chemical changes known as weather-ing. The first indication of weathering is a colour change; woods that are originally dark coloured will tend to fade and light coloured woods will darken. As weathering advances all woods tend to turn silver gray in colour.

These changes are caused by the action of the sun and rain. The ultraviolet light of the sun causes the chemical components of wood to break down at the surface, then the rain leaches the components out of the wood.

Repeated swelling and shrinking of the wood surface due to wetting and drying or freezing and thawing causes the surface grain to raise and also results in checking and cracking. The surface may also be attacked by stain or decay fungi, which may result in softening of the surface. Over a long period of time, the surface fibres will erode away.

Since weathering is primarily caused by the action of the sun and rain, it may be prevented by covering stored wood materials.

2

Wood Building Products

Protection in Storage

Proper storage and handling of wood and wood products will reduce deterioration and material damage, and eliminate costly replacement or repair of materials.

When storing wood materials on site, the following guidelines should be followed to prevent decay, weathering and other moisture related problems:

- Stack wood in bundles at least 150mm (6") off the ground.

- Bundles of wood materials should have enough supports to prevent sagging.

- Cover bundles with tarpaulins or store in a shed.

- Factory wrappings on glulam, kiln dried lumber, I-joists or structural composite lumber (SCL) such as laminated veneer lumber (LVL) and parallel strand lumber (PSL) should be left on as long as possible.

Careless handling of wood materials can cause unnecessary damage. Damage can be minimized by storing materials as described above in protected out-of-the-way areas. Barricades should be erected around the material in areas of heavy vehicular traffic to protect it from damage. Long slender materials, such as beams or prefabricated trusses, should be lifted by using a strongback or closely spaced slings.

Glulam

Glued-laminated timber is a finished product that is manufactured from lumber that is less than 15% moisture content. In order to maintain its appearance and dry condition, it is important that it be adequately protected during storage. Factory wrapping should be maintained intact during storage and erection; preferably until immediately prior to installation of the roof covering. To prevent the accumulation of condensation the wrapping should be slit slightly on the underside of the member. Wrapping that is ripped or torn should be completely removed to prevent localized discolouration from sunlight. The member should then be rewrapped or covered until the roof is in place.

Glulam should be stored on level bare ground with at least 150mm (6") clearance from the ground and enough supports to prevent the members from sagging. The material should be blocked up to a slope to allow rapid drainage. When lifting glulam, the corners and edges should be protected by using nylon or fabric slings. Blocking or pads should be used between the slings and the member to prevent surface damage.

Other Engineered Wood Products

Trusses, wood I-joists, parallel strand lumber (PSL), laminated veneer lumber (LVL) and panels are all high value wood products deserving of care during storage and installation.

The moisture content of these products is usually low. In fact, part of their purchase cost is for the removal of moisture during the manufacturing process. Therefore, it makes good sense to protect this investment by storing these products on level supports and under cover.

Trusses are particularly delicate when not in their final upright position. Detailed information on their handling is found in Section 3.3.

Plywood and Oriented Strandboard (OSB)

Plywood, OSB and other panel products are manufactured at a low moisture content (6% or less). Therefore, absorption of moisture during storage can cause swelling and warping. If plywood is subjected to wetting and drying over a long period, the face veneers may also check. Therefore, wood panels should remain wrapped or covered during storage and it is good practice to store them under conditions that they will experience in service. Wood panels should be stored level, flat and have the corners and edges protected. Finish panels should be delivered to the job site just prior to use to minimize their exposure to site conditions.

Protection after Installation

In most cases lumber, timber and lumber products will be installed while they are still at a moisture content higher than the equilibrium moisture content of the in-service environment and so some shrinkage after installation can usually be expected. Therefore, to prevent problems from occurring after completion, the effect of shrinkage should be considered in the design and installation of structural and finish wood products.

Wood framing that is periodically wetted during construction will usually dry quickly since only the surface is affected. However, sheathed floor framing should be protected with polyethylene sheets if it is to be exposed for long periods of time. Failure to do so may result in squeaky and uneven floors after completion of the building. Alternatively, the floor may be left exposed if the floor sheathing is to be fastened to the framing with screws to prevent squeaks. The edges of the plywood, waferboard and OSB panels tend to absorb the greatest amount of moisture and are susceptible to swelling. Therefore, prior to applying the finish flooring, any unevenness resulting from swollen edges should be planed or sanded away.

Builders can also minimize the severity of drying defects after completion by scheduling work so that the framing remains exposed for some time before interior finishes are applied. If the installation of gypsum wallboard and other finishes can be delayed for about 30 days during warm dry weather, enough additional moisture loss will take place so that the effect of any further drying after completion will be minimal. Before applying interior finishes, the frame should be examined for warped members or other defects that may have occurred during drying.

Another concern in buildings under construction is the prevention of checking and splitting in sawn timber and glulam after installation. Once the building is enclosed, it is important for the contractor to remember that the heat within the structure should be applied as slowly as possible to allow the internal and surface moisture content of the members to gradually equalize and to minimize the severity of checking. Localized heating near wood members from propane heaters or other sources should also be avoided.

To avoid potential shrinkage problems in any structure, it is advisable to check the moisture content of the wood prior to installation to assure that it is dry enough for the intended application.

2

Wood Building Products

2.6   **Preservative Treatment**

Introduction

Wood products should be treated with a preservative where they will be used in ground contact or be exposed to wet conditions on a continuous basis. Treatment may also be required where the wood is unlikely to dry properly between seasonal or occasional wettings. Pressure treated material should always be used since brush treatments are not as effective in preventing decay.

Types of Preservatives

The most common preservatives used to treat sawn lumber and plywood for use in buildings are the following:

- ammoniacal copper arsenate (ACA)

- chromated copper arsenate (CCA)

ACA turns wood blue-green, while CCA turns wood a light green colour. Both preservatives are mixed with water and applied to wood under pressure. After treatment the preservatives are highly fixed in the wood.

Other preservatives such as creosote and pentachlorophenol are highly effective but are generally not used for areas with high exposure to people.

Pressure treated lumber and timber is produced in accordance with CSA Standard O80.2 *Preservative Treatment of Lumber, Timber, Bridge Ties, and Mine Ties by Pressure Processes.* This standard specifies the amount of preservative added to the wood (retention), which depends on the intended end use as follows:

- retention of 4.0 kg/m^3 (0.24 lbs/ft^3) for wood used above ground

- retention of 6.4 kg/m^3 (0.38 lbs/ft^3) for wood in ground contact

The standard also specifies the minimum acceptable penetration of the preservative into the wood. For example, jack pine lumber for use above ground requires minimum 10mm (3/8") and 90% of the sapwood penetrated while jack pine in ground contact requires minimum 13mm (1/2") and 90% of sapwood penetrated.

Specifiers are encouraged to specify treated wood products bearing the stamp of the Canadian Wood Preservers' Bureau (CWPB) which is assurance that the stated amount of penetration and retention has been achieved.

Lumber and plywood for permanent wood foundations (PWFs) is treated to CSA Standard 080.15 *Preservative Treatment of Wood for Building Foundation Systems, Basements and Crawl Spaces by Pressure Processes.* The minimum acceptable retention is 9.6 kg/m^3 (0.58 lbs/ft^3) for plywood and 8.0 kg/m^3 (0.48 lbs/ft^3) for lumber. Lumber and plywood for PWFs bears a stamp (Figure 2.10) which indicates that it is PWF material. Only materials with this stamp are permitted for PWF construction.

Glulam may be pressure treated in the same manner as sawn lumber using creosote, pentachlorophenol or water-based preservatives such as ACA and CCA. However, the use of water-based preservatives may lead to severe checking and splitting in service; therefore, a glulam manufacturer should be consulted prior to specifying this type of treatment.

2

Wood Building Products

Figure 2.10
Qualification stamp for PWF materials

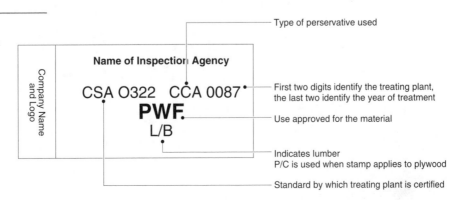

References

1. *Moisture Movement and Control in Light-frame Structures,* Gerald E. Sherwood and Anton TenWolde, USDA Forest Service, Madison, WI, 1982

2. *Multistorey Wood-frame Structures: Shrinkage Considerations and Calculations,* R. Rummelhart and J.A. Fantozzi, Western Wood Products Association, Portland, OR

3. *Wood Handbook: Wood as an Engineering Material,* Forest Products Laboratory, US Department of Agriculture, Washington, DC, 1987

4. *Wood Reference Handbook,* Canadian Wood Council, Ottawa, ON, 1995

5. *Pressure Treated Wood in Residential Construction,* Canadian Institute of Treated Wood, Ottawa, ON

Wood-Frame
Construction

Residential framing techniques also apply to commercial construction when member sizes and connections are designed accordingly.

Interior shear walls provide lateral stability for an office building subject to high seismic loading.

Partially completed buildings may be subjected to high wind loads and need to be braced accordingly.

To provide the required shear resistance for large buildings, close nail patterns may be required.

For this large commercial project, parallel chord trusses were assembled into units on the ground and lifted into place.

Parallel chord trusses are often used in wood-frame commercial construction for both floors and roofs.

Wood assemblies can be fabricated on the ground and lifted into place.

Wood-frame construction is a building technique that can be used for both residential and commercial construction.

To accommodate large window openings, additional framing members are used to carry vertical and horizontal loads.

Where the continuity of members is interrupted, additional framing is required to transfer loads to adjacent members.

Lintels transfer loads around windows and door openings.

When wood framing is used in larger buildings, uplift resulting from lateral loads may require tie down devices between floors *(top)* and at the foundation *(bottom)*.

For attaching wood framing to steel beams, a wood ledger should be provided for fastening purposes.

Many types of
light frame
connectors are
available.

Permanent
wood founda-
tions are used
for residential
applications and
sometimes for
larger buildings.

3.1 General Information

In North America, wood-frame construction is the construction technique of choice for millions of housing units. This construction technique, which uses small members spaced closely together in load sharing arrangements, offers economy and strength which can also be applied to large commercial buildings when provision is made for longer spans and larger loads.

For those buildings meeting the requirements of *NBCC* Part 9, the sizes of most members can be selected from tables. The variability of loadings to which Part 4 buildings are subjected means that members need to be individually designed rather than selected from tables. Much of the information in Chapter 3 applies to Part 9 buildings where loads and other conditions fall within certain norms. For Part 4 buildings, this information may have some applicability in terms of member arrangement and framing detail, but the adequacy of members for loading conditions must always be verified.

Wood-frame construction is economical because the roof and wall assemblies, comprised of main loadbearing members such as wall studs and roof rafters, in combination with sheathing and decking materials, serve a number of functions.

The combination of sheathing and framing provides rigidity for the resistance of lateral loads, a space for the installation of insulation, and robust interior and exterior surfaces for the application of exterior and interior finish materials.

The following sections are contained in this chapter:

3.2   Applications For Wood-Frame Construction

3.3   Framing Details

3.4   Fasteners and Framing Connectors

3

Wood-Frame Construction

3.2   Applications for Wood-Frame Construction

Introduction

Wood-frame construction is a building technique which makes use of small members spaced closely together. Strength is derived from the combined action of the main structural members (the framing) and secondary structural materials (sheathing or decking).

Framing is commonly comprised of dimension lumber or wood I-joists where long spans or high loads are encountered. Plywood and oriented strandboard (OSB) panels are most commonly for sheathing.

Wood-frame construction was first employed when water power facilitated the manufacture of lumber. Prior to that, timbers which were hand hewn were used because it was too labour intensive to reduce logs into lumber.

This building technique is efficient because members are easy to handle, load sharing amongst adjacent members results in strong but light-weight assemblies, and because lumber is economical to produce with modern methods of manufacture.

Wood-frame construction is the prevalent building technique for residential construction. However, the same attributes which have enabled wood-frame construction to dominate the North American residential building market, strength and economy, also apply to commercial construction.

Wood-frame construction is sometimes referred to as planar construction because the main and secondary structural members (framing and sheathing) are in the same plane, and structure, envelope, and insulation space share the same plane. This is in contrast to wood post and beam (Chapter 4) or typical steel construction where the frame and the building skin overlay each other, and the skin is not usually the main contributor of lateral strength to the wall.

All wood-frame construction is classified as light frame construction by the *National Building Code of Canada*. This terminology is not meant to imply that wood framing is light in terms of being suited only for light-duty applications. It means that the members used are small in cross section to the extent that special fire protection characteristics afforded Heavy Timber construction (Section 4.3) are not applicable and therefore, other measures are required to ensure that wood-frame construction meets or exceeds the degree of fire safety required by the building code for each occupancy type.

The same wood framing techniques and materials used for residential construction can be used for commercial construction. Part 9 of the *NBCC* applies to buildings of certain size (specifics are dealt with in more detail in following sections). Buildings which qualify under Part 9 use standard framing designs based upon satisfactory past performance and do not require specific engineering input. Buildings which exceed the size or complexity criteria for Part 9 buildings must be designed according to Part 4 of the *NBCC*, and the structural elements of such buildings must be engineered.

Structural performance is achieved in such buildings in several ways. In the case of loadbearing partitions, the 38 x 89mm (2" x 4" nom.) walls common to residential construction may have to be increased to 38 x 140 or 184mm (2" x 6" or 8" nom.) to accommodate larger loads and increased ceiling heights. For joists, it may be necessary to reduce spacing, use deeper dimension lumber joists, or use wood I-joists.

Similarly, dimension lumber headers and lintels may have to be supplanted by parallel strand lumber (PSL) or laminated veneer lumber (LVL) to increase capacity. This augmentation of member capacities permits wood framing used for commercial applications to meet the strength, deflection, and vibration criteria, and with due attention to design, also meet acoustic, thermal insulation, fire safety, and long term service criteria requirements.

For Part 9 buildings, building rigidity (the ability of the building to resist lateral loads such as those imposed by wind and seismic forces) is provided by the basic structure of the building. Exterior sheathing, interior panel wall finishes and interior

3

Wood-Frame Construction

partitions all contribute rigidity. In commercial frame buildings, lateral forces can be substantial and therefore extra measures must often be taken to provide the shearwall and diaphragm effects necessary to strengthen the building.

The Forintek Canada Corp. building in Vancouver is a good example of how residential wood-frame techniques can be augmented and applied to commercial applications. The Western Research Facility is a 9300m² (100 000 ft²) wood products research facility. Half the building, the office and laboratory portion, is wood-frame construction. The industrial half of the building is a mixture of wood-frame and post and beam construction.

Wherever possible, planar construction was used rather than hierarchical post and beam construction. This approach was based on using exterior walls and interior partitions as loadbearing structural elements. In this way, economy is effected by having walls perform multi-purpose functions.

The walls, which are required for enclosure or for separating interior spaces also support vertical loads thereby eliminating the need for beams and columns, and when sheathed in accordance with engineering standards, provide shearwall stiffening thereby eliminating the need for cross-bracing within the wall cavity.

In this way, the economy of wood-frame construction can be applied to a commercial building such as the Forintek building which has high serviceability requirements stemming from the nature of the precise laboratory work which is undertaken there.

Types of Wood Framing

There are two basic methods used to construct wood-frame buildings: platform and balloon framing.

Platform Framing

Platform framing is more commonly used for modern structures due to its simplicity and ease of erection. Its main advantage is that the floor assembly is built separately from the walls; therefore, the preceding floor provides a working surface on which to assemble and erect the walls and partitions. Generally, the wall framing is assembled and fastened together on the floor, then raised by hand into place. However, wall components can also be prefabricated off-site and then be erected in sections, thereby reducing on-site labour.

In platform framing, all of the walls are one story high and consist of a top plate (double or single), studs, and a bottom plate (Figure 3.1). The plates provide a nailing surface for sheathing and interior finishes. They also act as fire stops that resist the spread of fire from one floor to another in the wall cavity (Section 9.2).

Balloon Framing

Balloon framing is rarely used today, since it does not lend itself to easy site assembly. The main difference between this method and platform framing is that the studs for the exterior walls and some of the interior walls are continuous from the foundation sill plate to the top plate below the roof framing (Figure 3.2). The first floor joists rest on the sill plate adjacent to the studs. The second floor joists overlap the studs and bear on a 19 x 89mm (1" x 4" nom.) ribbon plate that has been recessed into the studs of the exterior wall. The joists are side nailed to the exterior studs and toe nailed to the supporting wall or beam at the opposite end. Since there are no wall plates to eliminate continuous passages within the walls, fire stops (usually 38mm (2" nom.) lumber blocking) are required between the studs and joists to resist the spread of fire.

Figure 3.1
**Platform frame
construction**

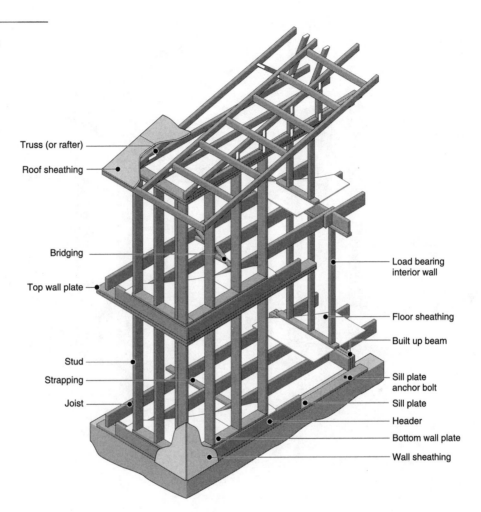

Truss (or rafter)

Roof sheathing

Bridging

Top wall plate

Load bearing
interior wall

Floor sheathing

Built up beam

Stud

Strapping

Joist

Sill plate
anchor bolt

Sill plate

Header

Bottom wall plate

Wall sheathing

3

Wood-Frame Construction

Figure 3.2
**Balloon frame
construction**

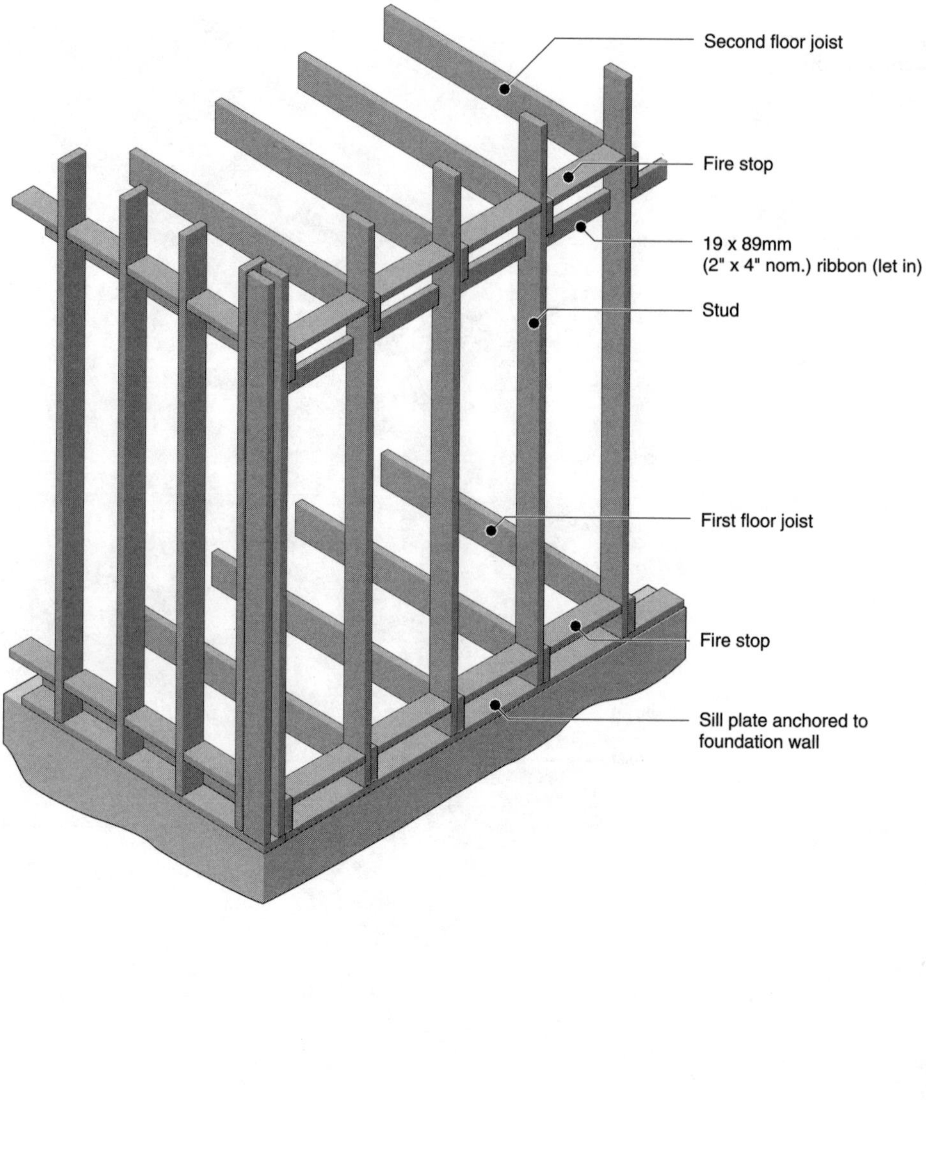

Second floor joist

Fire stop

19 x 89mm
(2" x 4" nom.) ribbon (let in)

Stud

First floor joist

Fire stop

Sill plate anchored to
foundation wall

Building Code Requirements

This section outlines the requirements for wood-frame construction under Part 9 and Part 4 of the *NBCC*.

Part 9 applies to buildings of 3 storeys or less in building height, having a building area on any storey not exceeding 600m^2 (6455 ft^2) and used for major occupancies classified as:

- Group C, *residential occupancies*

- Group D, *business and personal services occupancies*

- Group, *mercantile occupancies*

- Group F, Division 2 and 3, *medium and low hazard industrial occupancies*

The structural design of all other buildings must be done according to Part 4.

Wood Framing for Part 9 Buildings

The material, structural, and design requirements for wood-frame construction are outlined in Part 9, *Housing and Small Buildings* of the *NBCC*. Part 9 applies to:

- wood-frame construction in which the framing members are spaced not more than 600mm (2') on centre (beams supporting floors can be spaced further apart) and maximum clear spans do not exceed 12.20m (40')

- buildings where the floor live loads do not exceed 2.4 kPa (50 psf)

- buildings that are site assembled or factory made

- buildings having the major occupancies and not exceeding the height and area limits states previously indicated

If a building contains a number of portions that are completely enveloped by a minimum one-hour-rated vertical fire separation, each portion can be considered a separate building provided that it is a residential occupancy where the minimum unobstructed path from the nearest street to one entrance of each separated portion is 45m (148').

If a building is constructed according to the guidelines and specifications in Part 9, the structural design requirements for all members and connections are considered to be met for all typical loading situations.

The requirements for grades and sizes of structural elements such as beams, columns, floor joists, roof joists, ceiling joists, rafters, and sheathing are outlined in Section 9.23 of the *NBCC*.

Member sizes and grades for the structural elements can be chosen directly from tables, based on the span and loading conditions. To use the tables for roof framing members, the design roof snow load must be known for the area where the building will be constructed.

This can be calculated (in metric units) from the following formula:

$$S = C_b \times S_s + S_r$$

where:

S   is the design roof snow load

C_b is the basic snow load roof factor which is 0.5 where the entire width of the roof does not exceed 4.3m (14'), and 0.6 for all other roofs

S_s is the ground snow load listed in Chapter 1 of the Supplement to the *NBCC*

S_r is the associated rain load listed in Chapter 1 of the Supplement to the *NBCC*

3

Wood-Frame Construction

In no case can the design load be less than 1 kPa (20 psf). Once the roof load is known, the member size and lumber grade required can be determined.

The required size, grade, and spacing of floor joists, for the appropriate loading condition, can be taken directly from the *NBCC* tables. (Also refer to *The Span Book* published by the Canadian Wood Council.) However, if joists are used for residential balconies, they should be designed to carry the roof snow load or 1.9 kPa (40 psf), whichever is greater. The maximum spans for built-up, glulam, and steel beams supporting one or two floors for Part 9 applications are also given in the *NBCC* tables.

Exterior wall sheathing, based on *NBCC* Part 9, is not required to provide racking resistance against lateral loads, since tests have shown that interior finishes such as gypsum wallboard and interior partitions provide adequate stability.

Wood Framing for Part 4 Buildings

Wood-frame construction is an economical building method for large commercial buildings. Often these buildings exceed the criteria for Part 9 buildings in the following ways:

- the floor loading is higher

- long clear spans are required to provide open areas for offices, shopping, light industrial operations or warehousing

- the size may exceed the restrictions of Part 9

The *NBCC* does not provide specific construction guidelines for commercial buildings. Instead it requires that the structure be designed by an engineer in accordance with Part 4. Many of the framing techniques illustrated in the following sections may be used, but due to the heavier loadings and longer spans in commercial buildings, the member sizes and connections will require engineering design. In addition, Part 4 has special framing and connection details to provide shearwall and diaphragm action to resist the racking effects of lateral loads.

3.3   Framing Details

Introduction

Details in this section (all of Section 3.3) apply to Part 9 buildings. When used for Part 4 buildings, members and connections must be engineered to suit the loading conditions.

Floor Framing

The main floor in wood-frame buildings usually consists of wood joists, wood I-joists, or parallel chord trusses supported by the foundation walls at the perimeter of the building and by beams and columns in the interior (Figure 3.3). Loadbearing stud walls, as well as masonry or concrete walls, may also be used to support floor joists within the interior of the building.

The upper floor joists are usually supported by the exterior stud or masonry walls and by loadbearing interior stud walls (Figure 3.1).

Parallel chord wood trusses or wood I-joists will be used in place of solid wood joists where longer clear spans are required.

Figure 3.3
Nailing schedule for Part 9 floor framing

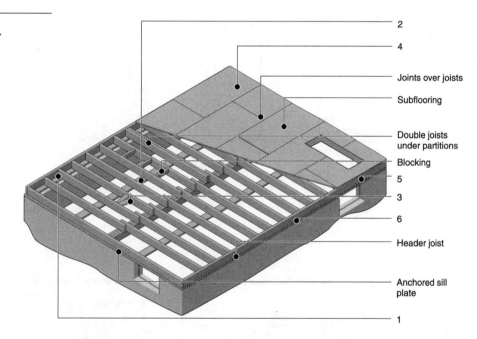

2
4
Joints over joists
Subflooring
Double joists under partitions
Blocking
5
3
6
Header joist
Anchored sill plate
1

3

Wood-Frame Construction

Application	Nailing schedule
1. Floor joist to plate, toe nail	Two 82mm (3-1/4") nails
2. Wood or metal strapping to underside of floor joists	Two 57mm (2-1/4") nails
3. Cross bridging to joists	Two 57mm (2-1/4") nails each end
4. Subfloor (<20mm [3/4"] thick) to joists	Common or spiral nails, or 45mm (1-3/4") ringed nails 51mm (2") @150mm (6") along edges and 300mm (12") along intermediate supports.
5. Header joist end nailed to joists	Three 82mm (3-1/4") nails
6. Header and end joists to sill plate	82mm (3-1/4") nails @ 600mm (24") o.c.

Note:
Nailing requirements for Part 4 buildings may be greater.

Columns

For wood-frame construction, steel, glulam, sawn timber, or built-up wood columns are usually used to support beams at interior locations.

For residential construction, steel pipe columns or adjustable teleposts are commonly used to support beams in the first floor. Steel pipe columns should have an outside diameter of at least 73mm (2-7/8") and a wall thickness of at least 4.76mm (3/16"). Adjustable steel teleposts

are most often used since they can easily be adjusted to length after installation or if settlement or shrinkage occurs after construction has been completed. Adjustable teleposts should conform to CAN/CGSB 7.2-M *Adjustable Steel Columns* and be approved by CMHC.

Bearing plates for steel pipe columns should be at least 100 x 100 x 6.35mm (4" x 4" x 1/4") thick, but they are not required at the top of the column if it is attached to a steel beam. Where steel columns support wood beams, the bearing

Figure 3.4
Column-to-beam connec-tion

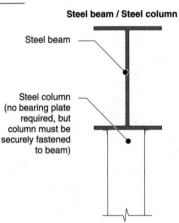

Steel beam / Steel column

Steel beam

Steel column (no bearing plate required, but column must be securely fastened to beam)

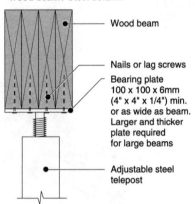

Wood beam / Steel column

Wood beam

Nails or lag screws

Bearing plate 100 x 100 x 6mm (4" x 4" x 1/4") min. or as wide as beam. Larger and thicker plate required for large beams

Adjustable steel telepost

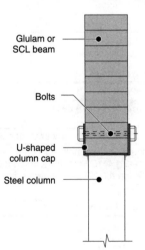

Glulam or SCL beam / Steel column

Glulam or SCL beam

Bolts

U-shaped column cap

Steel column

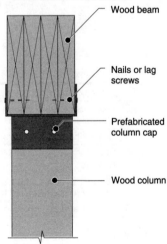

Wood beam / Wood column

Wood beam

Nails or lag screws

Prefabricated column cap

Wood column

plate must extend across its full width (Figure 3.4). Larger and thicker plates are recommended for deeper wood beams, and U-shaped brackets are required for deep and slender glulam or SCL beams to prevent rotation. The top bearing plate should be provided with holes so that nails, lag screws or bolts can be installed to anchor the column to a wood beam. The base plate is usually held in place by pouring the basement slab over the plate (Figure 3.5).

Rectangular wood columns should be 140 x 140mm (5-1/2" x 5-1/2") minimum, but

not less than the width of the supported member. Built-up columns of full length dimension lumber should have each ply fastened with 76mm (3") nails at 300mm (12") on centre.

Columns smaller than the minimum sizes above can be used where the load carrying capacity of the column is checked in accordance with Part 4 of the *NBCC* and found to be adequate.

Beams that rest on wood stud walls should have additional studs or a column placed in the wall below the beam (Figure 3.15).

3

Wood-Frame Construction

Figure 3.5
**Column
supports**

Steel column

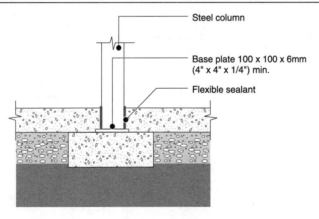

Steel column

Base plate 100 x 100 x 6mm
(4" x 4" x 1/4") min.

Flexible sealant

Wood column

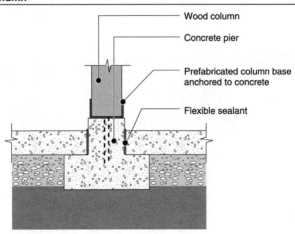

Wood column

Concrete pier

Prefabricated column base
anchored to concrete

Flexible sealant

Wood columns can be anchored to wood beams by toe nailing or by using prefabricated column-cap connectors (Figure 3.4). The base of wood columns should be supported on a small footing pier that raises the base of the column above the level of the basement slab (Figure 3.5). A prefabricated column base may be used to anchor the column to the pier. For Part 4 applications, all columns and column-to-beam connections must be engineered.

Beams

For residential construction, floor beams in wood-frame buildings are usually wood or steel. Steel beams are generally wide-flange sections. Wood beams can either be comprised of sawn lumber, glulam, or be built-up from dimension lumber or structural composite lumber (SCL).

Figure 3.6
Joist-to-beam connections

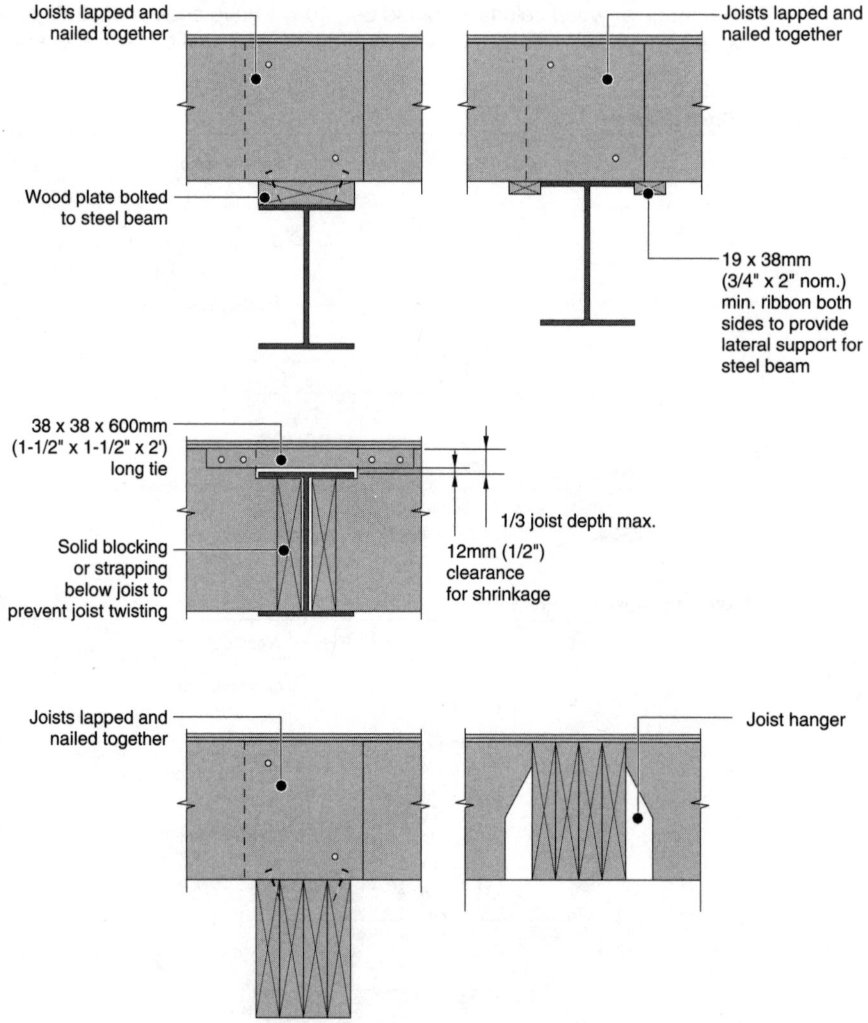

Joists lapped and nailed together

Wood plate bolted to steel beam

Joists lapped and nailed together

19 x 38mm (3/4" x 2" nom.) min. ribbon both sides to provide lateral support for steel beam

38 x 38 x 600mm (1-1/2" x 1-1/2" x 2') long tie

Solid blocking or strapping below joist to prevent joist twisting

1/3 joist depth max.

12mm (1/2") clearance for shrinkage

Joists lapped and nailed together

Joist hanger

Part 9 of the *NBCC* provides span tables for steel, built-up lumber, and glulam beams. Sawn timber and SCL beams must be designed in accordance with Part 4 of the *NBCC*. (SCL manufacturers provide span tables for selection of the appropriate beam size for residential buildings.)

Steel beams must be shop primed and meet the requirements for Grade 300 W steel (yield strength = 300 MPa) in accordance with CSA Standard G40.21, *Structural Quality Steels*. The top flange of steel beams must be laterally supported (Figure 3.6).

All beams must have even and level bearing. For steel beams this may be accomplished by welding a steel bearing plate to the end of the beam and providing a layer of grout below the plate. The minimum required length of bearing at end supports is 89mm (4").

Wood beams built up from dimension lumber should be continuous between points of support, but Part 9 of the *NBCC* permits the beams to have joints at or within 150mm (6") of the end quarter of the clear span of the beam (Figure 3.7).

Figure 3.7
Joints in built-up beams

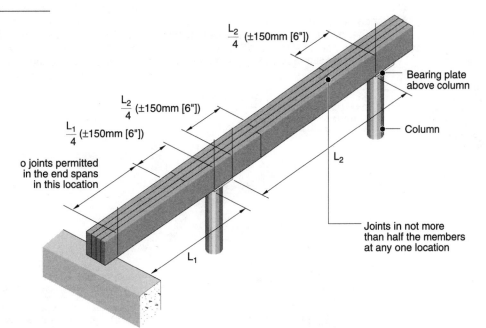

$\frac{L_2}{4}$ (±150mm [6"])

$\frac{L_2}{4}$ (±150mm [6"])

$\frac{L_1}{4}$ (±150mm [6"])

o joints permitted in the end spans in this location

Bearing plate above column

Column

L_2

L_1

Joints in not more than half the members at any one location

3

Wood-Frame Construction

Joints which occur at or near the end quarter must not occur in adjacent members at the same quarter point, and they must not reduce the effective beam width by more than half.

Members spliced at quarter points must be continuous over the adjacent supports. Each individual ply must be nailed with two rows of 89mm (3-1/2") nails spaced not more than 450mm (17-1/2") on centre. The nails near the end of each ply must be 100 to 150mm (4" to 6") from the end. The beams can also be bolted with 12.7mm (1/2") bolts at 1.2m (4') on centre, with end bolts not more than 600mm (2') from the end.

Simply supported beams should be tied together over interior supports. This may be done with nail-on steel straps or gusset plates. The column bearing plate may serve

as the tie as long as it is properly fastened to each beam. Built-up wood beams that have staggered butt joints are tied together by the nailing between laminations.

Beams framing into foundation walls can be supported on top of the wall or in a pocket below the top of the wall. In unit masonry walls, the top course of block must be filled with concrete directly beneath the beam. When wood beams frame into a foundation wall at or below ground level, they must be preservative treated or have a minimum 12mm (1/2") air space at the sides and end, and have 0.05mm (2 mil) polyethylene or Type S roll roofing separating the beam from the concrete. Beams that are located more than 150mm (6") above grade do not require polyethylene or roll roofing between the beam and the foundations (Figure 3.8).

Figure 3.8
Wood beam supported on foundation wall

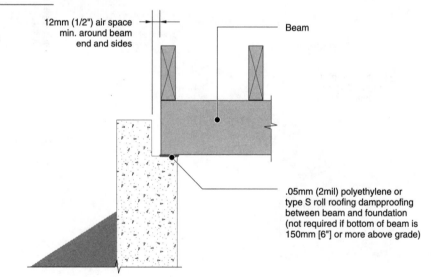

12mm (1/2") air space min. around beam end and sides

Beam

.05mm (2mil) polyethylene or type S roll roofing dampproofing between beam and foundation (not required if bottom of beam is 150mm [6"] or more above grade)

Wood Joists

Most wood floors are framed with 38 x 184mm (2" x 8" nom.) to 38 x 286mm (2" x 12" nom.) lumber. The most commonly available grades are No.1 and No.2 (because these grades are considered to have the same strength and stiffness properties, they are commonly sold as No.2 and Better). Joists are commonly spaced at 300 or 400mm (12" or 16") on centre, although 600mm (24") spacing may be used with thicker subfloors.

Part 9 of the *NBCC* provides span tables for the selection of the appropriate joist size for a given span. Two sets of tables are provided: one set for *General Cases,* which are most common, and one set for *Special Cases,* such as joists with ceilings attached to wood furring or joists with concrete toping. Spans in excess of 5.5m (18') are possible with No.1/No.2 grade lumber depending on the loading and bracing arrangements and species group. The CWC has published *The Span Book* which provides additional information to that found in the *NBCC.*

Since the 1990 edition of the *NBCC*, an additional criteria for floor vibration has been included for span tables to help improve the performance of wood joist floor systems. Depending on load, species, and joist restraint, floor spans are controlled by strength, deflection, or vibration.

The span tables provide maximum spans for solid wood joists installed with strapping and bridging only, and with or without bridging only. Strapping or bridging must be provided at intervals not exceeding 2.1m (7'). Strapping should be not less than 19 x 64mm (1" x 3" nom.) nailed to the underside of the floor joists and fastened at

each end to a sill or header. Strapping is not required if furring strips or a panel type ceiling is used. Bridging should consist of 19 x 64mm (1" x 3" nom.) or 38 x 38mm (2" x 2" nom.) cross bridging nailed between the joists. Solid 38mm (2" nom.) blocking can be used instead of bridging when strapping is also used.

Joists must have at least 38mm (1-1/2") bearing at supports. Restraint is also required at supports to prevent the joists from twisting. Furring strips or a ceiling finish will provide adequate restraint, but where these are not present, cross bridging or 38mm (2" nom.) solid blocking should be installed between joists. Alternatively, the joists may be toe nailed to the support, or end-nailed to the header joists, or continuous strapping may be fastened to the underside of the joists at the supports.

Design of floor joists for Part 4 buildings must be made using the minimum specified loads listed in the *NBCC* for each type of occupancy.

Connection of Joists to Foundation

In all buildings, it is important that a good connection be made between the wood framing superstructure and the foundation. This is of course particularly true in areas of high wind or seismic loadings. The effects of underestimating the importance of a good connection is well documented by some failures which resulted from Hurricane Andrew in southern Florida in 1992. While initial reaction to this catastrophic storm was to blame the building materials used, closer examination showed that code requirements for securing the building to the foundation were not met.

3

Wood-Frame Construction

Figure 3.9
Foundation to floor connection details

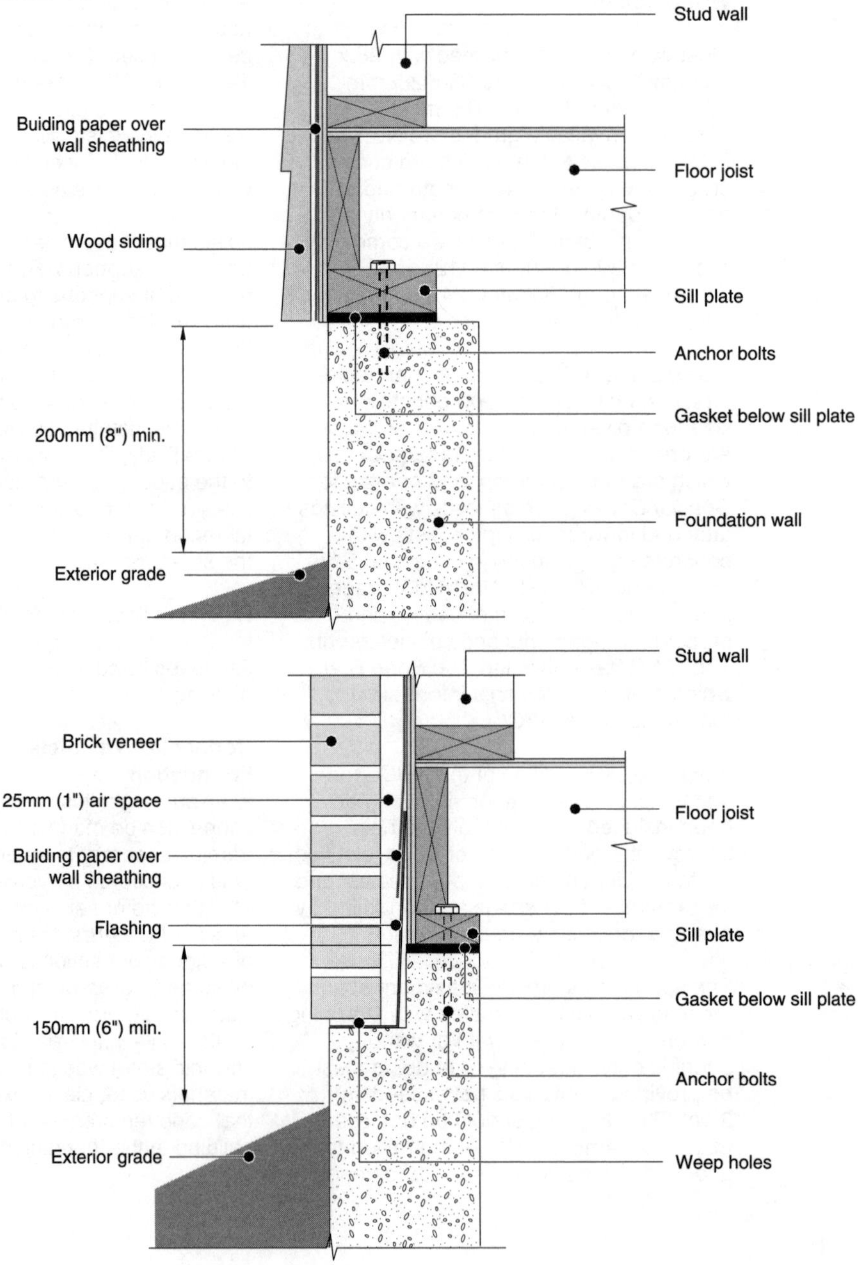

Stud wall

Buiding paper over wall sheathing

Wood siding

Floor joist

Sill plate

Anchor bolts

Gasket below sill plate

200mm (8") min.

Foundation wall

Exterior grade

Stud wall

Brick veneer

25mm (1") air space

Buiding paper over wall sheathing

Flashing

Floor joist

Sill plate

Gasket below sill plate

150mm (6") min.

Anchor bolts

Exterior grade

Weep holes

Typical connection details for connecting joists to the foundation for Part 9 buildings are shown in Figure 3.9. Where wood or vinyl siding is used, the top of the foundation may be flat with the header joist and sill plate located flush with the outside edge of the foundation wall. Where brick veneer is used with a poured concrete foundation, the brick is usually supported on a ledge in the wall below the sill plate. In either case the sill should be located at least 150mm (6") above grade.

The joists are toe nailed to a sill plate that is fastened to the foundation wall with minimum 12.7mm (1/2") diameter anchor bolts spaced not more than 2.4m (8') on centre for Part 9 buildings, and with anchors of appropriate design to resist uplift forces resulting from lateral loads for larger buildings.

It is important for both large and small buildings that a good foundation to super-structure attachment be created. Anchor bolts or other types of hold-down devices must be well embedded (no less than 100 mm) in the concrete foundation.

Anchor bolts must have the correct amount of projection so that nuts can be secured with full thread contact. The holes in the sill plate must be located carefully to match anchor locations. Undue oversizing of the holes to facilitate fitting of the sill plate means that washers will no longer be capable of establishing adequate contact with the sill plate, and resistance to uplift will be drastically reduced.

The header joist must be toe nailed to the sill plate with 82mm (3-1/4") nails at 600mm (2') on centre and be end nailed to the joist with two 82mm (3-1/4") nails.

Dampproofing is required between the sill and the concrete when the grade is closer than 150mm (6") (exterior wood siding should not be closer than 200mm [8"] to grade level).

Connection of Joists to Beams

Joists may be supported on top of a wood beam or be face mounted to the sides of the beam by means of joist hangers. If the joists rest on top of the beam, they must be overlapped, and the ends must be restrained by toe nailing with two 82mm (3-1/4") nails in each joist. This nailing also provides necessary lateral support for the top of the wood beam.

Joists supported by steel beams can rest on top of the steel beams or be notched into the beams. If the joists rest on top, 19 x 38mm (1" x 2" nom.) strips must be nailed to the joists tight to the top flange to give the beam lateral support, or the beam must be provided with a wood nailing plate to which the joists are toe nailed.

If the joists are supported on the bottom flange and notched, 38 x 38mm (2" x 2" nom.) ties connecting joist ends are required to provide support for the subfloor (Figure 3.6). A 12mm (1/2") gap should be provided between the ties and the top flange of the steel beam to allow for shrinkage.

Support of Walls

Non-loadbearing walls that run parallel to the floor joists must be supported by doubled joists or by blocking between the adjacent joists. The blocking should be 38 x 89mm (2" x 4" nom.) lumber spaced not more 1.2m (4') apart, and the supporting joists should be spaced no further than 200mm (8") apart.

Loadbearing interior walls at right angles to the floor joists must not be further than 900mm (3') from the joist support when the wall does not support a floor, and not further than 600mm (2') from the support when the wall supports one or more floors (Figure 3.10).

Figure 3.10
Location of loadbearing walls perpendicular to joists

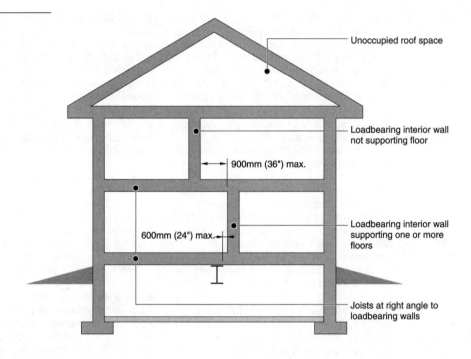

Unoccupied roof space

Loadbearing interior wall not supporting floor

900mm (36") max.

Loadbearing interior wall supporting one or more floors

600mm (24") max.

Joists at right angle to loadbearing walls

Figure 3.11
Notches and holes in wood joists

Notch restrictions

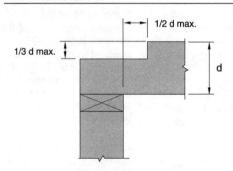

1/2 d max.

1/3 d max.

d

Hole Restrictions

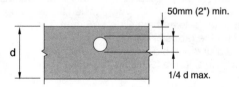

50mm (2") min.

d

1/4 d max.

Holes and Notches in Joists

Joists are often notched or drilled after installation to accommodate electrical or plumbing services. Holes drilled in roof, floor or ceiling framing must not be larger than 1/4 of the depth of the member, and must be located more than 50mm (2") from the edges (Figure 3.11).

Notches on the top edge of joists are allowed, provided they are not deeper than 1/3 the joist depth, and are not beyond half the joist depth from the edge of bearing.

Larger holes may be located closer to the edge, but the depth of the member must be increased by the size of the hole. Notches on the top edge can be larger and be located further from the edge of bearing if the depth of the joist is increased by the size of the notch. Notches on the bottom edge are not permitted.

Floor Openings

When framing around large openings (Figure 3.12), the trimmer joists must be doubled where they support header joists longer than 800mm (2.6'). The header joists should be doubled if they exceed 1.2m (4') in length. Sizes of header joists longer than 3.2m (10.5') should be determined by calculation in accordance with Part 4 of the *NBCC*. When header joists exceed 2m (6.5'), the size of the trimmer joists should also be determined by calculation.

In accordance with Part 9 of *NBCC*, the nailing of this framing should be as follows:

- Each header should be end nailed to the adjacent trimmer joist with five 82mm (3-1/4") nails or three 101mm (4") nails.

- The adjacent header joist should be nailed to the tail joist with five 82mm (3-1/4") nails or three 101mm (4") nails.

- Double header or trimmer joists should be nailed together with 76mm (3") nails at 300mm (12") on centre.

Alternatively, a superior and simpler connection may be achieved with joist hangers or framing anchors.

3

Wood-Frame Construction

Figure 3.12
Framing around openings

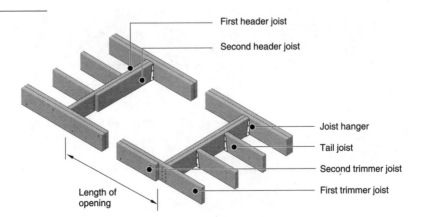

First header joist

Second header joist

Joist hanger

Tail joist

Second trimmer joist

First trimmer joist

Length of opening

Cantilevered Joists

Floor joists can be cantilevered past the exterior walls to provide additional floor space in upper rooms (Figure 3.13). For Part 9 applications, floor joists that support roof loads cannot be cantilevered more than 400mm (16") beyond their supports for 38 x 184mm (2" x 8" nom.) joists, or 600mm past the supports for 38 x 235mm (2" x 10" nom.) joists. Cantilevered joists which support roof and floor loads must be designed in accordance with Part 4 of the *NBCC*.

When cantilevered joists are perpendicular to the main floor joists, the tail joists should extend inward from the support at least six times the length of the cantilever. Each floor joist should be end nailed to the adjacent ply of a double header with five 82mm (3-1/4") nails or three 101mm (4") nails and the double header should be nailed together with 76mm (3") nails at 300mm (12") on centre. Alternatively, joist hangers with suitable joist nailing may be used to provide a superior connection. Framing anchors may also be used.

Subfloor

Modern floor systems are usually sheathed with panel products such as plywood or OSB, but Part 9 of the *NBCC* also permits the use of particleboard and lumber subflooring. In addition, panels of any wood based material may be used as long as they meet CSA Standard O325.0, *Construction Sheathing*. Tongue and groove panels are often used to eliminate the need for a panel underlay or blocking below panel edges.

Plywood and OSB panels should be installed with the surface grain at right angles to the floor joists. The end joints should be staggered and be nailed along the edges with 51mm (2") common or spiral nails or 45mm (1-3/4") ringed nails at 150mm (6") centres, and 300mm (12") at intermediate supports. Common nails are not often used since they provide less withdrawal resistance. When resilient flooring is applied directly to the subflooring, ringed nails should be used.

Figure 3.13
Cantilevered joist perpendicular to main joists

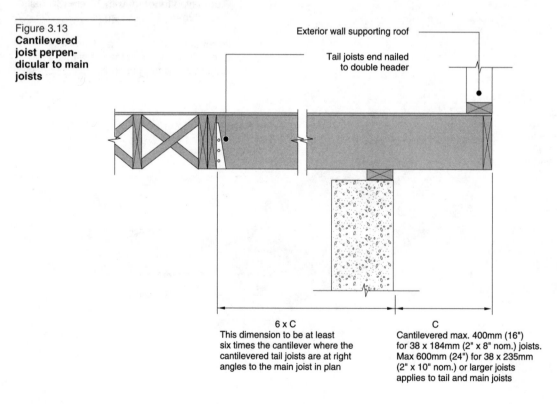

Exterior wall supporting roof

Tail joists end nailed to double header

6 x C
This dimension to be at least six times the cantilever where the cantilevered tail joists are at right angles to the main joist in plan

C
Cantilevered max. 400mm (16") for 38 x 184mm (2" x 8" nom.) joists. Max 600mm (24") for 38 x 235mm (2" x 10" nom.) or larger joists applies to tail and main joists

The edges of the subfloor usually have to be supported. This may be accomplished by using tongue-and-groove panel edges or by supporting the edges with 38 x 38mm (2" x 2" nom.) blocking securely nailed to the joists.

The minimum required thickness of plywood, and OSB subflooring for typical joist spacing is shown in Table 3.1. Table 3.2 provides the maximum spacing for panels conforming to CSA O325.0.

The performance of any floor system can be increased if, in addition to normal fastening, the subfloor is glued with elastomeric adhesive and is fastened with 45mm (1-3/4") No.8 wood screws at 300mm (12") on centre. If panels with tongue and grooved edges are used, additional stiffness can be obtained if glue is applied between the joints. The extra fastening allows the floor systems to act as a composite unit.

For Part 4 buildings, the thickness and span of floor sheathing must be designed in accordance with the minimum specified loads for each type of occupancy.

3

Wood-Frame Construction

Table 3.1
Required thickness of plywood and OSB/wafer-board subfloor

Maximum spacing of supports		Thickness of subflooring			
		Plywood and OSB (O-2 grade)		Waferboard (R-1 grade) and OSB (O-1 grade)	
mm	in.	mm	in.	mm	in.
400	16	15.5	5/8	15.9	5/8
500	19.2	15.5	5/8	15.9	5/8
600	24	18.5	3/4	19.0	3/4

Notes:
1. Where 19mm (3/4") matched wood-strip flooring is laid at right angles to joists, the following thicknesses may be used:
   • 12.5mm (1/2") plywood and O-2 grade OSB
   • 12.7mm (1/2") R-1 grade waferboard and O-1 grade OSB
2. Where a separate panel underlay or concrete topping is applied to subfloor over joists spaced at 400mm (16") on centre or less, the thickness shown in Note 1 may be used. This does not apply to a finish floor consisting of glued ceramic tiles.

Table 3.2
Maximum support spacing for CSA O325 subfloor panels

Maximum spacing of supports		Panel mark	
mm	in.	Subfloor	Used with panel-type underlay
400	16	1F16	2F16
500	19.2	1F20	2F20
600	24	1F24	2F24

Note:
1. In panel marks, 1 = edges unsupported and 2 = edges supported.

Panel Underlay

A 6mm (1/4") thick (minimum) panel underlay must also be installed over the subfloor under the following conditions:

- when the subfloor edges are not supported and the finished floor consists of resilient flooring, parquet flooring, felted-synthetic-fibre floor coverings, or carpeting

- where resilient flooring is used over an OSB subfloor

- where ceramic tiles are to be applied with adhesive

The underlay should consist of hardwood or softwood plywood, OSB, waferboard, particleboard, or hardboard, and the underlay joints should not coincide with the sheathing joints beneath.

Where ceramic tiles are to be glued, the underlay should be at least 11mm (7/16") thick where the joist spacing is greater than 300mm (12"). A 6mm (1/4") underlay is acceptable for glued ceramic tiles over joists spaced at 300mm (12") on centre or less (although a thicker underlay may be preferred). In either case, the subfloor must have its edges supported.

For larger and commercial applications, the installation of a 38mm (1-1/2") concrete topping can be used to provide a solid base for finish flooring with the added benefit of additional sound isolation and floor stiffness.

Floor Trusses

Floor trusses are an alternative to conventional joist floor systems. They can be designed to be either top or bottom chord bearing and can be designed and manufactured for long spans thereby reducing the need for interior supports. Electrical or other services can easily run between the truss webs. As a rough estimate of the depth required for parallel chord floor trusses, allow for a depth-to-span ratio of 1 to 12.

Part 9 of the *NBCC* does not provide floor truss designs. The design is carried out by the manufacturer in accordance with Part 4 of the *NBCC*.

Wood I-Joists

Wood I-joists are another alternative to conventional floor systems and have become quite popular in recent years. The ability to obtain long clear spans using relatively shallow members is a major advantage of this product. Most of the framing techniques used for conventional floor systems are applicable to wood I-joists which are used in combination with laminated veneer lumber (LVL) beams.

As with floor trusses, wood I-joists are designed by the manufacturer. Most suppliers have span tables for the selection of the appropriate grade, depth, and spacing for their product.

The webs of wood I-joists can be drilled to accommodate electrical, plumbing, and other services, and some manufacturers provide prepunched holes in the webs which can be used for this purpose. The manufacturers literature should be consulted for the permissible size and location of web holes. The flanges must not be cut or notched.

Wood I-joists often require nailed web stiffeners at the ends and at locations of concentrated loads. The location and details are outlined in the manufacturer's literature.

Wall Framing

In platform construction, wall framing consists of vertical studs, horizontal top and bottom plates, and lintels to carry loads over openings (Figure 3.14).

Studs

Stud walls are usually framed with 38 x 89mm (2" x 4" nom.) or 38 x 140mm (2" x 6" nom.) Stud grade or better lumber. Fingerjoined Stud grade lumber meeting the requirements of *Special Product Standard SPS 3* is suitable for wall stud applications.

Figure 3.14
Typical wall framing and fastening

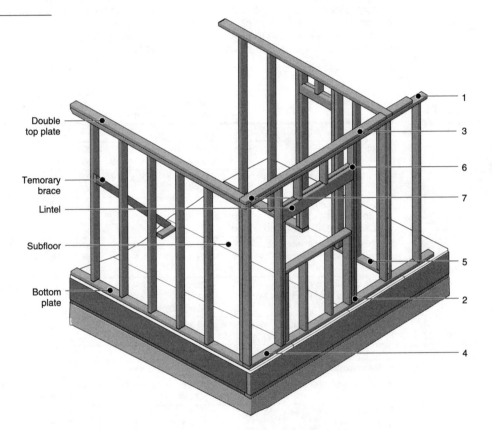

Double top plate

Temorary brace

Lintel

Subfloor

Bottom plate

3

Wood-Frame Construction

Application	Nailing schedule
1. Stud to wall plate (each end), toe nail or end nail	Four 63mm (2-1/2") or two 82mm (3-1/4") nails
2. Double studs at openings or studs at walls or wall intersections and corners	76mm (3") nails at 750mm (30") o.c.
3. Double top wall plates nailed together	76mm (3") nails at 600mm (24") o.c.
4. Bottom wall plate or sole plate to joists or blocking	82mm (3-1/4") nails at 400mm (16") o.c.
5. Interior wall to framing or subflooring	82mm (3-1/4") nails at 600mm (24") o.c.
6. Lintel nailed to studs (each end)	Two 82mm (3-1/4") nails
7. Lapped top plate at wall intersection	Two 82mm (3-1/4") nails

Bearing walls are typically framed with 38 x 140mm (2" x 6" nom.) studs spaced at 400mm (16") on centre and partition walls generally have 38 x 89mm (2" x 4" nom.) studs spaced at 600mm (24") on centre. The minimum requirements, however, are specified by Part 9 of the *NBCC* and they are given in Table 3.3. Although Part 9 permits 38 x 89mm (2" x 4" nom.) studs for exterior walls, 38 x 140mm (2" x 6" nom.) studs are often specified to provide additional insulation space. Stud walls for Part 4 buildings must be designed for the expected vertical and lateral loads.

Studs should be continuous for the full storey height except at openings where they can be cut shorter to support lintels. Studs must be placed perpendicular to the wall sheathing, but in certain situations studs on the flat are permitted (Table 3.3). All loadbearing studs must by laterally supported by sheathing on at least one side.

Table 3.3
Size and spacing of studs

Supported loads including dead loads	Minimum stud size mm	in. nom.	Maximum stud spacing mm	in.	Maximum unsupported height m	ft
Interior walls						
No load	38 x 38	2 x 2	400	16	2.4	8
(flat)	38 x 89	2 x 4	400	16	3.6	12
Attic inaccessible by stairway	38 x 64 [1]	2 x 3	600	24	3.0	10
	38 x 89 [1]	2 x 4	600	24	3.6	12
Attic accessible by stairway plus one floor, or roof load plus one floor, or inaccessible attic plus two floors	38 x 89	2 x 4	400	16	3.6	12
Roof load, attic accessible by stairway, attic inaccessible by a stairway plus one floor	38 x 89	2 x 4	600	24	3.6	12
	38 x 64	2 x 3	400	16	2.4	8
Attic accessible by stairway plus two floors, or roof load plus two floors	38 x 89	2 x 4	300	12	3.6	12
	64 x 89	3 x 4	400	16	3.6	12
	38 x 140	2 x 6	400	16	4.2	14
Attic accessible by stairway plus three floors or roof load plus three floors	38 x 140	2 x 6	300	12	4.2	14
Exterior walls						
Roof, with or without attic storage	38 x 64	2 x 3	400	16	2.4	8
	38 x 89	2 x 4	600	24	3.0	10
Roof, with or without attic storage, plus one floor	38 x 89	2 x 4	400	16	3.0	10
	38 x 140	2 x 6	600	24	3.0	10
Roof, with or without attic storage, plus two floors	38 x 89	2 x 4	300	12	3.0	10
	64 x 89	3 x 4	400	16	3.0	10
	38 x 140	2 x 6	400	16	3.6	12
Roof, with or without attic storage, plus three floors	38 x 140	2 x 6	300	12	1.8	6

Notes:
1. Studs may be used flat in walls supporting only a load from an attic inaccessible by stairway, provided stud height is no more than 2.4m (8'), stud spacing is no more that 400mm (16"), studs are clad on at least one side with plywood or OSB sheathing fastened to the face of the studs with acceptable adhesive, and the tributary width of the roof supported by the studs is not more than 2.1m (7').
2. Studs on flat can be used in gable ends of roofs that contain only unfinished space or in non-load-bearing interior walls.
3. Loadbearing studs must be laterally supported by cladding or blocking.

Where a beam rests on top of a stud wall, a post built up from studs should be provided in the wall directly below the beam and be designed for the loading conditions (Figure 3.15). Where the beam is dropped below the wall plate, the post can be framed as shown.

Wall Plates
Stud walls are framed with top and bottom plates nailed to the studs. Usually the lumber used for the plates is the same size and grade as the studs. In bearing walls, a double top plate and single bottom plate are used to account for misalignment of

Figure 3.15
**Built-up posts
in stud walls**

Beam suported on top of wall

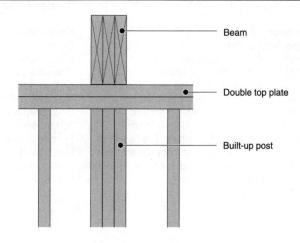

Beam

Double top plate

Built-up post

3

Wood-Frame Construction

Beam dropped below top plate

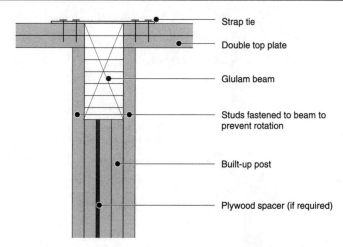

Strap tie

Double top plate

Glulam beam

Studs fastened to beam to prevent rotation

Built-up post

Plywood spacer (if required)

joists or trusses with the studs. Single top and bottom plates are used in partition walls.

In loadbearing walls, joints in double top plates should be staggered at least one stud spacing. The top plate should be lapped and tied at the corners or intersecting walls. Single top plates of partitions must also be adequately tied to bearing walls (Figure 3.16).

Erection

In platform construction, stud walls are usually framed and sheathed on the subfloor then raised and temporarily braced until the upper floor or roof is completed (Figure 3.14). Temporary bracing for each wall section should consist of a 38 x 89mm (2" x 4" nom.) diagonal brace at 45° fastened to the stud and the floor at a spacing not greater than 5m (17'). The wall framing should then be fastened to the floor framing.

It should be noted that the installation of sheathing significantly increases wind loads on partially completed buildings. In the rush to roof a building, incomplete fastening of lower floor sheathing, in combination with dead loads such as roofing materials stockpiled on the roof, can have dangerous consequences in the event of high winds. Additional storeys should be added only when an adequate degree of rigidity has been provided to the floors below.

Framing at Exterior Corners and Wall Intersections

The wall framing at exterior corners and wall intersections must provide adequate support for the vertical edges of interior and exterior cladding materials, and establish a good tie between adjoining walls (Figure 3.17). At the intersection of partitions, blocking between studs can also be used to support the edges of gypsum wallboard (Figure 3.18).

Figure 3.16
Ties for top plates in stud walls

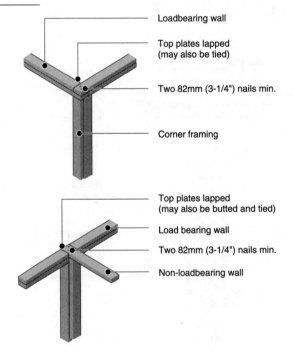

Loadbearing wall

Top plates lapped
(may also be tied)

Two 82mm (3-1/4") nails min.

Corner framing

Top plates lapped
(may also be butted and tied)

Load bearing wall

Two 82mm (3-1/4") nails min.

Non-loadbearing wall

Note:
Alternatively, walls may be tied with 75 x 150 x 0.91mm
(3" x 6", 20 gauge) galvanized steel straps fastened
to each wall with three 63mm (2-1/2") nails.

Figure 3.17
Multiple stud arrangements for exterior corners and wall intersections

At exterior corners

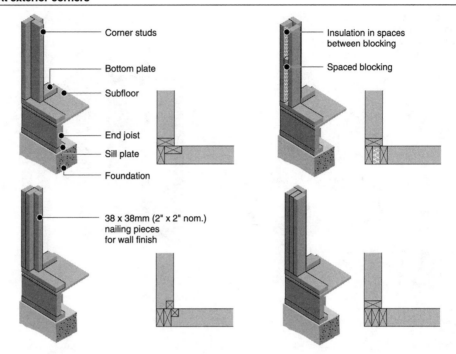

Corner studs

Bottom plate

Subfloor

End joist

Sill plate

Foundation

Insulation in spaces between blocking

Spaced blocking

38 x 38mm (2" x 2" nom.) nailing pieces for wall finish

At intersection of interior partition and exterior wall

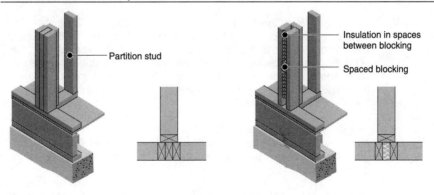

Partition stud

Insulation in spaces between blocking

Spaced blocking

3

Wood-Frame Construction

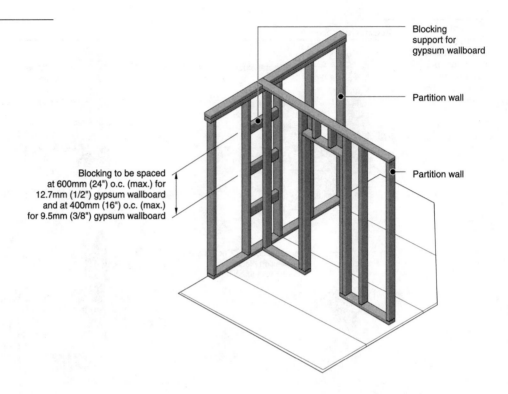

Blocking
support for
gypsum wallboard

Partition wall

Blocking to be spaced
at 600mm (24") o.c. (max.) for
12.7mm (1/2") gypsum wallboard
and at 400mm (16") o.c. (max.)
for 9.5mm (3/8") gypsum wallboard

Partition wall

Framing at Wall Openings

Lintels are used to carry roof or floor loads over window, door, and other openings in walls. For small openings in loadbearing walls, lintels may be either two pieces of 38mm (2" nom.) lumber, or one piece of 89mm (4" nom.) wide lumber.

Larger openings in walls supporting roof and ceiling loads can be obtained using glulam or three- to five-ply dimension lumber lintels.

Maximum span tables for lintels are provided in the 1995 *NBCC* and The *Span Book,* 1995 edition, published by the Canadian Wood Council.

Where the lintel is two ply or more, the studs at the sides of the opening must be doubled. The inner ply or cripple stud supports the lintel and extends from the lintel to the bottom of the wall plate and the outer stud extends from the bottom plate up past the end of the lintel (Figure 3.19). For glulam and three- to four-ply dimension lumber lintels, a minimum of three studs is required for bearing.

For Part 4 applications, lintels must be designed for their specific load conditions.

Lintels must be adequately tied to the adjacent walls. This is usually accomplished by running the top plate of the wall continuous over the lintel (Figure 3.20). Alternatively, the lintel can be made flush with the top of the wall and be tied to the wall with wood plates or steel straps.

Figure 3.19
**Lintels over
openings**

Small openings

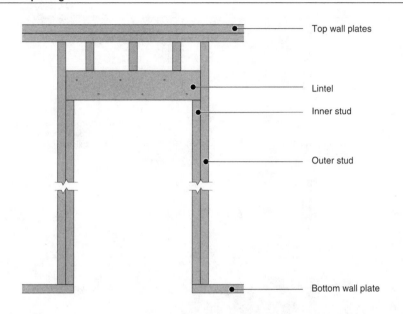

Top wall plates

Lintel

Inner stud

Outer stud

Bottom wall plate

Large openings

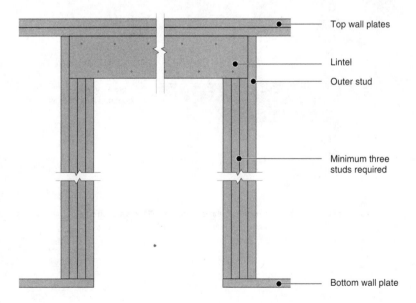

Top wall plates

Lintel

Outer stud

Minimum three
studs required

Bottom wall plate

Note:
Where lintels are made of two or more members, the members must be
fastened with two rows of 82mm (3-1/4") nails at 450mm (18") on centre.
Lintel members may be separated by filler pieces to make the lintel width
the same as the studs.

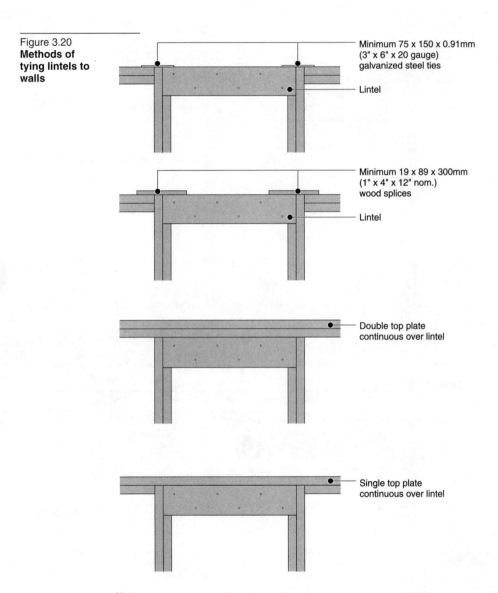

Figure 3.20
**Methods of
tying lintels to
walls**

Minimum 75 x 150 x 0.91mm
(3" x 6" x 20 gauge)
galvanized steel ties

Lintel

Minimum 19 x 89 x 300mm
(1" x 4" x 12" nom.)
wood splices

Lintel

Double top plate
continuous over lintel

Single top plate
continuous over lintel

Note:
Ties must be fastened with a minimum three 63mm (2-1/2") nails each side.

Wall Sheathing

For buildings meeting Part 9 requirements, wall sheathing for wood-frame construction is only required where exterior cladding, such as vertical siding or stucco, requires intermediate fastening between supports or solid backing. However, it is good building practice to use sheathing, as it provides additional strength and rigidity to the structure.

For Part 4 buildings, engineering assessment of the vertical and lateral loads will determine the need for wall sheathing to provide lateral bracing for wall studs and to develop shearwall action to resist lateral loads.

Several materials are listed in the *NBCC* for use as sheathing, but plywood and oriented strandboard (OSB) are most commonly used because they give superior strength and rigidity. In some cases, plywood or OSB panels are used only at the corners of the building and the remaining wall area is sheathed with a different material. This may reduce the cost of the sheathing material, while maintaining adequate strength. The minimum thickness of wall sheathing materials is given in Table 3.4 for Part 9 applications.

Plywood and OSB sheathing can be applied vertically or horizontally and should be fastened as shown in Figure 3.21.

Sheathing paper is generally required beneath siding, stucco, or masonry veneer to act as a second barrier to the entry of wind and rain (see Chapter 7). It must conform to CAN2-51.32 *Sheathing Membrane, Breather Type.*

3

Wood-Frame Construction

Table 3.4
Minimum thickness and specifications for wall sheathing

Type of sheathing	Minimum thickness, mm (in.)				Material standards
	Supports at 400mm (16")		Supports at 600mm (24")		
Lumber	17.0	(3/4)	17.0	(3/4)	See 1995 *NBCC* Table 9.3.2.1
Fibreboard (insulating)	9.5	(3/8)	11.1	(1/2)	CSA A247
Gypsum sheathing	9.5	(3/8)	12.7	(1/2)	CSA A82.27, ASTM C97
Plywood (exterior type)	6.0	(1/4)	7.5	(5/16)	CSA O121, CSA O151, CSA O153
OSB	6.0	(1/4)	7.5	(5/16)	CSA O437.0 Grade O-2
Waferboard and OSB	6.35	(1/4)	7.9	(5/16)	CSA O437.0 Grades R-1 and O-1
Expanded polystyrene	38	(1-1/2)	38	(1-1/2)	CAN/CGSB-51.20-M Types 1 and 2
Expanded polystyrene	25	(1)	25	(1)	CAN/CGSB-51.20-M Types 3 and 4
Urethane and Isocyanurate	38	(1-1/2)	38	(1-1/2)	CGSB 51-GP-21M Types 1, 2, and 4
Urethane and Isocyanurate	25	(1)	25	(1)	CGSB 51-GP-21M Type 3
Urethane and Isocyanurate	25	(1)	25	(1)	CAN/CGSB-51.26-M Types 1 and 2, faced
Phenolic, faced	25	(1)	25	(1)	CAN/CGSB 51.25-M
Rigid board mineral fibre	25	(1)	25	(1)	CSA A101 Type 2

Figure 3.21
**Vertical and
horizontal
application of
panel type
sheathing**

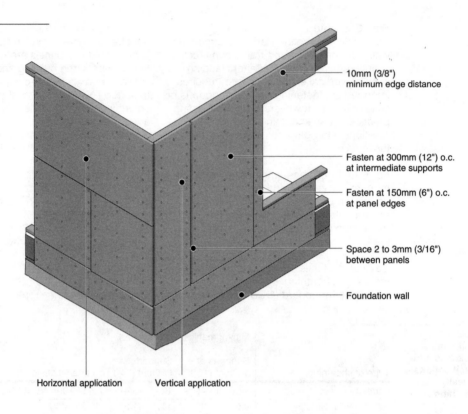

10mm (3/8")
minimum edge distance

Fasten at 300mm (12") o.c.
at intermediate supports

Fasten at 150mm (6") o.c.
at panel edges

Space 2 to 3mm (3/16")
between panels

Foundation wall

Horizontal application   Vertical application

Note:
Fastening for panel sheathing can be 51mm (2") common or spiral nails, 45mm ringed
nails, or staples (38mm [1-1/2"] long up to 10mm [3/8"] thick panels and 51mm [2"] long
for 10 to 20mm [3/8" to 3/4"] thick panels).

Roof Framing

Wood as a building material lends itself to the construction of many roof shapes (Figure 3.22). Gable, hip, and flat roofs can either be framed conventionally on site using rafters or they can be built using prefabricated roof trusses.

Conventional Roof Framing

For residential construction, roofs can be conventionally framed either by using a system of rafters supported at each end by beams and bearing walls, or by using a system of tied rafters supported on exterior walls with lateral restraint of the supporting walls provided by collar ties, dwarf walls, or diagonal struts.

The maximum permissible span for roof joists, ceiling joists, and rafters of different species, grades, and sizes of lumber is given in Part 9 of the 1995 *NBCC* for various spacings and roof loadings. Tables 3.5 and 3.6 provide the minimum nailing requirements for roof members.

3

Wood-Frame Construction

Figure 3.22
Roof shapes

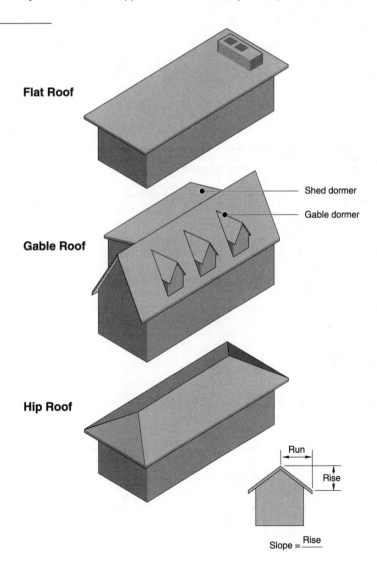

Flat Roof

Gable Roof

Shed dormer

Gable dormer

Hip Roof

Run

Rise

$$\text{Slope} = \frac{\text{Rise}}{\text{Run}}$$

Table 3.5
Nailing for roof framing

Application	Nail length mm	in.	Quantity
Ceiling joist to plate - toe nail each end	82	3-1/4	2
Roof rafter, roof truss or roof joist to plate - toe nail	82	3-1/4	3
Rafter plate to each ceiling joist	101	4	2
Rafter to joist (with ridge supported)	76	3	3
Rafter to joist (with ridge unsupported)	76	3	(Table 3.6)
Gusset plate to each rafter at peak	57	2-1/4	4
Rafter to ridge board - toe nail, - end nail	82	3-1/4	3
Collar tie to rafter - each end	76	3	3
Collar tie lateral support to each collar tie	57	2-1/4	2
Jack rafter to hip or valley rafter	82	3-1/4	2
Roof strut to rafter	76	3	3
Roof strut to loadbearing wall - toe nail	82	3-1/4	2

Table 3.6
Minimum rafter to joist nailing for unsupported ridges, 76mm (3") or longer nails

Roof slope	Spacing mm (in.)	Building width ≤ 8m (24') Roof snow load, kPa (psf) ≤1.0 (20)	1.5 (30)	≥2.0 (40)	Building width ≤ 9.8m (32') Roof snow load, kPa (psf) ≤1.0 (20)	1.5 (30)	≥2.0 (40)
Rafter tied to every joist							
1 in 3	400 (16)	4	5	6	5	7	8
	600 (24)	6	8	9	8	–	–
1 in 2.4	400 (16)	4	4	5	5	6	7
	600 (24)	5	7	8	7	9	11
1 in 2	400 (16)	4	4	4	4	4	5
	600 (24)	4	5	6	5	7	8
1 in 1.71	400 (16)	4	4	4	4	4	4
	600 (24)	4	4	5	5	6	7
1 in 1.33	400 (16)	4	4	4	4	4	4
	600 (24)	4	4	4	4	4	5
1 in 1	400 (16)	4	4	4	4	4	4
	600 (24)	4	4	4	4	4	4
Rafter tied to joist every 1.2m							
1 in 3	400 (16)	11	–	–	–	–	–
	600 (24)	11	–	–	–	–	–
1 in 2.4	400 (16)	7	10	–	9	–	–
	600 (24)	7	10	–	–	–	–
1 in 2	400 (16)	6	8	9	8	–	–
	600 (24)	6	8	9	8	–	–
1 in 1.71	400 (16)	5	7	8	7	9	11
	600 (24)	5	7	8	7	9	11
1 in 1.33	400 (16)	4	5	6	5	6	7
	600 (24)	4	5	6	5	6	7
1 in 1	400 (16)	4	4	4	4	4	5
	600 (24)	4	4	4	4	4	5

Notes:
1. Ceiling joists lapped or fastened with gussets. Use at least one more nail per joist splice than required for the rafter to joist connection.

The tied rafter system (Figure 3.23) can be used when the roof slope is 1 in 3 or greater. The rafters are cut to length with the appropriate angle cut at the ridge and eaves. At the bearing walls, the rafters can be birdsmouth cut and extend past the wall, or they can be cut flush with the wall, and, if desired, outriggers can be nailed to the ends to provide an overhang (Figure 3.24). A bearing length of at least 38mm (1-1/2") should be provided in either case.

Since the ridge is unsupported, the rafters must be tied together at the bearing walls with rods or ceiling joists to prevent outward movement. Ceiling joists are most commonly used for this purpose. They can either be continuous, or be spliced over vertical supports by lapping the ends or by fastening with gusset plates. Ceiling joist splices should be fastened with at least one more nail than specified in Table 3.8

for the appropriate roof slope. At the ridge, each rafter pair should be located directly opposite each other, and be fastened together using gusset plates or by nailing to a ridge board (Table 3.5). If a ridge board is used, the rafters can be offset by a distance equal to their thickness.

Collar ties of at least 38 x 89mm (2" x 4" nom.) lumber can be used to provide inter-mediate support to reduce the span of rafters. Collar ties longer than 2.4m (8') should be laterally supported near the centre with 19 x 89mm (1" x 4" nom.) bracing running at right angles to the ties. Dwarf walls or diagonal struts (at angle not less than 45°) can also be used to reduce the rafter span.

Dwarf walls are generally supported by the ceiling joists and must be securely fastened to the roof and ceiling framing to

3

Wood-Frame Construction

Figure 3.23
Tied rafter system

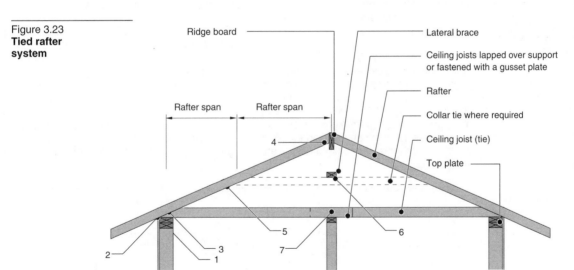

Nailing for roof framing

1. Ceiling joist to plate (toe nail each end)	Two 82mm (3-1/4") nails
2. Rafter, truss, roof joist to plate (toe nail)	Three 82mm (3-1/4") nails
3. Rafter to joist (with ridge unsupported)	(Table 3.6)
4. Rafter to ridge board, - toe nail - end nail	Four 57mm (2-1/4") nails Three 82mm (3-1/4") nails
5. Collar tie to rafter (each end)	Three 76mm (2") nails
6. Collar tie lateral support to collar tie	Two 57mm (2-1/4") nails
7. Ceiling joist at splice	(Table 3.6)

prevent movement. If dwarf walls enclose finished rooms, solid blocking should be installed between the supporting joists. The additional roof load imposed by a dwarf wall should be considered when the size of the ceiling joists below is determined. Usually an increase in the size to the next standard depth will be adequate.

For hip and valley rafters (Figure 3.25) the *NBCC* requires that these rafters be at least 50mm (2") deeper than the common rafters. However, larger valley rafters should be considered for long spans, or for where the length of the supported joist is large. Fastening for jack rafters is given in Table 3.5.

For gable and shed dormers (Figure 3.26), the rafters at each side of the dormer are doubled to support the side studs. A double header is installed at each end of the dormer opening to support the ends of the jack and common rafters. Dormers without side walls can be framed in a similar manner.

Gable end walls may be framed using double rafters supported by studs that have angled end cuts to match the slope of the rafters (Figure 3.27). The studs are in turn supported on the lower end wall. If an over-hang greater than 400mm (16") is desired, ladder truss framing can be used at the end wall, in which case, the lookout rafters are

cantilevered over the gable end wall, and the ends are fastened to a double rafter. The distance between the double rafter and the end wall should be at least twice the length of the cantilever.

Where a cathedral or vaulted ceiling is desired, the rafters must be supported on a ridge beam (Figure 3.28), or tie rods must be provided to resist outward thrust. In this situation, the beam and supporting posts must be designed in accordance with Part 4 of the *NBCC*. Support for the ridge is also required where the roof slope is less than 1 in 3, even if the rafters are tied together with ceiling joists. Support may be provided by a beam or dwarf walls.

In flat roof construction, the rafters usually support the ceiling as well as the roof loads. For this reason, they are referred to as roof joists and they must be sized from the appropriate table in the *NBCC*.

A minimum slope of 1 in 25 is required for roof drainage. This can be obtained by tapering each joist or by adding a tapered strip to the top of each joist. Where an overhang is required, lookout joists are cantilevered over the wall and supported by a doubled joist at the interior end and by a rafter header at the eave (Figure 3.29). The cantilevered length should be no greater than half of the interior span.

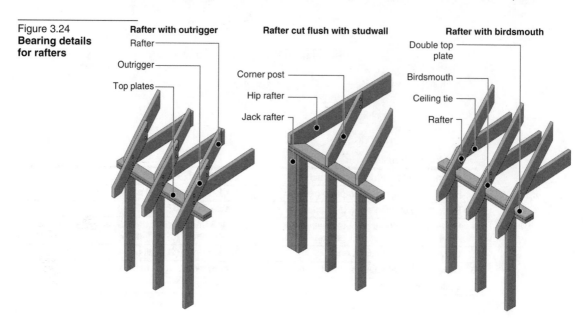

Figure 3.24
Bearing details for rafters

Rafter with outrigger

Rafter cut flush with studwall

Rafter with birdsmouth

Rafter
Outrigger
Top plates

Corner post
Hip rafter
Jack rafter

Double top plate
Birdsmouth
Ceiling tie
Rafter

Figure 3.25
**Hip and valley
rafter framing**

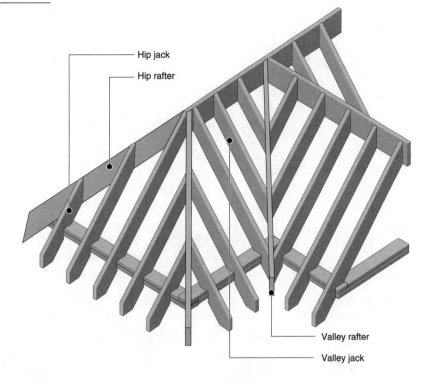

Hip jack

Hip rafter

Valley rafter

Valley jack

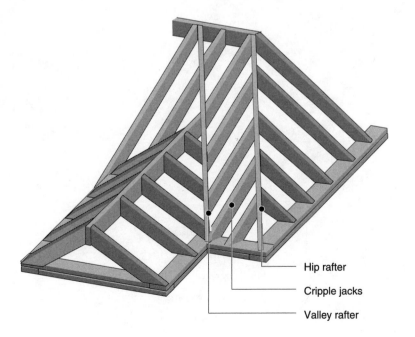

Hip rafter

Cripple jacks

Valley rafter

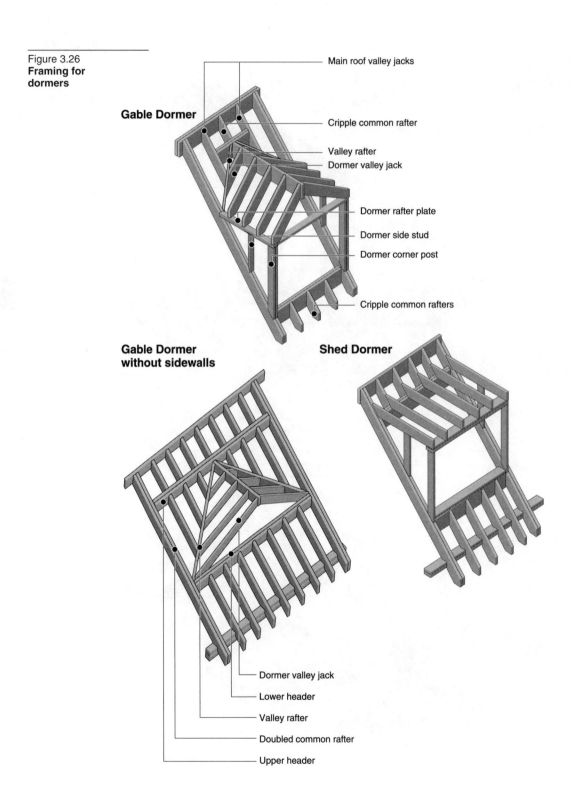

Figure 3.26
Framing for dormers

Gable Dormer

Main roof valley jacks

Cripple common rafter

Valley rafter

Dormer valley jack

Dormer rafter plate

Dormer side stud

Dormer corner post

Cripple common rafters

Gable Dormer without sidewalls

Shed Dormer

Dormer valley jack

Lower header

Valley rafter

Doubled common rafter

Upper header

Figure 3.27
Framing for gable ends

Gable end

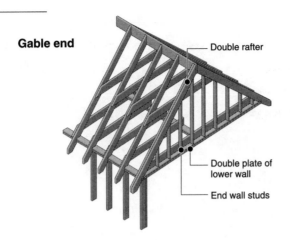

- Double rafter
- Double plate of lower wall
- End wall studs

Gable end with overhang

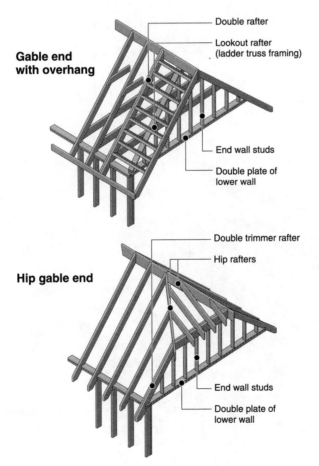

- Double rafter
- Lookout rafter (ladder truss framing)
- End wall studs
- Double plate of lower wall

Hip gable end

- Double trimmer rafter
- Hip rafters
- End wall studs
- Double plate of lower wall

3

Wood-Frame Construction

Figure 3.28
**Cathedral
ceiling support**

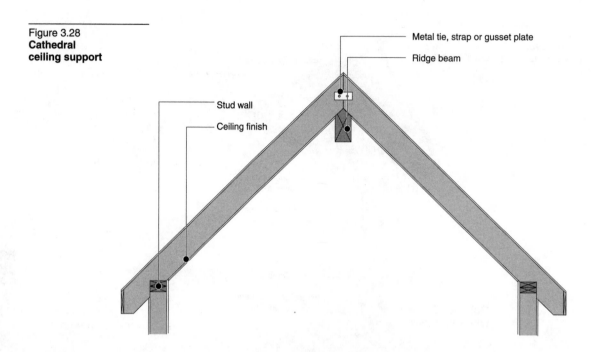

Metal tie, strap or gusset plate

Ridge beam

Stud wall

Ceiling finish

Figure 3.29
**Flat roof
construction**

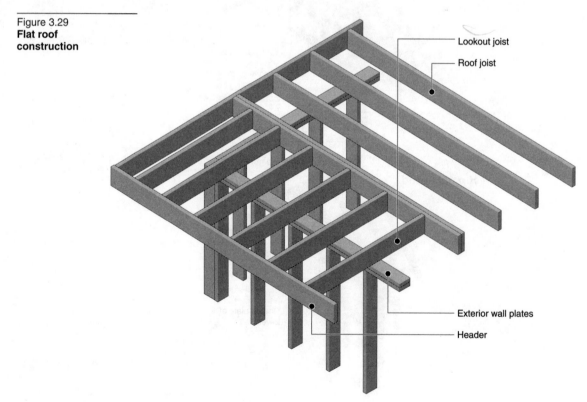

Lookout joist

Roof joist

Exterior wall plates

Header

Prefabricated Roof Trusses

Prefabricated roof trusses (Section 2.3) are by far the most common system used for roof framing today. They are premanufactured and can be installed quickly, allowing the building to be rapidly enclosed. Wood trusses are engineered and are widely used in single- and multi-family residential, institutional, agricultural and commercial construction. Their high strength-to-weight ratios permit long spans, offering greater flexibility in floor plan layouts. They can be designed in almost any shape or size, restricted only by manufacturing capabilities, shipping limitations and handling considerations.

The truss plate manufacturer, on behalf of the truss fabricator, is usually responsible for the design of the trusses. Once the trusses are delivered to the job site, the installer (builder, building contractor, licensed contractor, erector or licensed erector) accepts full responsibility for the trusses unless the truss fabricator has been contracted to erect the trusses.

With each truss shipment, a roof plan, a truss layout drawing (Figure 3.30) showing the location of each truss type, and a shop drawing for each truss should be included. The shop drawings (Figure 3.31) show a sketch of the truss with an engineer's seal if this has been specified. In addition, the following important information is shown on these drawings:

- overall truss dimensions

- truss design, loading, and analysis

- location of all supports

- truss spacing

- web and chord sizes and grades

- plate size, type, and location for each joint

- location and size of all permanent lateral bracing required for the chords and webs

Unless otherwise arranged, the installer is responsible for properly receiving, unloading, storing, handling and bracing the wood trusses to protect life and property.

3

Wood-Frame Construction

Figure 3.30
Truss reference and layout plan

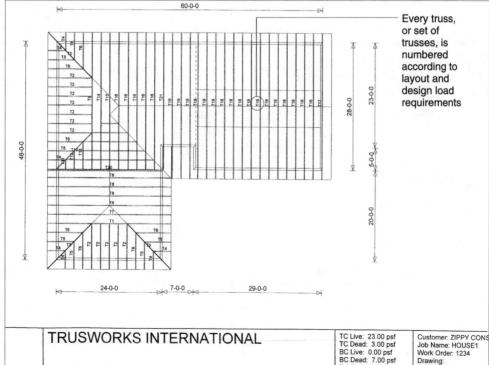

Every truss, or set of trusses, is numbered according to layout and design load requirements

TRUSWORKS INTERNATIONAL

TC Live: 23.00 psf
TC Dead: 3.00 psf
BC Live: 0.00 psf
BC Dead: 7.00 psf
Total: 33.00 psf
Stress Increase 1.33 psf
Spacing 24.00" o.c.

Customer: ZIPPY CONS
Job Name: HOUSE1
Work Order: 1234
Drawing:
Designed by:
Checked by:
Date: 11-29-96

Figure 3.31
**Typical truss
shop drawing**

TPIC97	CWC		WO: TEST01		TI: CWCTR1	QTY: 1

TOP CHORDS: 2x4 SPF #1/#2 (N)
BOT CHORDS: 2x4 SPF #1/#2 (N)
WEBS: 2x3 SPF #1/#2 (N)
All COMPRESSION Chords are assumed to be
continuously braced unless noted otherwise.
MAX LIVE LOAD DEFLECTION:
L/876 at JOINT # 8
L=-0.34" D=-0.11" T=-0.45"
MAX HORIZONTAL DEFLECTION:
T= 0.11"
Defl Criteria based on TPIC: 1.33*LL + DL

RMB: 1.10* (Fb, Fc, Ft, Fv)
Importance Factor: 1.00
TPIC Building Type: HSB

Analysis based on Simplified Analog Model.
Analysis is based upon MANUALLY entered load
    Top Chord Live Load = 37.0 psf.
CONNECTOR PLATES ARE ForeTruss
FT20 (20ga) and FT18 (18ga)

..TC...FORCE...CSI	..BC...FORCE...CSI
1- 2 -4587 0.91	10- 9 4265 0.98
2- 3 -3983 0.83	9- 8 2776 0.69
3- 4 -3990 0.83	8- 7 2776 0.72
4- 5 -4594 0.91	7- 6 4271 0.97

=============Joint Locations==============
1) 0- 0- 0   5) 26- 0- 0   9) 8-11- 4
2) 6-10-14   6) 26- 0- 0   10) 0- 0- 0
3) 13- 0- 0   7) 17- 0-12
4) 19- 1- 2   8) 14- 0- 0

----------- TOTAL DESIGN LOADS -----------
Uniform	PLF	From	PLF	To
TC Vert L	-111	-1-10- 8	-111	27-10- 8
TC Vert D	-7	-1-10- 8	-7	27-10- 8
BC Vert D	-25	0- 0- 0	-25	26- 0- 0

----MAX. REACTIONS PER BEARING LOCATION-----
X-Loc	Vert	Horiz	Uplift	Y-Loc	Type
0- 2-12	1449	0	0	BOT	PIN
25- 9- 4	1450	0	0	BOT	H-ROLL

---MAX. LIVE/DEAD LOAD REACTIONS PER X-LOC--
X-Loc	Vert-React	Uplift-React	Y-Loc
0- 2-12	1100/ 349	0/ 0	BOT
25- 9- 4	1100/ 349	0/ 0	BOT

13-0-0   13-0-0
4.00   -4.00
5X5
2X3   2X3
5-3-3   4-7-15
0-3-15   0-3-15
3X12   4X5   3X6   4X6   3X12

26-0-0
10   6
1450# 5.50"   1450# 5.50"
9   8   7
1-10-8   1-10-8
(R1-11-11)   (R1-11-11)
26-0-0
DESIGN LOADS SHOWN ARE FACTORED
scale = 0.2252

DESIGN INFORMATION
THIS DESIGN IS FOR AN INDIVIDUAL
BUILDING COMPONENT AND HAS BEEN
BASED ON INFORMATION PROVIDED BY THE
CLIENT. THE ENGINEER DISCLAIMS ANY
RESPONSIBILITY FOR DAMAGES AS A
RESULT OF FAULTY OR INCORRECT
INFORMATION. SPECIFICATION AND/OR
DESIGNS FURNISHED TO ENGINEER BY
THE CLIENT.SYSTEMES FORETRUSS IS
ONLY RESPONSIBLE FOR THE STRUCTURAL
INTEGRITY OF THIS BUILDING
COMPONENT FOR THE CONDITIONS SHOWN
ON THIS DRAWING. THE STRUCTURAL
INTEGRITY OF THE BUILDING AND THE
VERIFICATION OF THE DIMENSIONS AND
THE DESIGN LOADS USED ARE THE
RESPONSIBILITY OF THE BUILDING
DESIGNER.   **CODE**
THIS TRUSS HAS BEEN DESIGNED IN
ACCORDANCE WITH NBC/OBC AND CSA
ENGINEERING GUIDLINES.

LUMBER
1.LUMBER USED MUST BE THE SAME GRADE
AND SIZE AS INDIQUATED ON THE
DRAWING.
2.LUMBER USED MUST NOT BE TREATED BY
ANY FIREPROOFING MATERIAL OR ANY
OTHER CORROSIVE CHEMICAL AGENTS.
3.LUMBER MUST BE FREE OF SPLITS AND
CRACKS.

CONNECTOR PLATTES
1.PLATES SHALL BE LOCATED ON BOTH
FACES OF THE TRUSS WITH NAILS
FULLY IMBEDED AND SHALL BE SYM.
ABOUT THE CENTRE OF THE JOINT.
2.PLATES SHALL NOT BE INSTALLED OVER
KNOTHOLES,KNOTS OR DISTORTED GRAIN.

CALCULATION
1.COMPRESSION CHORDS (TOP OR BOTTOM)
Are ASSUMED TO BE CONTINUOUSLY
BRACED BY SHEATING UNLESS OTHERWISE
SPECIFIED.
2.WHERE BOTTOM CHORDS IN TENSION
ARE NOT FULLY BRACED LATERALLY BY
A PROPERLY APPLIED RIGID CEILING,
THEY SHOULD BE BRACED AT A MIN.
10'-0" O.C.
3.USE OF THIS TRUSS IS IN DRY
ENVIRONMENT.

**FABRICATION HANDLING
AND INSTALLATION**
1.PRIOR TO FABRICATION, THE FABRICATOR
SHALL REVIEW THIS DRAWING TO VERIFY
THAT THE INFORMATION IS IN
CONFORMANCE WITH HIS PLANS.
2.CALCULATION IS BASED ON A GOOD
QUALITY CONTROL AT FABRICATION.
3.MEMBERS SHALL BE CUT FOR TIGHT
FITTING WOOD TO WOOD BEARING.
4.NO DRILLING OR CUTTING OF WEBS
ARE PERMITTED.
5.HANDLING AND ERRECTION OF TRUSSES
MUST BE HANDLED BY QUALIFIED PERSON
IN ACCORDANCE WITH
"HANDLING, INSTALLATION & BRACING",
TPIC.
6.USE CARE DURING BANDING OR
BUNDLING, DELIVERY AND INSTALLATION
TO AVOID DAMAGE.
7.THIS TRUSS MUST BE FIXED STRAIGHT
AND PLUMB TO BEARING PLATE USING
MIN. 4-(4-1/2") NAILS.
8.CONNECTION AND ANCHORAGE OF THE
TRUSS TO BEARING PLATE ARE THE
RESPONSIBILITY OF THE BUILDING
DESIGNER.
9.TEMPORARY AND PERMANENT BRACING
FOR HOLDING TRUSSES IN A STRAIGHT
AND PLUMB POSITION AND FOR
RESISTING LATERAL FORCES SHALL BE
DESIGNED AND INSTALLED BY OTHERS.

SPLICES
LOCATE 'IN-PANEL' SPLICES AT APPROX.
1/4 OF PANEL LENGTH FROM ADJACENT
JOINT AS SHOWN ON TRUSS DRAWING

Systemes ForeTruss Inc.

WARNING: READ ALL NOTES ON THIS SHEET.
**A COPY OF THIS DRAWING TO BE GIVEN TO ERECTING
CONTRACTOR.**
BRACING WARNING
BRACING SHOWN ON THIS DRAWING IS NOT ERECTION BRACING, WIND BRACING, PORTAL
BRACING OR SIMILAR BRACING. BRACES SHOWN ON THIS TRUSS DRAWING ARE FOR
LATERAL SUPPORT OF TRUSS MEMBERS ONLY TO REDUCE BUCKLING LENGTH. BRACES
SHALL BE: (1) 1X4 FOR RESIDETIAL BLDG. IN ACCORDANCE TO SECTION #9 OF NBC
AND 2X4 FOR COMMERCIAL AND AGRICULTUR BLDG. IN ACCORDANCE TO SECTION #4 OF
NBC. (2) PLACED HORIZONTALLY AND NAILED TO MEMBERS WITH MIN. 3- 3" NAILS.
PROVISIONS MUST BE MADE TO ANCHOR LATERAL BRACING AT ENDS AND SPECIFIED
LOCATION DETERMINED BY THE BUILDING DESIGNER.

Eng. Job:		WO: TEST01
Dwg: LSD		Truss ID: CWCTR1
Dsgnr:	Chk:	Date: 6-09-97

TC Live	37.0 psf	DurFac - Lbr: 1.00
TC Dead	3.0 psf	DurFac - Plt: 0.80
BC Live	0.0 psf	O.C. Spacing: 24.0"
BC Dead	10.0 psf	Design Criteria: TPIC
		Code Desc: P9-NBC
TOTAL	50.0 psf	V:06.03.97- 4456- 6

Figure 3.31
(cont'd)
**Typical truss
shop drawing**

Lumber specifications

Connector plate specifications

Member load distribution

Design load distribution

Joint locations

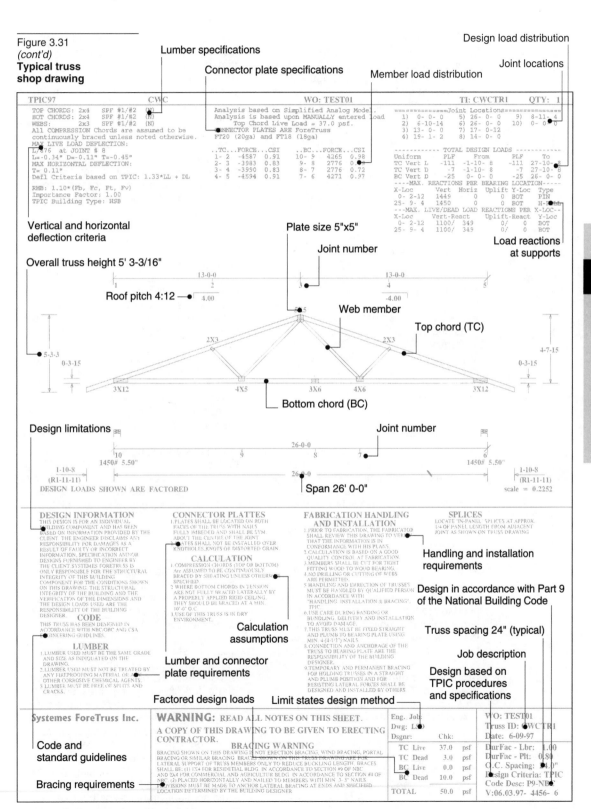

Vertical and horizontal
deflection criteria

Plate size 5"x5"

Joint number

Load reactions
at supports

Overall truss height 5' 3-3/16"

Roof pitch 4:12

Web member

Top chord (TC)

Bottom chord (BC)

Design limitations

Joint number

DESIGN LOADS SHOWN ARE FACTORED

Span 26' 0-0"

Handling and installation
requirements

Design in accordance with Part 9
of the National Building Code

Truss spacing 24" (typical)

Job description

Design based on
TPIC procedures
and specifications

Calculation
assumptions

Lumber and connector
plate requirements

Factored design loads

Limit states design method

Code and
standard guidelines

Bracing requirements

Systemes ForeTruss Inc.

WARNING: READ ALL NOTES ON THIS SHEET.
A COPY OF THIS DRAWING TO BE GIVEN TO ERECTING CONTRACTOR.
BRACING WARNING

Truss Framing

Roof trusses can be manufactured in many different shapes, slopes, and styles (Figure 2.6,). A standard gable roof (Figure 3.32) is the simplest arrangement, with gable end trusses at both ends and common trusses spaced in between.

Buildings with intersecting ridge lines can be framed as shown in Figure 3.32. Valley trusses are supported on top of the common trusses to form the intersecting ridge. The ends of the common trusses can be supported by a girder truss if a clear span opening is required below. The girder trusses usually consists of a number of common trusses nailed together.

A hip roof consists of two hip ends built up of flat hip trusses in a step down system (Figure 3.33). In this system, common trusses are located between the two hip ends and the height of the hip trusses is decreased with each subsequent truss beyond peak of the hip. Parallel chord trusses may be used to form flat roofs.

Trusses can also be cantilevered by extending the structural portion of the truss beyond the support to create an overhang. Since the bottom chord of a cantilevered truss is in compression, it is important that it is adequately braced with lumber or sheathing. Blocking may also be required between cantilevered or raised heel trusses over top of the wall to prevent the trusses from rotating (Figure 3.34). The truss design drawings should indicate where these details are required.

All trusses should be fastened to the bearing walls with toe nails (Table 3.5), or light gauge metal uplift anchors can be used to produce a superior connection. For larger buildings subject to high wind loads, the truss-to-bearing wall connection must be designed to resist the potential loads.

Storage, Handling and Erection of Trusses

Trusses are slender elements. They are very strong when placed in the vertical position, but can be easily damaged or broken if racked or bent in the lateral direction. Damage or failure can occur at the joints (connector plates) or within the lumber members.

When trusses arrive at the job site they should be checked for any permanent damage such as cross breaks in the lumber, missing or damaged metal connector plates, excessive splits in the lumber, or any damage that could impair the structural integrity of the truss.

Whenever possible, trusses should be unloaded in bundles on relatively smooth ground. They should not be unloaded on rough terrain or uneven spaces that could result in undue lateral strain possibly distorting the metal connector plates or damaging parts of the trusses such as overhangs and soffit returns (Figure 3.35).

Wood trusses can be stored horizontally or vertically (Figure 3.35). If stored in the horizontal position, trusses should be supported on blocking spaced at 2.4 m (8') to 3m (10') centres to prevent lateral bending and lessen moisture gain from the ground. When stored in the vertical position, trusses should be placed on a stable horizontal surfaced and braced to prevent toppling or tipping. If trusses need to be stored for an extended period of time measures must be taken to protect them from the elements, keeping the trusses dry and well ventilated.

During unloading and erection, trusses should be handled with care. Proper lifting equipment is to be used at all times. They should be transported in the vertical position to minimize the strain on the plated joints.

Wood trusses can be installed by hand (Figure 3.36) if their size and configuration are such that they can be handled into place without causing an excessive lateral deflection of the truss. Any lateral deflection greater than 75mm (3") is considered excessive.

Trusses installed by mechanical means (Figure 3.37) should be supported at intervals of 7.5m (25') or less. Adequate rigging (crane, fork lift, slings, tag lines, spreader bars, etc.) should be used to ensure safety and prevent damage. Lifting devices (slings, chains, cables, nylon strapping, etc.) should be connected to the truss top chord with a closed-loop attachment. Trusses will be placed according to framing plans. They will be held with the hoisting equipment until the ends of the trusses are securely fastened and temporary braced.

Figure 3.32
**Typical truss
arrangements**

Gable roof truss system

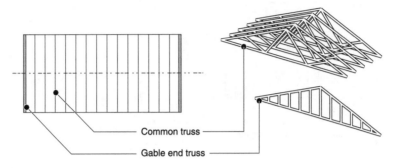

Common truss

Gable end truss

Girder and valley truss system

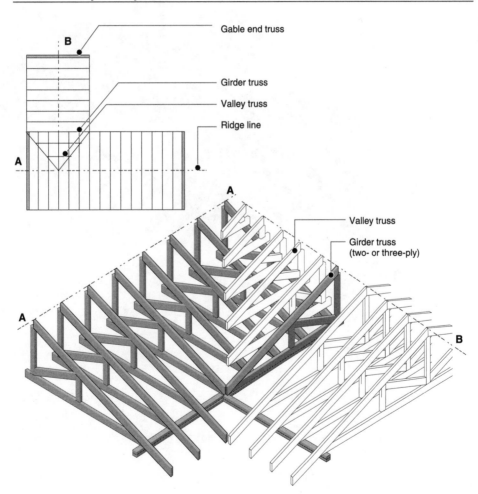

Gable end truss

Girder truss

Valley truss

Ridge line

Valley truss

Girder truss
(two- or three-ply)

3

Wood-Frame Construction

Figure 3.33
**Hip roof
system**

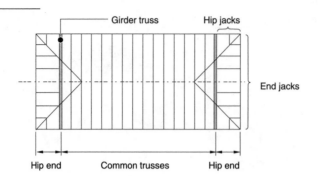

Girder truss

Hip jacks

End jacks

Hip end   Common trusses   Hip end

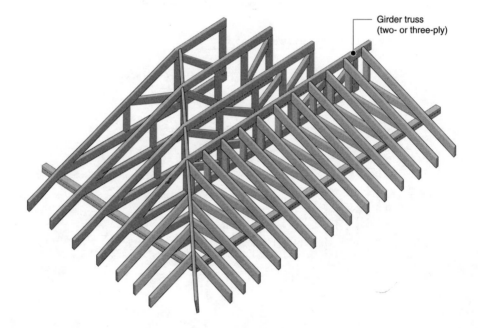

Girder truss
(two- or three-ply)

Figure 3.34
**Bracing for
cantilevered
and raised
heel trusses**

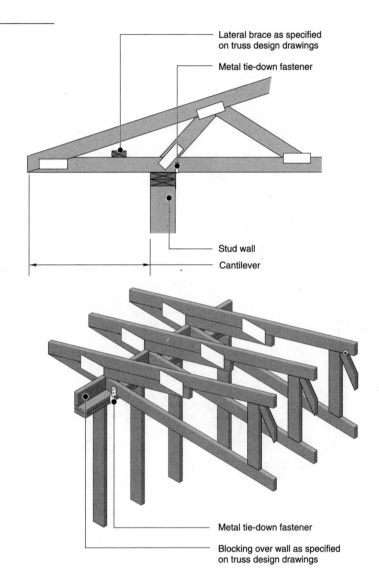

Lateral brace as specified
on truss design drawings

Metal tie-down fastener

Stud wall

Cantilever

Metal tie-down fastener

Blocking over wall as specified
on truss design drawings

Figure 3.35
Truss storage

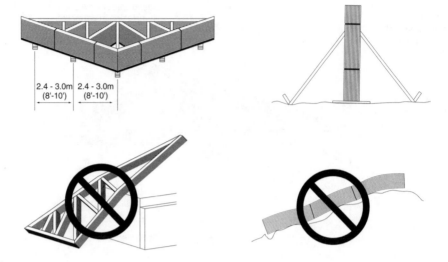

Figure 3.36
**Hand
installation
of trusses**

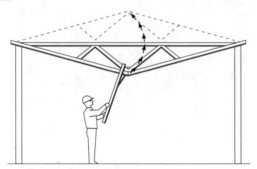

Trusses with spans less than or equal to 6m (20')
should be supported at the peak.

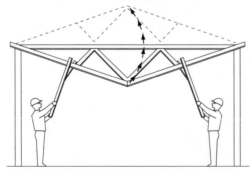

Trusses with spans less than or equal to 9m (30')
should be supported at quarter points.

Figure 3.37
**Mechanical
installation
of trusses**

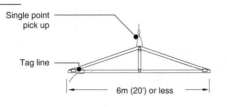

Single point
pick up

Tag line

|← 6m (20') or less →|

Do not lift single trusses with spans
greater than 9m (30') by the peak

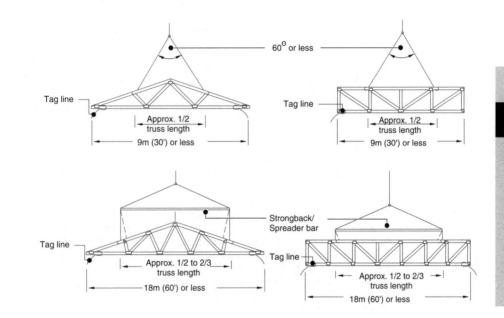

60° or less

Tag line

Approx. 1/2
truss length

9m (30') or less

Tag line

Approx. 1/2
truss length

9m (30') or less

Strongback/
Spreader bar

Tag line

Approx. 1/2 to 2/3
truss length

18m (60') or less

Tag line

Approx. 1/2 to 2/3
truss length

18m (60') or less

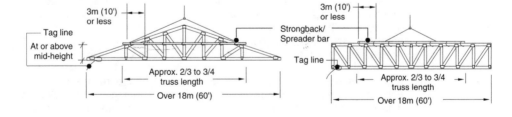

3m (10')
or less

Tag line
At or above
mid-height

Approx. 2/3 to 3/4
truss length

Over 18m (60')

3m (10')
or less

Strongback/
Spreader bar

Tag line

Approx. 2/3 to 3/4
truss length

Over 18m (60')

3

Wood-Frame Construction

Another method of erection for trusses greater than 15m (50') long is to assemble a block of them together on the ground and then lift the assembly into position. The advantage of this method is that it is usually much easier to work and handle the trusses on the ground thereby preventing lateral strain on the joints. Also, by erecting trusses in units, it is easier to ensure they are adequately braced so that they will not collapse during high winds prior to final assembly of the roof system.

Bracing

Both temporary and permanent bracing is required for trusses. The extent to which each type is required depends on the configuration and the end use conditions. For example, trusses in a building with no ceiling below the trusses will require bracing of the lower chord whereas a ceiling, where present, might provide the required stability to the lower chords.

In some cases, temporary and permanent bracing is required for the same condition in which case forethought should be given to the attachment of temporary bracing so that it can also be made to serve as the permanent bracing, thereby eliminating double work. For example, bracing of the top plane is always required on a temporary basis. If the truss manufacturer has specified that bracing of the top chord is required on a permanent basis, the temporary bracing should be installed on the underside of the top chords so that it does not have to be removed and be reinstalled when the panel sheathing is installed.

It is the responsibility of the installer to ensure that temporary bracing is provided to prevent damage or collapse during construction. Temporary bracing (also called installation bracing) is also required to keep trusses plumb, to assure correct truss spacing, and to prevent the trusses from tipping over in the wind during erection. For large spans or long buildings, it is recommended that permanent bracing and roof sheathing be installed as soon as a sufficient number of trusses is erected. This is to provide additional stability to the structure and reduce the likelihood of a collapse.

Trusses should not be left overnight without all temporary bracing in place. In addition, trusses must not be overloaded during erection with concentrated loads such as stacks of roof sheathing or bundles of shingles.

Temporary Bracing

The following types of temporary bracing are required:

- bracing of first truss

- bracing to prevent toppling

- bracing of top chord plane

- bracing of web member plane

- bracing of bottom chord plane

Temporary Bracing of First Truss (Figure 3.38)

- Long span trusses should be securely braced at the end of the building; shorter trusses can be supported laterally by a single gable end brace.

- Ground braces (Figure 3.38) should be located directly in line with all rows of top chord continuous lateral bracing to hold the top chord in plane and to prevent strain on the truss plate and bracing connections.

- Scabs should not be nailed to the end of the building to brace the first truss, since they may break off and allow total collapse.

Temporary Bracing to Prevent Toppling

- As the trusses are installed, temporary bracing is required to hold the trusses plumb and secure until permanent bracing, decking or sheathing is in place.

- Temporary bracing should not be less than 38 x 89mm (2" x 4" nom.) lumber and should be at least 3m (10') long. The use of short spacer pieces of lumber between adjacent trusses is not adequate.

- Temporary bracing should be fastened with two 90mm (3-1/2") double-headed nails at every intersection with the trusses.

Figure 3.38
**Ground
bracing
for trusses**

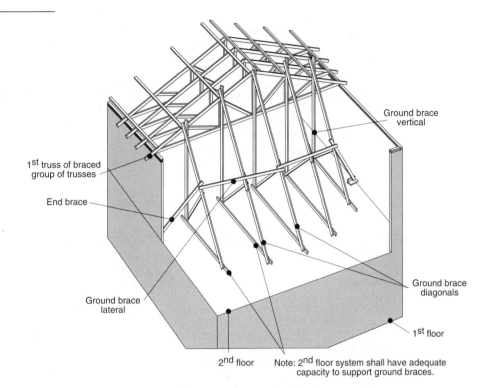

Ground brace
vertical

1st truss of braced
group of trusses

End brace

Ground brace
lateral

Ground brace
diagonals

1st floor

2nd floor   Note: 2nd floor system shall have adequate
capacity to support ground braces.

Ground brace
diagonal

Ground brace
vertical

1st truss of braced
group of trusses

Ground brace
lateral

End brace

Backup
ground stake

Strut

Driven
ground stakes

Typical horizontal tie member
with multiple stakes

Note:
Locate ground braces of first truss directly in line with all rows of top chord continuous lateral bracing
(either temporary or permanent)

3

Wood-Frame Construction

- When the sheathing is being applied, removing the bracing to adjust the spacing of trusses should be avoided. This may cause the trusses to topple if a key connection is removed. Therefore exact spacing of trusses should be maintained as temporary bracing is applied.

Temporary Bracing of Top Chord Plane (Figure 3.39)

- Top chords should be temporarily braced with continuous lateral bracing installed within 150mm (6") of the ridge line or centre line. Subsequent lines of bracing should be installed at approximately 2.4m (8') intervals between the ridge line of sloped trusses or centre line of flat trusses and the eaves.

- Diagonals, set at 45° between the lateral bracing, provide stability to the top chord.

- On longer span trusses, lateral bracing and diagonals may require closer spacing.

- To ensure that the trusses are held securely during installation of the sheathing, continuous lateral bracing should be located on the underside of the top chord (if possible) so that it does not have to be removed as the sheathing is applied.

Temporary Bracing of Bottom Chord Plane (Figure 3.40)

- To hold the proper spacing of the bottom chord, continuous lateral bracing at no greater than 2.4 (8') on centre along the truss length should be secured to the bottom chord. This should be installed on the trusses for the full length of a building.

- Diagonal bracing at 45° between laterals will stabilize this bracing system.

Temporary Bracing of Web Member Plane (Figure 3.41)

- Temporary bracing of the web member plane is usually installed at the same location specified on the architectural plan for permanent bracing. The location of permanent lateral bracing on the web members is specified on the shop drawings. It reduces the buckling length of the individual web members. Diagonal web bracing can form part of the temporary and permanent web bracing system.

- Sets of diagonals should not be spaced more than 6m (20') apart (clear space between end of one set of braces and start of another set).

Figure 3.39
Top chord plane temporary bracing

SPAN	MINIMUM PITCH	TOP CHORD LATERAL BRACE SPACING	TOP CHORD DIAGONAL BRACE SPACING
Up to 9.8m (32')	4/12	2.40m (8')	9.15m (30')
Over 9.8 to14.6m (32' - 48')	4/12	1.80m (6')	4.30m (14')
Over 14.6 to18.3m (48' - 60')	4/12	1.50m (5')	3.05m (10')
Over 18.3m (60')	See a registered professional engineer		

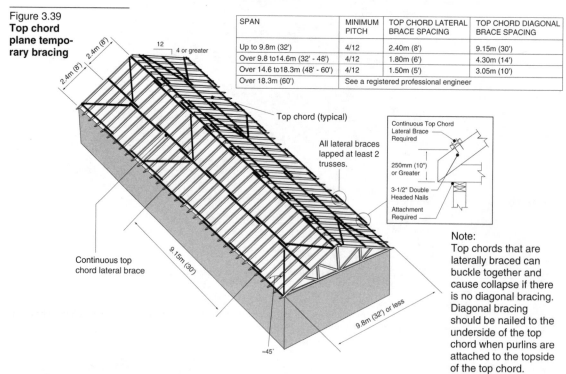

Continuous top chord lateral brace

Top chord (typical)

All lateral braces lapped at least 2 trusses.

Continuous Top Chord Lateral Brace Required

250mm (10") or Greater

3-1/2" Double Headed Nails

Attachment Required

Note:
Top chords that are laterally braced can buckle together and cause collapse if there is no diagonal bracing. Diagonal bracing should be nailed to the underside of the top chord when purlins are attached to the topside of the top chord.

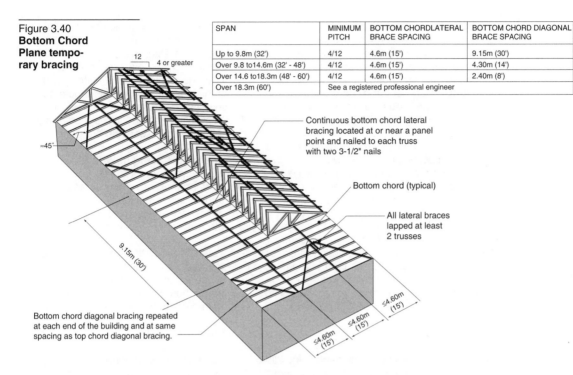

Figure 3.40
Bottom Chord Plane temporary bracing

SPAN	MINIMUM PITCH	BOTTOM CHORDLATERAL BRACE SPACING	BOTTOM CHORD DIAGONAL BRACE SPACING
Up to 9.8m (32')	4/12	4.6m (15')	9.15m (30')
Over 9.8 to14.6m (32' - 48')	4/12	4.6m (15')	4.30m (14')
Over 14.6 to18.3m (48' - 60')	4/12	4.6m (15')	2.40m (8')
Over 18.3m (60')	See a registered professional engineer		

12 4 or greater

≈45°

Continuous bottom chord lateral
bracing located at or near a panel
point and nailed to each truss
with two 3-1/2" nails

Bottom chord (typical)

All lateral braces
lapped at least
2 trusses

9.15m (30')

≤4.60m (15')

≤4.60m (15')

≤4.60m (15')

Bottom chord diagonal bracing repeated
at each end of the building and at same
spacing as top chord diagonal bracing.

3

Figure 3.41
Web Member Plane temporary bracing

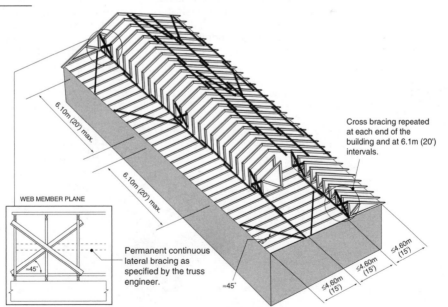

6.10m (20') max.

6.10m (20') max.

Cross bracing repeated
at each end of the
building and at 6.1m (20')
intervals.

WEB MEMBER PLANE

≈45°

Permanent continuous
lateral bracing as
specified by the truss
engineer.

≈45°

≤4.60m (15')

≤4.60m (15')

≤4.60m (15')

Permanent Truss Bracing

Permanent truss bracing prevents overall lateral movement of the complete roof assembly and provides lateral resistance and restraint for compression webs and chords where required. Permanent bracing is either specified by the truss designer or by the building designer.

Permanent lateral bracing prevents chord or web buckling and is shown on the truss drawings. The top chord must always be fully braced by the roof sheathing or by closely spaced bracing. Unless otherwise stated on the truss drawings, braces for residential trusses should be 19 x 89mm (1" x 4" nom.) minimum and 38 x 89mm (2" x 4" nom.) minimum for commercial or farm trusses spaced less than 600mm (24") on centre. All lateral braces must be anchored with vertical or horizontal braces to the roof or side walls (Figure 3.42).

Permanent Bracing of Top Chord Plane

- If plywood or OSB sheathing is installed directly to the top chords, a continuous diaphragm is created to resist lateral movement at the top chord. Additional bracing in this plane is generally not required.

- If purlins are used, their spacing must not exceed the buckling length at the top chord. Diagonal bracing should be applied to the underside of the top chord to prevent lateral shifting of the purlins. Diagonal bracing should be installed on both sides of the ridge or centre line and should be repeated at intervals not exceeding 6m (20').

Permanent Bracing in Web and Bottom Chord Planes

- Permanent bracing in web and bottom chord planes is usually applied as temporary bracing and is specified on the truss shop drawings.

- Lateral bracing of compression web members is a typical method used to prevent buckling. Lateral braces must be anchored by using diagonals or other approved methods. The method of anchorage should be specified by the building designer.

- Lateral bracing of the bottom chord helps to maintain truss spacing and can resist buckling caused by stress reversal. Multiple bearing or cantilevered trusses can result in compressive forces in the bottom chords and require additional bracing.

Figure 3.42
Permanent bracing for trusses

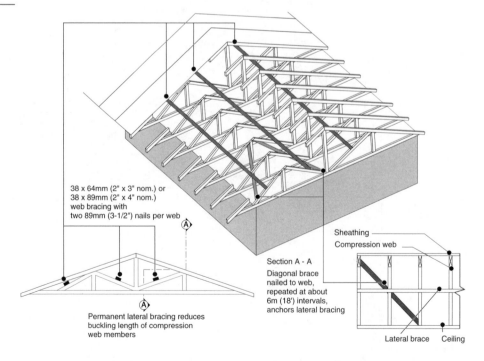

38 x 64mm (2" x 3" nom.) or
38 x 89mm (2" x 4" nom.)
web bracing with
two 89mm (3-1/2") nails per web

Ⓐ

Permanent lateral bracing reduces
buckling length of compression
web members

Section A - A
Diagonal brace
nailed to web,
repeated at about
6m (18') intervals,
anchors lateral bracing

Sheathing
Compression web

Lateral brace   Ceiling

Wood I-Joists

Wood I-joists can be used as an alternative to obtain roofs with rafter spans longer than lumber members. Wood I-joists must be supported at each end by beams or walls since they are not generally used as tied rafters. Wood I-joists can be purchased with or without predrilled cross ventilation holes where roof ventilation is required.

Wood I-joists and LVL or PSL beams, where required, are usually designed by the manufacturer. Framing techniques and construction details for these products are provided by the manufacturers.

Roof Sheathing

Sheathing provides a nailing base for the roof covering and also provides lateral support for the roof framing members. Plywood and OSB panels are generally used to sheath the roof. Lumber sheathing is also permitted by the *NBCC*, but is not commonly used.

The minimum thickness of plywood, and OSB sheathing for Part 9 applications is shown in Table 3.7. Table 3.8 provides the maximum spans for sheathing panels conforming to CSA Standard O325.0, *Construction Sheathing.*

Plywood and OSB panels should be installed and fastened as shown in Figure 3.43. They should be installed with the surface grain or face orientation running at right angles to the framing. A 2 to 3mm (1/8") gap should be left between adjacent panels to prevent buckling if swelling occurs. However, roof sheathing at valleys and hips should be fitted tightly to give a solid base for the roof flashing. Where required, panel edges should be supported by 38 x 38mm (2" x 2" nom.) blocking or metal H-clips.

Where roofs are designed under Part 4 to develop diaphragm action, nailing patterns, and panel orientations must meet the requirements of the engineering design.

Typical Framing Details for Large Buildings

Roofs

Wood trusses are often used to provide large open areas (Figure 3.44). Clear spans of more than 30m (100') have been constructed with pitched trusses. Parallel chord trusses can also be used and can be built with mansard parapets at one or both ends. The trusses are supported by wood stud walls, by concrete block fire walls, or by beams and columns.

3

Wood-Frame Construction

Table 3.7 **Minimum thickness of roof sheathing**	Maximum spacing of supports		Plywood and O-2 grade OSB				OSB and waferboard O-1 and R-1 grades				Lumber	
			Edges supported		Edges unsupported		Edges supported		Edges unsupported			
	mm	in.	mm	in.	mm	in.	mm	in.	mm	in.	mm	in. nom.
	300	12	7.5	5/16	7.5	5/16	9.5	3/8	9.5	3/8	17.0	3/4
	400	16	7.5	5/16	9.5	3/8	9.5	3/8	11.1	7/16	17.0	3/4
	600	24	9.5	3/8	12.5	1/2	11.1	7/16	12.7	1/2	19.0	3/4

Note:
1. Panel edge support may be provided by 38 x 38mm (2" x 2" nom.) blocking or metal H-clips.

Table 3.8 **Maximum spans for roof sheathing panels conforming to CSA Standard O325.0**	Maximum spacing of supports		Panel mark	
			Edges supported	Edges unsupported
	mm	in.		
	400	16	2R16	1R16
	500	19.2	2R20	1R20
	600	24	2R24	1R24

Figure 3.43
**Installation of
panel roof
sheathing**

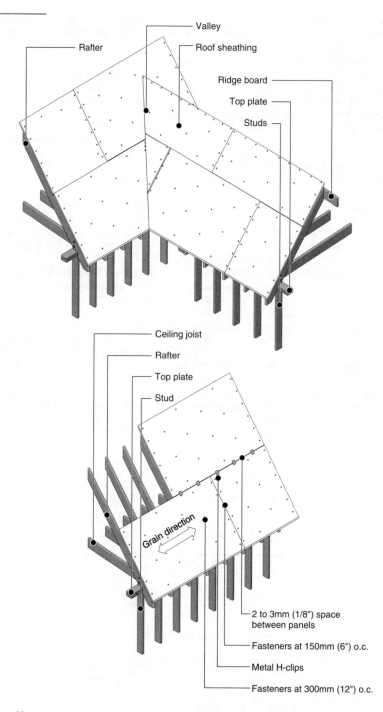

Valley

Rafter

Roof sheathing

Ridge board

Top plate

Studs

Ceiling joist

Rafter

Top plate

Stud

Grain direction

2 to 3mm (1/8") space
between panels

Fasteners at 150mm (6") o.c.

Metal H-clips

Fasteners at 300mm (12") o.c.

Note:
1. Fasten roof sheathing with 51mm (2") common or spiral nails, 45mm (1-3/4") ringed nails, or
    staples 30mm (1-1/4") long for panels up to 10mm (3/8") thick and 51 mm (2") long for panels
    10 to 20mm (7/16" to 3/4") thick. Staples must be driven parallel to the framing.

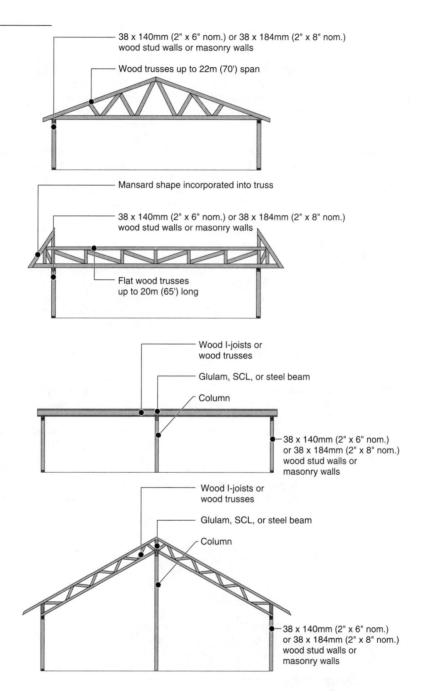

Figure 3.44
Long span roofs

38 x 140mm (2" x 6" nom.) or 38 x 184mm (2" x 8" nom.) wood stud walls or masonry walls

Wood trusses up to 22m (70') span

Mansard shape incorporated into truss

38 x 140mm (2" x 6" nom.) or 38 x 184mm (2" x 8" nom.) wood stud walls or masonry walls

Flat wood trusses up to 20m (65') long

Wood I-joists or wood trusses

Glulam, SCL, or steel beam

Column

38 x 140mm (2" x 6" nom.) or 38 x 184mm (2" x 8" nom.) wood stud walls or masonry walls

Wood I-joists or wood trusses

Glulam, SCL, or steel beam

Column

38 x 140mm (2" x 6" nom.) or 38 x 184mm (2" x 8" nom.) wood stud walls or masonry walls

3

Wood-Frame Construction

Large buildings can be framed with wood trusses or wood I-joists supported by walls around the perimeter and beams on the interior. Glulam, LVL, PSL, or steel beams may be used with wood or steel columns. The roof may be flat with a small slope for drainage or pitched with a ridge beam at the peak.

Floors

Floors in large commercial buildings are often built using 406 to 610mm (16" to 24") deep wood I-joists or floor trusses to obtain long spans. Since wood I-joists and trusses are available in long lengths, they may be installed to be continuous over a number of supports to speed erection and provide a stiff, economical floor.

Where span and load conditions permit, floors may be built with conventional wood joists. Generally 38 x 286mm (2" x 12" nom.) joists are spaced at 300 or 400mm (12" or 16") to provide spans up to about 5.5m (18') on heavily loaded floors.

Walls

Wood stud walls and concrete block walls are commonly used in large commercial buildings. Stud walls 6m (20') or more in height have been used to provide high ceiling clearance. Studs may consist of 38 x 140 or 184mm (2" x 6" or 8" nom.) or larger lumber, and wood I-joists have also been used with LVL plates for high walls subjected to high wind loads.

Framing for Wind and Seismic Loads

Lateral loading is applied to buildings due to the action of wind and earthquakes which tend to cause the structure to sway sideways. To prevent excessive sway, wood-frame roofs and floors are often constructed to act as horizontal beams or diaphragms (Figure 3.45). The diaphragm transfers the lateral load to the end walls, which are built as shearwalls. These shearwalls transfer the lateral load from the roof to the foundation.

Shearwalls and Diaphragms

The main components in shearwall and diaphragm construction are sheathing, intermediate framing members, chords, and struts (Figure 3.46). The sheathing may be plywood or oriented strandboard (OSB). The nail connection between the sheathing and framing is the essential means of load transfer to the perimeter chords and struts. The size and spacing of the nails will be shown in the structural drawings. Closer nail spacings and increased sheathing thickness will increase the capacity of shearwalls and diaphragms.

Diaphragms are essentially horizontal beams. The sheathing acts as the web of the beam and is fastened directly to the framing members. Intermediate blocking may be used at unsupported panel edges to obtain a stronger diaphragm. The top

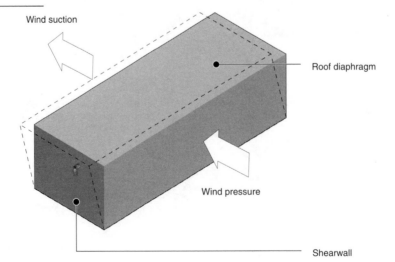

Figure 3.45
Effect of wind pressure

Wind suction

Roof diaphragm

Wind pressure

Shearwall

Figure 3.46
**Shearwall and
diaphragm
details**

Plan of diaphragm

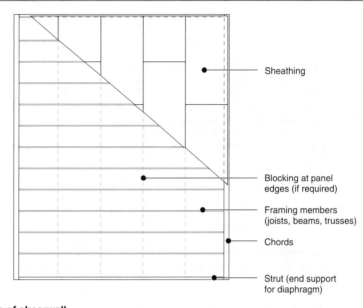

Sheathing

Blocking at panel
edges (if required)

Framing members
(joists, beams, trusses)

Chords

Strut (end support
for diaphragm)

Elevation of shearwall

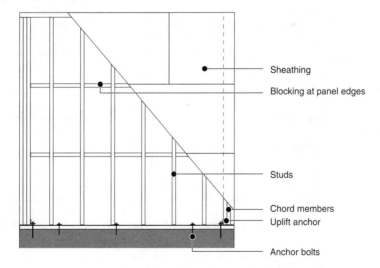

Sheathing

Blocking at panel edges

Studs

Chord members

Uplift anchor

Anchor bolts

3

Wood-Frame Construction

plates of the wall, or the perimeter floor header joist may be used as the chord, which acts like the flange of the beam. Where a chord is not continuous, it must be spliced with nails or bolts.

Shearwalls are similar in construction to diaphragms in that the sheathing must be adequately fastened to the stud wall framing and perimeter chord members. Blocking is always required between framing members where the sheathing edges are unsupported. The chord members are generally two- or three-ply studs and must be fastened to the foundation with special tie-downs (Figure 3.47) to prevent the wall from lifting away from the foundation when the building is subjected to lateral loading from wind or earthquake effects.

Where supplemental hold-down devices are required, it is important that continuity be maintained at floor junctions in platform frame construction so that the entire structure is securely attached to the foundation.

Openings in shearwalls and diaphragms can effect the performance of the structure, and therefore additional framing and connections around openings may be needed to transfer loads. The bottom plate of the wall must also be fastened to the foundation with anchor bolts in the manner conventional to residential construction to resist sliding.

In wood-frame construction, nailing is the form of connection used to affix sheathing to framing to develop required shear and diaphragm strengths. Although board sheathing, particularly when laid diagonally to the framing, contributes shear strength to an assembly, far higher strengths are

possible when plywood or OSB panel sheathing is used. The strength developed, as set out in CSA O86, is dependent upon:

- panel sheathing thickness

- species of framing

- nail size

- nail spacing

Part 9 buildings are considered to have enough rigidity from usual features such as closets, partitions, and interior gypsum wallboard finishing, all of which tend to stiffen the building, that particular attention to shearwall and diaphragm strength is not normally required. However, for all buildings falling outside the parameters of Part 9, lateral loads from wind and earthquake loading can be substantial, and shearwall and diaphragm requirements must be analyzed and must be built into the structure.

Shearwall and diaphragm action in wood-frame construction structure has performed well when severely tested as in the case of recent earthquake and hurricane events in the southern United States. The use of many small fasteners rather than fewer large connectors, as in the case of post and beam construction, means that a multitude of load paths are provided for transferring lateral loads through the structure and into the foundation.

As more commercial large-scale wood projects are built, it is important to ensure that the required shearwall and diaphragm strength is constructed. Although large wood-frame buildings resemble residential-type buildings in terms of the materials and

Figure 3.47
Hold-down devices for shearwalls

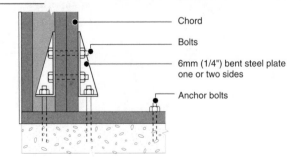

Chord

Bolts

6mm (1/4") bent steel plate one or two sides

Anchor bolts

building techniques used, residential contractors undertaking larger projects may be taken by surprise at the nailing and blocking requirements for larger buildings. To avoid debates during construction, it is recommended that the required nailing patterns be clearly indicated by both the drawings and the specifications.

While there is no question that gypsum wallboard adds rigidity to wall assemblies, and some US model codes provide shearwall strength values for wallboard, CSA O86 at present does not provide values. This means that shearwall strength must come form the wood panel sheathing products, and the gypsum wallboard is an added margin of safety. The present approach is based on one school of thought that questions the ability of the nail or screw to gypsum wallboard interface to remain reliable after cyclic loading, but testing underway at the time of publication may result in changes in the next edition of CSA O86.

Bracing
Bracing may be used as an alternative to shearwalls and diaphragms. Typically, horizontal cross-bracing is added in the roof and vertical cross-bracing in the walls. Steel rods are also used as bracing members since they are easy to fasten and can be tightened with a turnbuckle.

Uplift
The action of wind on a building also causes uplift on the roof, especially in commercial buildings with large door openings. Therefore, roof trusses should be anchored to the walls with metal framing anchors or metal tie-down straps since toe nailing does not usually have adequate capacity to resist these forces.

Permanent Wood Foundations (PWFs)

For Part 9 buildings (and for some Part 4 buildings), PWFs (Figure 3.48) offer some advantages compared to concrete foundations. This topic is covered in *Permanent Wood Foundations,* recently published by the CWC. For this reason, only basic information is provided here.

Wood foundations maximize usable floor space by allowing the structure to serve as the support as well as the housing for the insulation. Basements with permanent wood foundations remain dry and comfortable due to a water tight membrane on the exterior of the foundation and a superior moisture drainage system around and below the basement.

Wood foundation walls can be supported on treated wood footing plates butted together at the ends and placed directly on a continuous granular drainage layer. Soil pressure at the bottom is resisted by either a concrete or a PWF wood-frame floor, and at the top by the floor framing system.

Economy can result from the fact that the foundation and superstructure can be framed by the same building trade, and because the wall panels can be easily prefabricated, installation may be less prone to weather delays than concrete foundations.

For unfinished basements, PWFs are economical in areas where ready mix concrete is expensive or not available. The economy of PWFs is particularly apparent in situations where residential basements are to be finished to be used for living space. This is because the PWF wall framing serves as the foundation, the space for the installation of insulation, and the framework for affixing vapour barriers and the interior wall finish.

3

Wood-Frame Construction

Figure 3.48
**Permanent
wood
foundation**

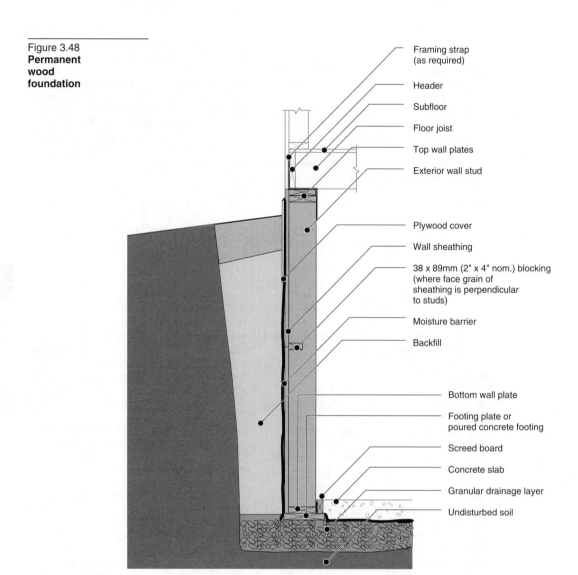

Framing strap
(as required)

Header

Subfloor

Floor joist

Top wall plates

Exterior wall stud

Plywood cover

Wall sheathing

38 x 89mm (2" x 4" nom.) blocking
(where face grain of
sheathing is perpendicular
to studs)

Moisture barrier

Backfill

Bottom wall plate

Footing plate or
poured concrete footing

Screed board

Concrete slab

Granular drainage layer

Undisturbed soil

3.4   Fasteners and Framing Connectors

Introduction

Wood-frame construction is characterized by the use of many small fasteners, usually nails, and light frame connectors to transfer loads. When properly engineered and constructed, the resulting structural assembly offers many paths for the transfer of forces. When overloaded, such assemblies tend to fail by creeping rather than by sudden release as might be the case when high capacity fasteners and column-and-beam hierarchies are used.

Nails, Spikes, and Staples

The most commonly used fasteners in wood-frame construction are nails and spikes. They must conform to CSA Standard B111 *Wire Nails, Spikes, and Staples.*

In Canada, nails and spikes are specified by their length and gauge based on the Imperial Standard Wire Gauge. Spikes are similar to nails except that they are longer and for an equivalent length, of heavier gauge than nails. Nails are usually 25 to 150mm (1" to 6") long, while spikes are available from 100 to 350mm (4" to 14") long.

For wood framing, nails must be common steel wire or common spiral nails. To minimize the possibility of splitting the wood members, spiral nails can be used. They should be staggered in the direction of the grain and kept well away from the edges. At least half of the nail should penetrate into the second member.

Subflooring should be fastened with common, spiral, or ringed nails, but if better capacity is required it can be glued with an elastomeric adhesive and be secured with nails or screws.

Staples are sometimes used as an alternative to nails for fastening roof and wall sheathing up to 19mm (3/4") thick. Staples should have a minimum diameter of 1.6mm (1/16") and a crown not less than 9.5mm (3/8").

To expedite construction, there are many tools available such as pneumatic nail and staple guns, and power driven screw drivers. Nailing guns have been developed for specific applications, such as framing, finishing, roofing, and floor fastening. Spiral nails ranging from 51 to 83mm (2" to 3-1/4") are usually used for the pneumatic framing nailers.

Fastenings for outdoor applications or for damp environments should be hot dipped galvanized. Other materials and coatings for nails, spikes, and staples are available to suit various situations and end use conditions.

Framing Connectors

Framing anchors and joist hangers are the most commonly used type of framing connector in wood-frame construction (Figure 3.49). They are manufactured from light gauge galvanized sheet steel, usually 1.6, 1.3, or 1.0mm (16, 18, or 20 gauge).

Framing anchors are the most versatile framing connectors, since they can be adapted for most joint configurations. Often they are installed in pairs to avoid eccentricity and therefore most types are available in right and left handed versions.

Joist and beam hangers are used to connect joists to beams and beams to beams in wood-frame construction. They are available in two types: top mount and face mount. Top mount hangers have a tab that is bent over and nailed to the top of the beam. Face mount hangers are nailed to the face of the beam. Special hangers are also available for wood trusses and I-joists.

Framing anchors and hangers are often designed for attachment with special large diameter 32 or 38mm (1-1/4" or 1-1/2") nails. In order to obtain the safe working load specified by the manufacturer, the proper type and number of nails must be used.

Other products used in framing applications are post and sill plate anchors, H-clips, post caps, backup clips (for interior finish), straps, plates or angles (Figures 3.50 and 3.51).

Figure 3.49
**Framing
connectors**

All purpose framing anchor

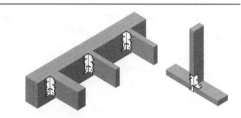

Tie-down framing anchor

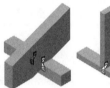

Triple grip framing anchor

Joist and purlin hangers

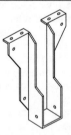
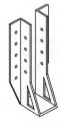
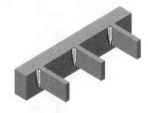

Face mount   Top mount

Figure 3.50
Miscellaneous connectors

Post caps

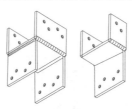
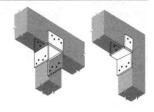

Post anchor

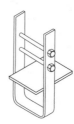

Sill plate anchors

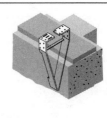

Straps

3

Wood-Frame Construction

Figure 3.51
Miscellaneous connectors

Nail-on plates

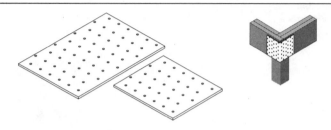

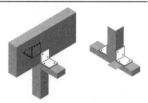

Framing angle

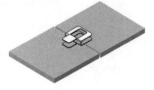

H-clip

Back-up drywall clip

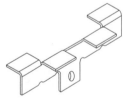

Typical Connection Details

The connection details shown in this section (Figures 3.52 to 3.54). are commonly used in large wood-frame commercial construction. These details provide the concept of the connection only. The actual number and size of fasteners should be specified on the structural drawings or by the truss or wood I-joist manufacturer.

It is important that all roof joists or trusses be anchored to the supporting wall or beam to resist uplift. Also, bracing or blocking is usually required at the support to prevent the truss or joist from rotating.

Where a wood roof or floor provides lateral support for concrete or masonry walls, ties must be provided from the wall to the framing members at regular intervals along the building. Typically the ties must be spaced no greater than 2m (6.5') along the wall and they must be capable of carrying a load of at least 3 kN/m (200 plf) perpendicular to the wall.

The tie should be a metal strap or a bracket bolted to the framing and anchored to the wall. Toe nailing is not an acceptable method of anchoring to the wall.

Figure 3.52
**Fastening
trusses or
wood I-joists
to masonry
walls**

Truss or wood I-joist on masonry pier

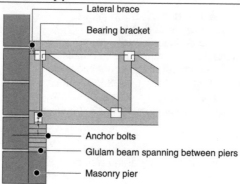

— Lateral brace
— Bearing bracket
— Anchor bolts
— Glulam beam spanning between piers
— Masonry pier

Truss or wood I-joist on wood ledger

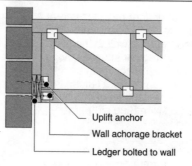

— Uplift anchor
— Wall achorage bracket
— Ledger bolted to wall

Wood I-joist on ledger

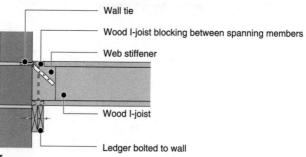

— Wall tie
— Wood I-joist blocking between spanning members
— Web stiffener
— Wood I-joist
— Ledger bolted to wall

Wood I-joist on hanger

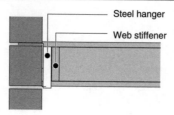

— Steel hanger
— Web stiffener

Figure 3.53
**Fastening
trusses or
wood I-joists
to stud walls**

Gable truss

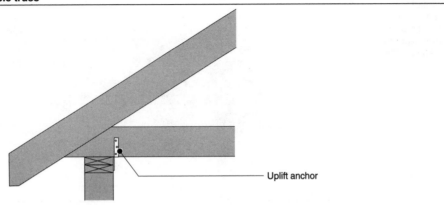

Uplift anchor

Flat truss - Top chord bearing

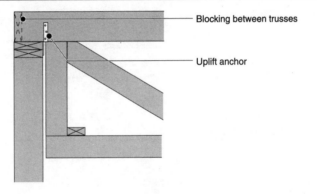

Blocking between trusses

Uplift anchor

Flat truss - Bottom chord bearing

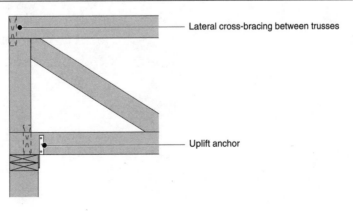

Lateral cross-bracing between trusses

Uplift anchor

Figure 3.53
(cont'd)
**Fastening
trusses or
wood I-joists
to stud walls**

Flat roof joist

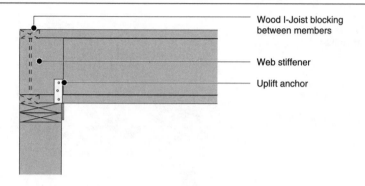

Wood I-Joist blocking
between members

Web stiffener

Uplift anchor

Continous joists

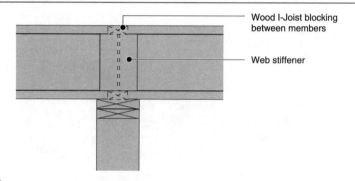

Wood I-Joist blocking
between members

Web stiffener

Sloped roof joist

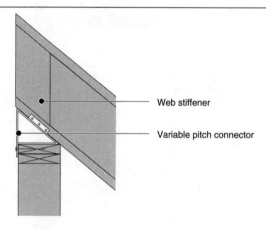

Web stiffener

Variable pitch connector

Figure 3.54
Fastening trusses or wood I-joists to beams

Flat truss to glulam beam

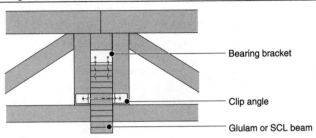

- Bearing bracket
- Clip angle
- Glulam or SCL beam

Flat truss to glulam beam

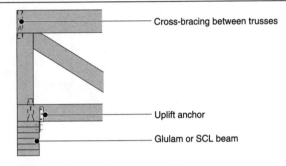

- Cross-bracing between trusses
- Uplift anchor
- Glulam or SCL beam

Flat truss to steel beam

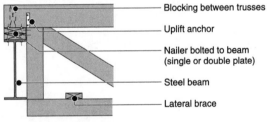

- Blocking between trusses
- Uplift anchor
- Nailer bolted to beam (single or double plate)
- Steel beam
- Lateral brace

Flat truss to steel beam

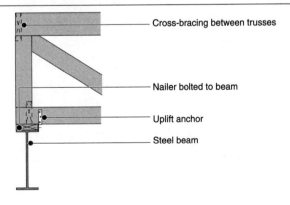

- Cross-bracing between trusses
- Nailer bolted to beam
- Uplift anchor
- Steel beam

3

Wood-Frame Construction

Figure 3.54
(cont'd)
**Fastening
trusses or
wood I-joists
to beams**

Wood I-joist to glulam beam

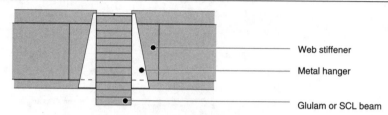

Web stiffener

Metal hanger

Glulam or SCL beam

Wood I-joist to steel beam

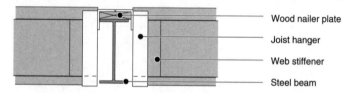

Wood nailer plate

Joist hanger

Web stiffener

Steel beam

Special Requirements for Wood I-Joists

It is important that hangers and connectors used for supporting wood I-joists be specifically designed for that purpose. Hangers developed for conventional lumber or glulam beams often use large nails and space them in a pattern that will split the joist flanges and web stiffeners. Hanger selection considerations for wood I-joists should include nail length and diameter, nail location, joist bearing capacity, composition of the supporting member, physical fit, and load capacity. For example, hangers appropriate for a wood I-joist to glulam beam support may not be compatible for a wood I-joist to wood I-joist connection.

In general, nails into the flanges should not exceed 3.8mm (0.15") in diameter, with a recommended length no greater than 38mm (1-1/2"). Nails into web stiffeners should not exceed 4.2mm (0.17") in diameter. Specific information can be obtained from the manufacturer.

Figure 3.55
Support of wood I-joist webs

3

Wood-Frame Construction

Wood I-joist to beam connection

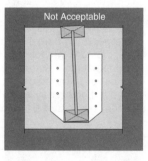
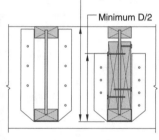

D

Minimum D/2

Not Acceptable

Top and bottom flanges must be laterally restrained against rotation and against web buckling

Top supported connection

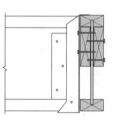

Not Acceptable

The top flange of the support joist must be supported to prevent cross grain bending and rotation

Bottom supported connection

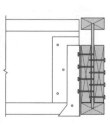

Not Acceptable

Hanger nails must extend past the supporting joists web member into the backer blocking

Nails through the sides of the hanger, when used in combination with web stiffeners, can be used to reduce the joist's minimum required bearing length. Nails help transfer loads directly from the joist web into the hanger, reducing the load transferred through direct bearing in the bottom hanger seat.

Hangers should be capable of providing lateral support to the top compression flange of the joist (Figure 3.55). This is usually accomplished by a hanger flange that extends the full depth of the joist. As a minimum, hanger support should extend to at least mid-height of a joist used with web stiffeners. Some connector manufacturers have developed hangers specifically for use with wood I-joists that provide full lateral support without the use of web stiffeners.

When top flange style hangers are used to support one wood I-joist from another (especially the wider flanged wood I-joists), web stiffeners need to be installed tight to the bottom side of the support joists to flange (Figure 3.50) to prevent cross grain bending and rotation of the top flange.

When face nail hangers are used for joist to joist connections, nails into the support joist should extend through and beyond the web element. Filler blocks should also be attached sufficiently to provide support for the hanger.

Multiple joists need to be adequately connected together to achieve desired performance. This requires proper selection of a nailing patterns and attention to web stiffener and blocking needs.

The low torsional resistance of most wood I-joists is also a design consideration for joist to joist connections. Eccentrically applied side loads, such as a top flange hanger hung from the side of a double joist, create the potential for joist rotation. Bottom flange restraining straps, blocking, or directly applied ceiling systems may be needed on heavily loaded eccentric connections to resist rotation.

References

1. *Canadian Wood-Frame House Construction,* Canada Mortgage and Housing Corporation, Ottawa, ON, 1997

2. *Permanent Wood Foundations,* Canadian Wood Council, Ottawa, ON, 1993

3. *Span Book, The ,* Canadian Wood Council, Ottawa, ON, 1995

4. *Wood Reference Handbook,* Canadian Wood Council, Ottawa, ON, 1995

3

Wood-Frame Construction

Post and Beam
Construction

Post and beam construction is characterized by large members which are spaced far apart.

Where many large openings occur in post and beam construction, additional cross-bracing may be required and can be made to be architecturally appealing.

Pre-installation of fasteners and prefinishing of members can reduce labour costs.

Preassembly of post and beam assemblies can save erection time.

Wood infill framing is often used in post and beam construction for partitions and exterior walls, and may be designed to provide shear wall effect.

Side-plates can be concealed internally to create a cleaner looking connection.

Glulam rivets are effective means of connecting large members that require no drilling or dapping to prepare the joint.

Connectors for post and beam construction may be stock ordered pieces or may have to be custom manufactured.

Washers must be used with bolts and lag screws.

Hangers may be stock items or custom manufactured depending on the size of members used.

Special dapping tools are required for installing split rings and shear plates.

When post and beam members are of a certain dimension, the assembly qualifies as Heavy Timber construction as defined by the *NBCC*.

Where members are to be left exposed, prefinishing of hardware is recommended to eliminate rust staining.

While techni-
cally not post
and beam on
account of its
shape, glulam
arches can
similarly provide
large, clear
spans.

4.1 General Information

Post and beam construction is a method of construction which makes use of large members spaced far apart in non-load-sharing arrangements. It is often used for large spans or loadings, or where the structure of the building is to be left exposed to exhibit the aesthetic qualities of the wood members.

The North American model building codes have recognized the ability of large wood members to remain structurally intact for a certain period of time when exposed to fire. For this reason, the model codes, of which the *National Building Code of Canada (NBCC)* is one, afford large wood members meeting certain minimum size requirements, special fire resistance ratings. When post and beam members meet these minimum size requirements, the members qualify as Heavy Timber construction as defined by the *NBCC*.

This chapter describes the characteristics of post and beam construction and, where applicable, references Heavy Timber construction. The following major subject items are covered:

4

Post and Beam Construction

4.2   Description of Post and Beam Construction

Introduction

In post and beam construction (Figure 4.1), the roof and floors are comprised of decking supported by purlins. The purlins frame into beams that in turn are connected to columns. It is a hierarchical construction method which is similar in arrangement to structural steel building construction.

The large wood members are connected together with bolted steel connections or some other type of high capacity connection.

In some cases, mortise and tenon joints connected with hardwood dowels are still used where it is desired to have the architectural appearance unique to this method of connection.

Figure 4.1
**Typical post
and beam
construction**

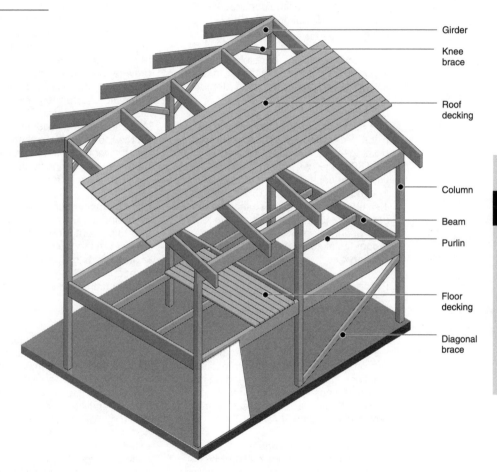

Girder

Knee brace

Roof decking

Column

Beam

Purlin

Floor decking

Diagonal brace

4

Post and Beam Construction

Usually the structural members are left exposed in the completed building as an architectural feature.

Large clear span structures can be built using post and beam construction. For example, a warehouse layout for glulam beams and columns might have bays 10 x 15m (30' x 50'). The post and beam construction method is often used in combination with frame construction which is used to infill wall openings and to frame around windows and doors.

Sawn timber, glulam, parallel strand lumber (PSL), and heavy timber trusses are typically used for the main members.

Decking
The decking is usually tongue and groove plank deck, although in older industrial buildings vertically nail laminated 38 x 89mm (2" x 4" nom.) deck was often used. The decking should always be dried to a moisture content of 15% (maximum 19%) before installation so that the tongue and groove joint does not become loose after drying in service. Details for the proper installation of decking are shown in Section 4.6.

Purlins, Beams and Columns
The purlins, beams, or columns may be sawn timber, glulam or PSL. The purlins may sit on top of the beams or frame into the face of the beams. The beams may rest on top of the posts, or, for multistorey buildings, they may be mounted on the face of the posts. Details for these and other post and beam connections are provided in Section 4.4.

Bracing and Anchorages
Unlike wood-frame construction which derives its resistance to lateral loads from the interaction of the sheathing and the framing members, post and beam construction requires additional members or framing to provide the required racking strength.

Diagonal bracing must be provided between columns at regular intervals to keep the structure plumb and to resist wind forces. The bracing may be comprised of wood members or steel rods. Knee braces between the posts and beams are often used to provide wind resistance, particularly where full height diagonal bracing is not desirable. Also, nailed shear panels consisting of wood studs and structural sheathing may be inserted between columns to provide wind resistance. These panels must be properly designed and anchored to the foundation as outlined in Section 3.3.

Wind acting on a building also causes uplift on the roof. For this reason it is important that the roof members and the supporting beams and columns be tied together to resist these uplift forces.

The columns must be securely anchored to the foundation to hold the building in place and to prevent wind from lifting the building away from the foundation. This anchorage is particularly critical at the diagonal brace locations since the bracing pulls or pushes on the column base when wind acts on the building.

Walls and Partitions
Exterior walls and partitions may be constructed using conventional stud wall framing between columns (Figure 4.2). Commercially available composite panels may also be used to enclose the building. These panels have a rigid insulation core with a gypsum wallboard face on the interior side and a panel sheathing face on the exterior side. The panels are usually connected together with tongue and groove joints and are fastened with nails to the exterior surface of the timber framework.

Figure 4.2
**Framing
spaces
between
columns**

Infill by coventional framing

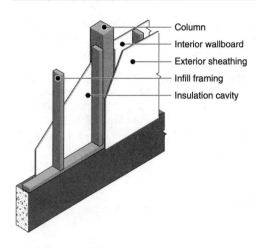

- Column
- Interior wallboard
- Exterior sheathing
- Infill framing
- Insulation cavity

Infill using non-structural panels

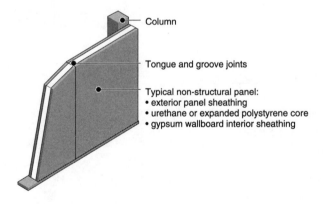

- Column

- Tongue and groove joints

- Typical non-structural panel:
  - exterior panel sheathing
  - urethane or expanded polystyrene core
  - gypsum wallboard interior sheathing

4

Post and Beam Construction

Clear Span Roof Systems

Although not considered to be post and beam construction, glulam arches can also be used to create large clear spans (Figure 4.3). Pitched-tapered beams are made of glulam to produce a pitched roof shape and a curved soffit. The roof slope for such structures is usually between 1:12 and 3:12. The roof deck is usually supported directly on the beams, which in turn are supported by columns at each end. Pitched-tapered beams are commonly used in swimming pool enclosures, churches, community halls, gymnasiums, and other similar structures.

Arches are usually fabricated from glulam. Various shapes are possible, including circular, straight (A-frame), or tudor.

The arch is usually built in two sections and connected at the peak. Under load the base of the arch is pushed outward. This push or thrust is either resisted by buttressed foundations or by a tie connecting the opposing arch bases together. The tie may be built into the floor or be located below it.

Figure 4.3
Clear span of heavy timber roofs

Pitched-tapered glulam beam

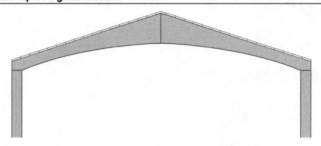

Glulam tudor arch

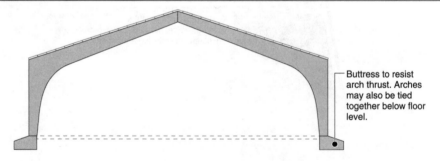

Buttress to resist arch thrust. Arches may also be tied together below floor level.

Heavy timber truss

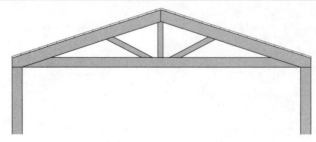

Arches are usually spaced from 1.2 to 5m (4' to 16') apart and can span 25m (80') or more. Arches may be used for any building where a large clear span is required including swimming pools, churches, arenas, solariums, agricultural and commercial buildings.

Sawn timber trusses may be constructed with sawn timber, glulam, or structural composite lumber (SCL). Flat and pitched roof shapes are common; however, curved glulam may be used to create bowstring (curved) trusses. The members are generally connected together using steel plates and bolts, and shear plates, or glulam rivets. The trusses may be supported on timber columns or masonry walls and can span up to 50m (165') depending on the type of truss. Truss spacing is typically between 3 and 6m (10' and 20') on centre.

Post and Beam Combined with Wood-Frame Construction

Post and beam construction is often combined with conventional wood-frame construction (Figure 4.4) in the following ways depending on fire safety considerations:

- Conventional framing or light trusses and panel sheathing are used in the roof while the remaining above grade structure is post and beam construction

- The structural frame is post and beam construction but joist or rafter framing and panel sheathing is used in place of plank decking.

- Loadbearing walls are used instead of columns.

Figure 4.4
Post and beam construction combined with wood-frame construction

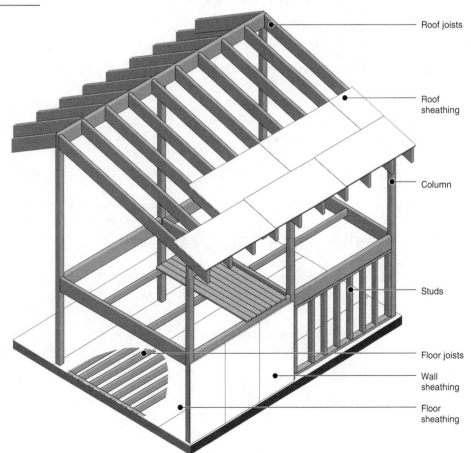

Roof joists

Roof sheathing

Column

Studs

Floor joists

Wall sheathing

Floor sheathing

4

Post and Beam Construction

Combined post and beam construction and wood-frame construction offers a number of practical advantages including the following:

- Concealment of Services:
  The extra planning required for the concealment of electrical conduits, plumbing, and heating ducts can be simplified by concealment in wood framing.

- Insulation and Finishes:
  Combining post and beam construction with light frame construction gives the designer flexibility in the choice of building materials such as insulation and interior finishes.
  Wood-frame construction roofs and walls may be insulated with flexible batt insulation in the space between members rather than with rigid insulation on top of the roof deck, which would normally be used for a post and beam plank roof.
  Conventional finishes such as gypsum wallboard may be used with wood-frame floors and roofs to provide contrast with the exposed timber members.

4.3   Heavy Timber Construction

Introduction

Heavy Timber construction, as defined in the *NBCC*, is a type of combustible construction in which a degree of fire safety is attained by placing limitations on the minimum sizes of wood structural members, on the thickness and composition of wood floors and roofs, and by the avoidance of concealed spaces under floors and roofs.

Heavy Timber construction is usually post and beam construction. However, not all post and beam construction has member sizes which qualify for the equivalency to 45-minute fire rating assigned to Heavy Timber construction. (Note that in all CWC publications, Heavy Timber spelled with capitals indicates reference to the fire codes.)

Heavy timber trusses may also qualify as Heavy Timber construction when composed of adequately sized members.

Part 3 of the *NBCC* assigns Heavy Timber construction an equivalency to conventional wood-frame construction having a 45-minute fire rating as long as the size of the members meets the requirements of Table 4.1, and floor and roof deck construction conforms to Table 4.2. Heavy Timber construction has inherent fire resistance because the layer of char that forms on the surface during burning insulates the core. Since the unburnt core suffers only a minor strength loss, a large member can burn for a significant amount of time before its capacity is reduced to the point of collapse.

Since the spacing of members in post and beam structures generally exceeds 600mm, the structure must be designed in accordance with Part 4 of the *NBCC*. This means that structural drawings must be prepared and sealed by a licensed professional engineer. However, joists used in residential timber buildings may be sized using the tables in Part 9. Part 9 may also be used for other light frame components provided the Part 9 loading requirements are met.

4

Post and Beam Construction

Table 4.1
Minimum dimensions of wood elements in Heavy Timber construction[1]

Supported assembly	Structural element	Solid sawn (w x d)		Glulam (w x d)		Round (dia.)	
		mm	in. (nom.)	mm	in. (actual)	mm	in. (nom.)
Roofs only	Columns	140 x 191	6 x 8	130 x 190	5-1/8 x 7-1/2	180	7
	Arches supported on the tops of walls or abutments	89 x 140	4 x 6	80 x 152	3-1/4 x 6	–	–
	Beams, girders, and trusses	89 x 140	4 x 6	80 x 152	3-1/4 x 6	–	–
	Arches supported at or near the floor line	140 x 140	6 x 6	130 x 152	5-1/8 x 6	–	–
Floors, floors plus roofs	Columns	191 x 191	8 x 8	175 x 190	6-7/8 x 7-1/2	200	8
	Beams, girders, trusses, and arches	140 x 241	6 x 10	130 x 228	5-1/8 x 9	–	–
		191 x 191	8 x 8	175 x 190	6-7/8 x 7-1/2	–	–

Notes:
1. Timber construction that meets the requirements of Part 3 and Part 9 of the *NBCC* for combustible construction required to have a 45-minute fire rating.
2. If combustible construction is permitted with no required fire rating, these minimum sizes are not required.

In addition to the minimum sizes of timber members, Part 3 of the *NBCC* also places the following restrictions on the construction methods used for Heavy Timber construction:

- wood columns must be continuous or superimposed on each other throughout all storeys

- superimposed wood columns must be connected by reinforced concrete, steel caps, or by timber splice plates connected with shear plates or split rings (Section 4.4)

- beam hangers or self-releasing boxes must be used to support beams framing into masonry walls (Section 4.4)

- beams must be closely fitted around columns with each end connected by ties or caps capable of transferring horizontal loads

These requirements are to ensure that all components of the structure, including connections and supporting assemblies, are capable of allowing the members to remain intact during a fire. In the case where beams and girders enter masonry, the connectors are designed to collapse without affecting the integrity of the masonry wall.

Table 4.2
Decking requirements for Heavy Timber construction[1]

	Deck[2]	Subfloor or finish floor[3,4]
Floor	64mm (3" nom.) T&G plank deck	12.5mm (1/2") panel sheathing subfloor
	38 x 89mm (2" x 4" nom.) vertically nail-laminated deck	19mm (3/4" nom.) T&G finish flooring laid perpendicular or diagonal to deck
Roof	28mm (1-3/32") T&G phenolic bonded plywood	not applicable
	38mm (2" nom.) T&G plank	
	38 x 64mm (2" x 3") vertically nail-laminated deck	

Notes:
1. Construction that meets the requirements of Part 3 and Part 9 of *NBCC* for combustible construction required to have a 45-minute fire rating.
2. Decking must be installed as outlined in Section 4.6. Splined deck may be used in place of tongue and groove (T&G) deck.
3. Subfloor or finish floor is required in addition to floor deck. All floor components, including the deck, must be laid not closer than 15mm (5/8") to the wall to provide for expansion, and the gap must be covered at the top or bottom.
4. Panel sheathing for subfloors includes phenolic bonded plywood, waferboard, or oriented strandboard.

4.4   Connections

Introduction

The large loads usually carried by post and beam members require connections using large fasteners such as bolts, lag screws, shear plates and split rings, often in combination with wood or steel side plates. Glulam rivets, in combination with steel side plates, are used for glued-laminated timber, and for parallel strand lumber (PSL).

Bolts

Bolts for wood connections must conform to ASTM Standard A307. They are available as either square headed machine bolts, finished hexagon bolts, or carriage bolts (Table 4.3). Countersunk heads can be used where a flush surface is desired.

Bolts are commonly available in imperial sizes, from 3" to 16" (75 to 405mm) long. When they are to be used in wet service or corrosive conditions, they should be galvanized (hot-dipped or plated). Where longer fasteners are required, A307 threaded rod can be substituted for bolts of the same diameter provided the rod is threaded at the ends only.

Washers (Table 4.4) should always be used between the wood and bolt head and nut to prevent crushing (washers are not used with countersunk heads or carriage bolts). When a steel side plate is used, the bolt head or nut can bear directly on the steel. Standard cut washers are acceptable for bolts and lag screws that are laterally loaded. Heavier plate or iron washers are required where the bolt is loaded in tension or where the bolt is used with a split ring or shear plate connector (Table 4.4).

Bolt holes should be drilled 1.0 to 2.0mm (1/32" to 1/16") larger than the bolt diameter to prevent any splitting or stress that could be caused by installation or subsequent wood shrinkage. Bolts should be tightened so that the faces of all connecting members are brought tightly together, but not over tightened to the point where the wood crushes. Shrinkage of sawn timber in service can cause the bolts to come loose; therefore, the tightness should be checked about one year after installation and the nuts retightened if necessary.

4

Post and Beam Construction

Table 4.3
Types of bolts for wood construction

Bolt type	Usual range of diameters	Uses	
Finished hexagon bolt	6.4 to 38mm (1/4" to 1-1/2")	Most types of wood construction including timber connector joints	
Square headed machine bolt	6.4 to 51mm (1/4" to 2")	Same as finished hexagon bolt but gradually being replaced by them	
Machine bolt with countersunk head	12.7 to 32mm (1/2" to 1-1/4")	Where flush surface required (may have to be used with countersunk washer)	
Carriage bolt	4.8 to 19 mm (0.19" [No.10] to 3/4")	Where head may be inaccessible during tightening	

Lag Screws

Lag screw materials and dimensions are specified in CSA Standard B34 *Miscellaneous Bolts and Screws.* Lag screws are commonly used in lieu of bolts in arrangements where only one side of a connection is accessible or where the main wood member is very thick and would require long bolts. Lag screws can be designed for use in tension since they are threaded. Washers are required between the lag screw head and the wood to prevent crushing.

Lag screws are available in imperial sizes from 3" to 12" (75 to 300mm) long and 1/4" to 1" (6.4 to 25mm) in diameter with square heads and cone points, but they can also be obtained with hexagon heads and gimlet points. Lag screws should be galvanized (hot dipped or plated) when they are used in wet environments.

Lag screw holes (Figure 4.5) should consist of a lead hole for the threaded portion, and a counterbore for the unthreaded portion The diameter of the counterbore should be the same as the shank of the lag screw, but the diameter of the lead hole must be smaller than the shank in order for the threads to grip the wood. When installing the lag screw it must be turned with a wrench, not driven with a hammer. Soap or any other non-petroleum based lubricant can be used to make turning easier.

Table 4.4
Washers for bolts and lag screws

Washer type	Uses	
Standard cut washer	Used for screws and bolts where the loading is lateral and should not be used with split rings and shear plates	
Square plate washer	Used for bolts, split rings and shear plates and suitable for tensile loads	
Round plate washer	Used for bolts, split rings and shear plates and suitable for tensile loads	
Ogee (cast iron) washer	Used for bolts, split rings and shear plates and suitable for tensile loads	
Malleable iron washer	Used for bolts, split rings and shear plates and suitable for tensile loads	
Bevel washer	Used where the bolt to member alignment is not perpendicular	

Figure 4.5 **Lag screws for wood construction**	Usual range of diameters	Uses	
	6.4 to 25mm (1/4" to 1")	In lieu of bolts where nut location would be inaccessible; sometimes used for split ring and shear plate joints	

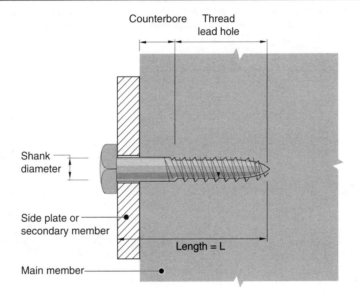

Drilling dimensions for lag screw holes	Counterbore	Lead hole		
		Dense hardwoods	D.Fir-L	Hem-Fir, S-P-F Northern
Diameter	same as shank	65 to 85% of shank	60 to 75% of shank	40 to 70% of shank
Depth	same as shank	threaded length	threaded length	threaded length

Note: For lead hole diameter, the larger percentage applies to larger lag screws.

4

Post and Beam Construction

Glulam Rivets

Glulam rivets, commonly marketed as
Griplam Nails, are high strength fasteners
developed specifically for use in glued-laminated timber (they may also be used for
PSL). Glulam rivets have a flattened oval
shank with a wedge shaped head and are
similar in appearance to nails (Figure 4.6).

Glulam rivets are commonly available in
lengths of 40, 65, and 90mm (1-1/2", 2-1/2",
and 3-1/2"). The rivets are made from high
yield point, high strength steel and are hot-
dipped galvanized to provide adequate
corrosion resistance for most environments.
Glulam rivets should not be used where
acid or salts can contact the connection, or
where steam is present.

Figure 4.6
Glulam rivets

Elevation

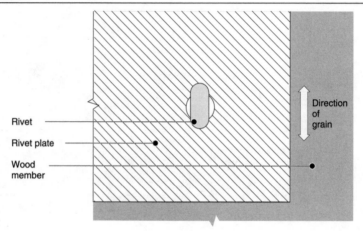

Section

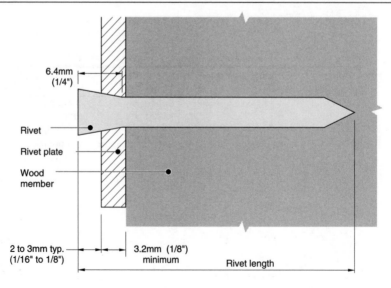

Glulam rivets must be used with at least 3.2mm (1/8") thick steel side plates that are predrilled (sometimes punched) with 6.7 to 7mm (1/4" to 9/32") holes to accommodate the rivets. Glulam rivets must be driven until the tapered head is firmly seated in the holes in the steel plate, while maintaining a minimum 2mm (5/64") head projection above the plate. They must be installed so that the flat face is parallel to the grain.

Either a standard or pneumatic hammer may be used to drive the rivet. Safety glasses should always be worn when driving glulam rivets because particles of galvanizing or hardened steel may break off when struck.

Glulam rivets have become the favoured connection for glulam members because of their many advantages over other connectors which include:

- Glulam rivets transfer greater loads for a given connector area than any other timber fastener. This results in a smaller connection which is often favoured for aesthetic reasons.

- The wood members need not be drilled, bored or grooved. This simplifies fabrication. Since material does not have to be removed from glulam to install the rivets, smaller members can be used.

- Glulam rivet connections can be easily verified during field inspection.

Split Ring and Shear Plate Connectors

Split ring (Figure 4.7) and shear plate (Figure 4.8) connectors are high strength fasteners that are used with either bolts or lag screws. Split rings are used for wood-to-wood connections, and shear plates are used for steel-to-wood connections. These connectors distribute the lateral forces over a larger bearing area than bolts or lag screws and therefore they have much higher capacities.

Split rings and shear plates are manufactured in imperial dimensions only. Split rings are available in 2-1/2" and 4" diameters. The 2-1/2" split ring is used with a 1/2" diameter bolt or lag screw and the 4" split ring requires a 3/4" bolt or lag screw. Shear plates can be purchased in 2-5/8" and 4" diameters. The 2-5/8" shear plate is used with a 3/4" bolt or lag screw and the 4" size may be used with either a 3/4" or 7/8" bolt or lag screw.

Split ring connectors (2-1/2" or 4" diameter) are manufactured from hot-rolled carbon steel SAE 1010, meeting the requirements of the Society of Automotive Engineers Handbook. The 2-5/8" diameter shear plate is manufactured from hot-rolled carbon steel SAE 1010 and the 4" diameter shear plate is manufactured from malleable iron meeting the requirements of ASTM Standard A47, *Malleable Iron Castings* (Grade 35018). Split rings and shear plates used in corrosive or wet conditions should be galvanized.

4

Post and Beam Construction

Figure 4.7
Split ring timber connectors (one split ring in a two-member joint)

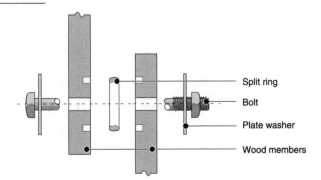

Split ring

Bolt

Plate washer

Wood members

Split ring connector

(available in 2-1/2" and 4" diameters)

Shear plates and split rings are installed in grooves in the wood members (Figures 4.7, 4.8, and 4.9). Special grooving tools are available from the connector supplier to accurately machine the grooves to specified tolerances (Figure 4.10).

A slight taper in the split ring allows it to wedge tightly into each groove at the interface when the members are butted face-to-face. Shear plates, when assembled, lie flush with the wood surface. Poorly fitting connectors will significantly reduce the capacity of a connection.

Figure 4.8
Shear plate timber connectors

Two shear plates with steel side plates

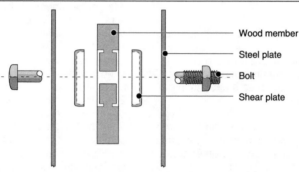

Wood member
Steel plate
Bolt
Shear plate

Two shear plates back-to-back in a wood-to-wood joint

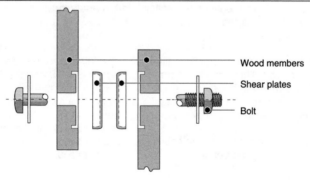

Wood members
Shear plates
Bolt

Figure 4.9
Shear plate timber connectors

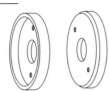

Pressed steel shear plates
(available in 2-5/8" diameter)

Malleable iron shear plates
(available in 4" diameter)

Figure 4.10
Groove cutting tools for timber connectors

Split ring tool

Shear plate tool

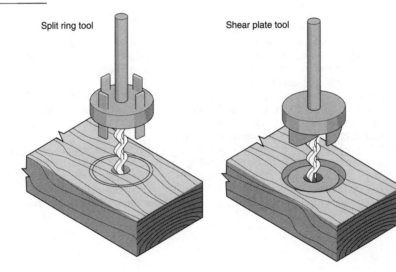

4

Post and Beam Construction

Heavy Framing Connections

This section provides details for many of the connections most commonly used for post and beam construction (Figures 4.11 to 4.14). These details are intended only to be used as guides. The quantities, sizes, spacings, edge and end distances of fastenings will depend on the loads to be carried and the member sizes. This information should be shown on the structural drawings. (For more information, refer to the *Wood Design Manual* and *Wood Reference Handbook*.)

The connection of wood columns to foundations must resist uplift and lateral loads, and the column must bear on a base plate that prevents moisture transfer from the support. Beams must also be anchored to the masonry or concrete and have a bearing plate to prevent moisture migration into the wood. In addition, an air space must be left around the sides and the end of the beam.

Beams must be prevented from rotating at points of bearing when the depth to width ratio of the beam is greater than 2.5. This may be accomplished by the use of wedges or clip angles for beam to masonry or beam to concrete connections. U-shaped brackets can be used to provide restraint for beam to column connections or purlins can be framed into the face of the beam to prevent rotation (Figure 4.14).

All beams and columns should be provided with an even and level bearing surface. Where members are supported on masonry, this may be accomplished by providing a layer of grout below the bearing plate.

Beam to column brackets and purlin to beam hangers are usually custom fabricated using welded steel plates and angles. However, where stock sizes of glulam and SCL are used, it is usually possible to obtain prefabricated hangers and brackets.

The steel for these connections should conform to either CSA Standard G40.21 or ASTM Standard A36.

For normal service conditions the hardware should be primed and painted. For wet conditions, steel plates and angles should be hot-dipped galvanized. For corrosive environments, stainless steel should be used.

Figure 4.11
**Columns to
masonry or
concrete**

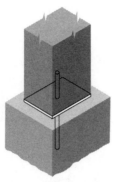

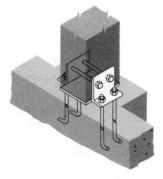

This simple base connection is effective when uplift and lateral forces are negligible. A base plate at least 3mm (1/8") thick prevents moisture transfer from the concrete support.

This connection resists both uplift and lateral loading. The base plate thickness depends on the area over which the load is distributed, but should not be less than 6mm (1/4").

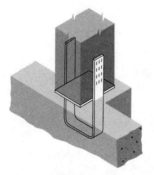

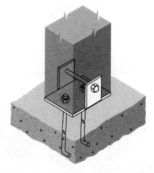

This U-shaped anchorage, fastened with glulam rivets, will resist both uplift and lateral loads. A 3mm (1/8") bearing plate should be used.

Some uplift and horizontal forces may be resisted by this connection. The end of the column must be countersunk to receive the anchor bolt and nut.

4

Post and Beam Construction

Figure 4.12
Beams to masonry or concrete

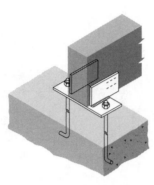

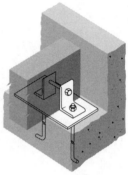

Glulam rivets are used for this detail. The side plates may be extended out to allow easy installation of fasteners if the masonry extends above the beam.

This standard beam-to-masonry connection resists both uplift and lateral forces. The bearing plate should be a minimum of 6mm (1/4") thick. Clearance should be left between the wall and beam for ventilation.

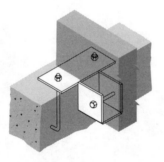

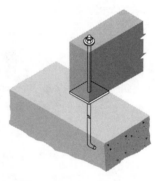

This is an acceptable method for limiting the projection of the beam above the foundation. A 6mm (1/4") clearance should be left between the anchor plate and the beam.

This simple anchorage for beams up to 600mm (24") deep resists both uplift and minor lateral forces and may be countersunk to provide a flush surface.

A bearing plate supports the beam and allows it to rotate out of the wall pocket if it collapses during a fire. The lugs transfer horizontal loads. This type of connection is required for Heavy Timber construction defined in Part 3 of the *NBCC*.

Figure 4.13
Beams to columns

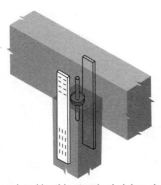

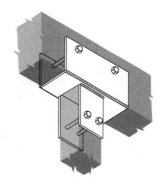

Uplift is resisted by this standard glulam rivet beam-to-column connection. The shear plates and dowel are only included when lateral forces are to be resisted.

When the beam and column are of different widths, this welded assembly may be used to transfer loads effectively.

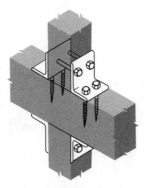

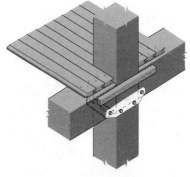

This detail may be used where a continuous beam is supported by a column and supports another column for the floor above. Lateral stability for the beam must be provided by purlin framing.

This connection fastens the beams together. Lag screws tie and support the beams through the side plate. The wood tie at the top of the beams provides support for the decking framing into the face of the column. This type of connection meets the Heavy Timber construction requirements of Part 3 of the *NBCC*.

This connection uses a steel plate in the sawn kerf. Machine bolt heads and nuts may be countersunk and plugged.

4

Post and Beam Construction

Figure 4.14
Purlins to beams

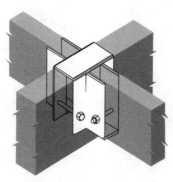

This connection is recommended where two purlins of moderate depth require support.

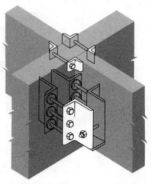

Deep purlins or beams may be connected by hangers. The clip angles at the top prevent rotation but do not restrain shrinkage in either member.

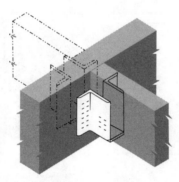

One-sided connections are well served by this arrangement, which uses glulam rivets.

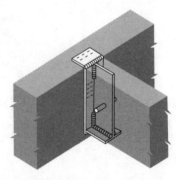

The vertical gusset prevents rotation of the purlin. The bearing plate may be recessed into the bottom of the purlin to provide a flush detail. The holes for the countersunk pin are plugged.

4.5   Detailing for Dimensional Change

Introduction

For post and beam construction comprised of sawn timber members, it is important to allow for shrinkage and expansion in the design. Sawn timbers are always dressed green and will shrink in service as they dry. Furthermore, since the members are large, the dimensional change as a result of shrinkage may also be large. Even manufactured wood products such as glulam and SCL, which are produced at a moisture content below 15%, may undergo some small shrinkage and expansion with seasonal changes in humidity.

Wood shrinks across the grain as it dries below a moisture content of about 30%. However, the dimensional changes along the grain due to drying are very small. The shrinkage of green timber across the grain may be up to 6% of the original dimension after acclimatizing to the conditions in a dry heated building. For example, a 286mm (12" nom.) deep member may shrink up to 17mm (11/16") after drying from 30 to 12% moisture content.

This change in dimension is a normal occurrence in a naturally occurring material. Understanding the dimensional changes in wood and detailing appropriately will result in designs which eliminate the following difficulties:

• splitting and checking through connections

• uneven floors

• distortion of roof or floor sheathing

• damaged finishes

The following information offers suggestions on how to negate the effects of dimensional changes for post and beam construction.

Arrangement of Framing Members

Where solid sawn purlins frame into a beam, the purlin should be installed slightly higher than the top of the beam (Figure 4.15). The height of the purlin above the

4

Post and Beam Construction

Figure 4.15
Purlin to beam connection

Sawn purlins flush with top of beam will cause distortion of sheathing

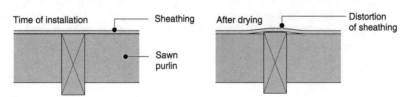

Sawn purlins raised above beam are recommended

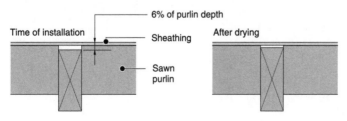

beam should be about 6% of the purlin depth. This will prevent the purlin from shrinking below the top of the beam and distorting the sheathing and finish flooring.

Framing members should also be arranged so that the amount of anticipated shrinkage on any given floor (and roof) is equal throughout the floor area. For instance, floor joists or purlins should be supported at each end by members that will shrink an equal amount otherwise the floor will be uneven after the structure dries.

Unequal shrinkage will occur where joists are supported by a concrete wall at one end and by a sawn timber beam at the other (Figure 4.16). In this situation, a sawn timber sill beam could be provided on top of the wall to equalize shrinkage or, the joists at the wood beam end could be set slightly higher than the joist elevation at the concrete wall.

Detailing of Connections

Connections should be detailed to prevent splitting, which lowers the load-carrying capacity of the fasteners. Splitting will occur when the connection hardware restrains shrinkage of a wood member as it dries. This occurs when long rows of bolts are used perpendicular to the grain, or where bolts are spaced far apart perpendicular to the grain. Splits due to restrained shrinkage may occur in glulam and structural composite lumber (SCL) in addition to green timber since seasonal humidity fluctuations cause expansion and contraction.

Some examples of good and poor connection detailing are as follows:

- Purlin hangers: the bolts through the purlin in the side plate should be located near the bottom of the hanger (Figure 4.17). If the bolt is placed near the top of the purlin, it may shrink away from the base plate and bear on the bolt. This may cause splitting of the purlin.

- Beam-to-column connections: the bolts in the side plates of the column cap should be placed near the bottom of the side plates (Figure 4.18). Placing bolts in the upper half of the beams may cause splitting.

- Multiple rows of bolts: where two or more rows of bolts are used in a splice plate connection, separate side plates should be provided where the distance between rows of bolts exceeds 125mm (4-7/8") (Figure 4.19). If a single side plate is used, a split may form when the wood member dries.

Figure 4.16
Wood joists supported on one end by masonry

Unequal shrinkage at ends of joists may cause an uneven floor

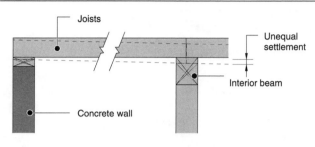

Joists

Unequal settlement

Interior beam

Concrete wall

Providing a sill beam to equalize shrinkage is recommended

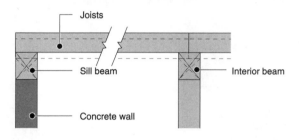

Joists

Sill beam

Interior beam

Concrete wall

4

Post and Beam Construction

Figure 4.17
Purlin hanger

Bolt near top of hanger will cause a split

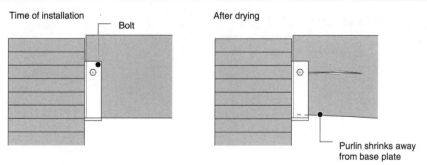

Time of installation

Bolt

After drying

Purlin shrinks away from base plate

Locating bolt near bottom of hanger recommended

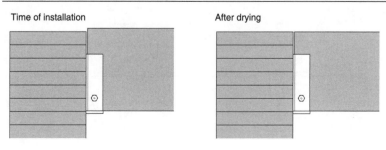

Time of installation

After drying

Figure 4.18
Beam-to-column connection

Bolts near top of side plate may cause a split

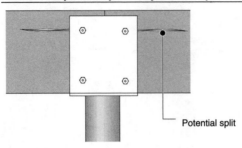

Potential split

Locating bolts near bottom of side plate will prevent splitting

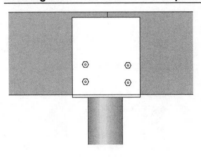

Figure 4.19
Splice plate connections

Single side plate may cause a split

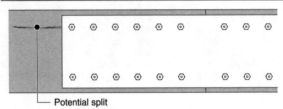

Potential split

Double side plates are recommended

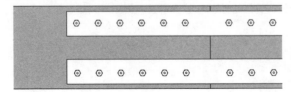

4.6   Erection

Introduction

Prior to erection of post and beam structures, shop drawings are usually prepared for each of the timber members showing the length, width, and depth of each member along with the size and location of any holes or grooves for fasteners. As much as possible, the members should be cut to the required size and be drilled or grooved in the shop prior to delivery to the site. This will help assure that the members and connections fit together accurately to specified tolerances.

When glulam arches are erected, each arch pair is raised, connected together and braced prior to installation of purlins, decking and other secondary members. Where the arches frame into a compression ring in a dome building, it is important that the arches be raised and connected to the ring in a symmetrical pattern to prevent the ring from rotating.

Heavy timber trusses are usually assembled on the ground at the site and then lifted into place. However, it may be possible to assemble the trusses in the shop if they are small enough to transport.

Erection equipment should be selected on the basis of the loads to be lifted, the overall height of the structure, and the working space available for erection. Long slender members and extra-heavy loads may require special lifting equipment, heavy rigging or spreader beams. When erecting large wood members, belt slings with padding or extra care in lifting and blocking between the sling and the members should be used to protect the factory finish. The erection of preassembled systems should not place undue or eccentric stresses on connections and therefore extra care in lifting, and temporary cross bracing may be required.

Temporary Bracing

Post and beam framing is unstable until the permanent bracing and other secondary members are in place. Adequate erection bracing must therefore be provided by the contractor to keep the framework stable and aligned until the secondary members are installed.

Erection bracing can consist of struts and shores or wire guy ropes with turnbuckles that allow easy adjustment. The bracing must be adequately connected to the timber members and the guys must have a sufficient number of clips at each loop in the rope. Blocking should be provided to prevent damage to the member. Often the permanent bracing can be installed while the structure is being erected to serve as the temporary bracing.

Temporary bracing should be designed to resist wind loading that might occur during the erection process. A sufficient number of braces must be used so that the member frame work remains stable and is not overstressed under wind loading.

Timber Decking

Tongue and groove planks are usually used for decking in post and beam buildings; however, decking may also be comprised of 38 x 64 or 89mm (2" x 3" or 4" nom.) or lumber nailed together on edge. This type of deck construction, called a nail laminated deck, was once used exclusively for heavily loaded floors in industrial and storage buildings (mill type buildings) and was referred to as a mill deck.

Installation
Plank and nail laminated deck may be arranged in a number of patterns. The most common patterns are:

- controlled random

- simple span

- two span continuous

4

Post and Beam Construction

The controlled random pattern (Figure 4.20) is the most economical method since random length material may be used. It must be laid in the following manner:

- the entire deck must extend over at least three spans

- end joints are not permitted in the outer half of end spans

- end joints which occur in adjacent courses must be staggered by 610mm (2') or more

- where end joints occur in the same general line they must be separated by at least two intervening courses

- planks that do not span over one support must be flanked by courses resting on both supports of that span and must be separated from the next unsupported

plank by at least six courses, each of which extends over at least one support (this is only permitted for nail-laminated decks and double tongue and groove planks more than 38mm (2" nom.) thick)

For simple span installation of plank decking, all pieces rest on two supports, and for two span continuous deck, all pieces must be rest on three supports. For simple span and two span continuous decks, all pieces are cut to a predetermined length, which generally makes these methods more expensive than the controlled random pattern. However, labour costs may be reduced because the arrangement of individual pieces does not have to be predetermined.

During installation of wood decking, each individual board must be nailed to the adjacent boards and to each support using proper nail sizes and specific arrangement of the planks (Figure 4.21).

Figure 4.20
Controlled random pattern for timber decking

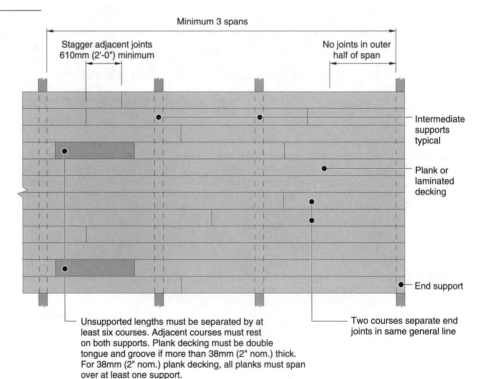

Minimum 3 spans

Stagger adjacent joints 610mm (2'-0") minimum

No joints in outer half of span

Intermediate supports typical

Plank or laminated decking

End support

Unsupported lengths must be separated by at least six courses. Adjacent courses must rest on both supports. Plank decking must be double tongue and groove if more than 38mm (2" nom.) thick. For 38mm (2" nom.) plank decking, all planks must span over at least one support.

Two courses separate end joints in same general line

Notes:
1. Random pattern is not permitted for bridges.
2. The other methods, Simple Span and Two Span Continous installation patterns, require that all butt joints occur over a support.

Figure 4.21
**Nailing for
timber decking**

Plank decking

64 and 89mm (2-1/2" and 3-1/2") Decking   **38mm (1-1/2") Decking**

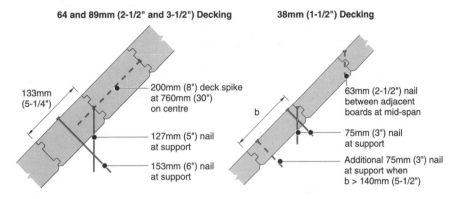

133mm
(5-1/4")

200mm (8") deck spike
at 760mm (30")
on centre

127mm (5") nail
at support

153mm (6") nail
at support

b

63mm (2-1/2") nail
between adjacent
boards at mid-span

75mm (3") nail
at support

Additional 75mm (3") nail
at support when
b > 140mm (5-1/2")

Note:
1. Planks 140mm (6" nom.) or less in width shall be nailed with 2 nails to each support.
   Planks more than 140mm (6" nom.) in width shall be nailed with 3 nails to each support.

Laminated decking

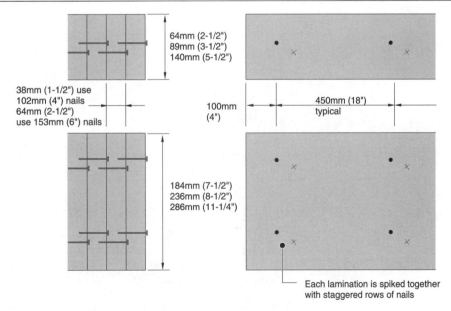

64mm (2-1/2")
89mm (3-1/2")
140mm (5-1/2")

38mm (1-1/2") use
102mm (4") nails
64mm (2-1/2")
use 153mm (6") nails

100mm
(4")

450mm (18")
typical

184mm (7-1/2")
236mm (8-1/2")
286mm (11-1/4")

Each lamination is spiked together
with staggered rows of nails

Notes:
1. Material for laminated decking should be minimum 38 x 64mm (2" x 3" nom.).
   The length of nails used should be no less than 102mm (4").
2. Each lamination shall be toe nailed to each support with 102mm (4") or longer nails.

4

Post and Beam Construction

References

1. *Wood Design Manual,* Canadian Wood Council, Ottawa, ON, 1995

2. *Wood Engineering and Construction Handbook,* Keith E. Flaherty and Thomas G. Williamson, McGraw Hill Publishing, 1989

Stairs and
Guards

Stringer spacing
is dependent
upon width,
occupancy type
and load.

Open stairs
require stronger
treads because
there is no riser
to distribute
load.

When stringers are supported by framing or by attachment to a wall, stringer spacing can be increased.

Stringers must be cut so that a minimum cross section remains for carrying the load.

Stairs must be positively attached at their tops and bottoms to resist vertical or horizontal displacement.

Risers allow a narrower tread to be used and reduce the thickness of the tread required.

Guards and balusters must be designed to resist horizontal and vertical loads.

5.1   Stairs and Guards

Introduction

The movement of people between floors is an important design consideration. The *National Building Code of Canada (NBCC)* gives direction on the construction of stairs and guards because of the obvious hazard these pose to injury from falling, and their importance to building evacuation during emergency. Specific information about fire safety requirements for exits is found in *Fire Safety Design in Buildings.*

This chapter provides information about structural requirements for stairs and guards, and some information pertaining to the installation of elevators in multistorey wood buildings. Some of the following information applies to stairs in general for both Part 9 and Part 4 requirements, and specific details are provided for wood stairs.

Stairs

Wood stairs consist of vertical risers and horizontal treads supported on two or more wood stringers (Figure 5.1). The stringers are the main load-carrying members and are supported by a header at the top and the lower floor at the bottom. The treads act as small beams and transfer the load to the stringers. The tread usually extends out past the face of the riser to create the nosing.

Stairs may be constructed with open or closed risers. Closed risers have a vertical board at the back of each tread. With open risers, the vertical board is omitted.

Part 9 of the *NBCC* specifies the acceptable step dimensions, which for stairs in dwelling units, are a maximum rise of 200mm (8"), a minimum run of 210mm (8-1/4"), and a minimum tread width of 235mm (9-1/4"). It is important that the rise and run be uniform throughout the stairs to avoid injury from tripping.

Stair Construction

One common method of building wood stairs is to build them on site using stringers that are cut or notched to accommodate the treads. These are called cut stringers (Figure 5.1). A finished 19mm (3/4") thick backboard is often placed between the stringer and the wall to serve as trim along the stairs. This trim can be matched to the baseboards along the floors and landings.

5

Stairs and Guards

Figure 5.1
Stairs constructed with cut stringers

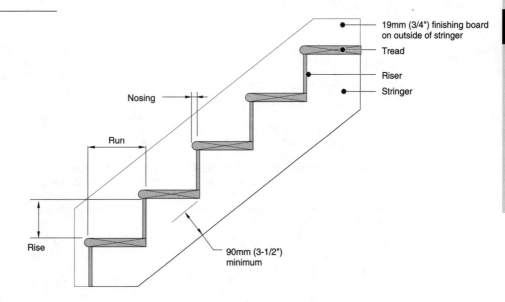

Nosing

Run

Rise

19mm (3/4") finishing board on outside of stringer

Tread

Riser

Stringer

90mm (3-1/2") minimum

Modern stairs are often premanufactured and delivered to the site as complete units. They are usually built with housed stringers which have grooves routed in the face of stringers (Figure 5.2). The risers and treads are placed in the grooves and are then glued using wood wedges to obtain and maintain firm contact between the stringers and the risers and treads.

The top of the riser is usually connected to the tread by chamfer blocks that are glued to both surfaces and nailed or screwed. The bottom of the riser is fastened to the tread with glue and nails or screws. The tread and riser connections can also be tongued and grooved. This method of construction results in a stair system which will not loosen or creak in service.

Stringers and Treads

The requirements for stair stringers and treads used in houses and small buildings are provided in Section 9.8 of the *NBCC*. Stringers must be made from lumber at least 38 x 235mm (2" x 10" nom.) with an effective depth of at least 90mm (3 1/2") when cut. However, if the stringer is supported along its length by a wall, the thickness may be reduced to 25mm (1").

The spacing of stringers must not exceed the following limits:

- 600mm (14") for stairs serving more than one dwelling unit

- 900mm (36") for stairs with open risers serving one dwelling unit

- 1200mm (48") for stairs with closed risers serving one dwelling unit

Lumber, plywood or OSB may be used for stair treads. The minimum acceptable thickness is 25mm (1" actual) when closed risers are used. For open risers the thick-ness must be increased to 38mm (1-1/2" actual) when the stringer spacing exceeds 750mm (30").

Stairs in buildings which must be designed under Part 4 of the *NBCC* will usually require larger stringers (or number of stringers) and treads than those required for Part 9 because of higher loadings.

Stairs in residential buildings which exceed the criteria for design under Part 9 must be designed under Part 4 using a minimum specified load of 1.9 kPA (40 psf). For other occupancies designed under Part 4, the minimum specified load for corridors of 4.8 kPa (100 psf) should be used to design the stair system.

Stair Width

The width of a stair will determine the number of stringers required. The required width for stairs depends on occupancy type, occupant load, and the arrangement of floors and exits to ensure that adequate capacity exists in the event of a need to evacuate.

The minimum widths are:

- 1100mm (44") for stairs that serve more than 3 storeys above grade or more than 1 storey below grade,

- 900mm (36") for stairs that serve not more than 3 storeys above grade or not more than 1 storey below grade

- 1650mm (65") for stairs serving patients' sleeping rooms

These minimum widths may need to be increased for certain occupancy types or where a stair serves more than one converging exit on the same floor. Stairs within dwelling units designed in accordance with Part 9 need not exceed 860mm (34").

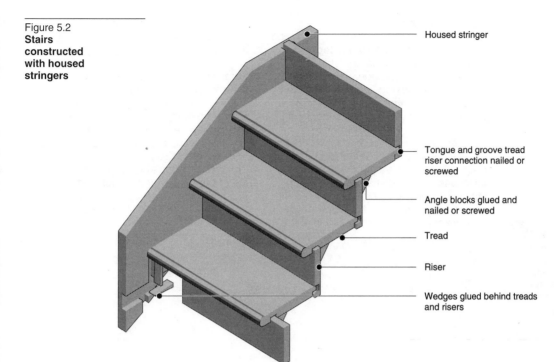

Figure 5.2
**Stairs
constructed
with housed
stringers**

Housed stringer

Tongue and groove tread
riser connection nailed or
screwed

Angle blocks glued and
nailed or screwed

Tread

Riser

Wedges glued behind treads
and risers

5

Stairs and Guards

Connection Details

The *NBCC* specifies that stair stringers be supported and secured at the top and bottom. This means that the stringer connections must be adequate to prevent the stair from moving vertically or sliding horizontally at either end. Failure to do so can result in an unstable and unsafe stair.

Cut stringers can be fastened to the header at the top end using nailed or bolted angles (Figure 5.3). Joist hangers may also be used where appropriate. At the base, the stringer should rest on top of the floor and be secured from sliding by a kicker plate. The kicker plate is nailed or bolted to the

floor (or concrete slab) and the stringer is notched around the plate. Bolted steel angles could also be used at the base.

Somewhat different details are usually used for connecting premanufactured stairs with housed stringers (Figure 5.4). There is usually no space for angles or hangers at the top end of the stringers so another means of providing vertical support must be used. Some stairs are manufactured with a hook at the top that fits over top of the header. If the hook method is not used, a built-up post can be added below each stringer and the stringers toe nailed to the header.

Figure 5.3
Connection details for stairs with cut stringers

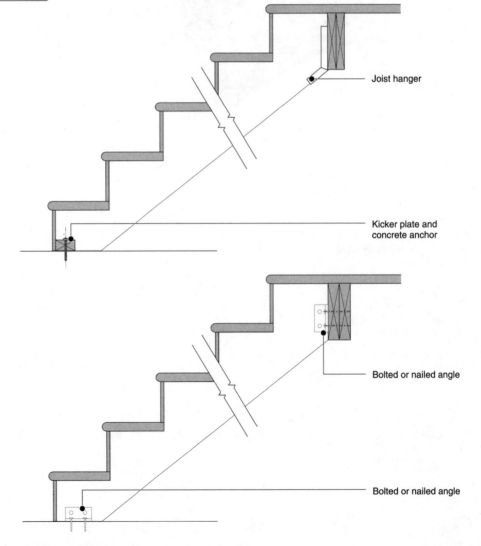

Joist hanger

Kicker plate and concrete anchor

Bolted or nailed angle

Bolted or nailed angle

Figure 5.4
Connection details for premanufactured stairs with housed stringers

Side view

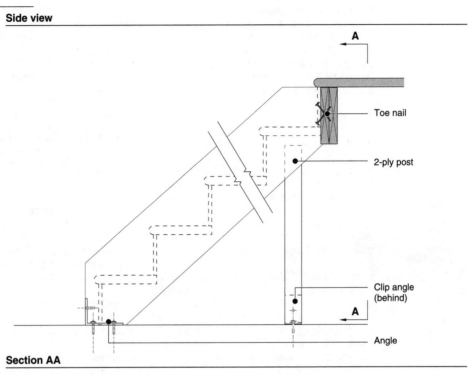

A

Toe nail

2-ply post

Clip angle (behind)

A

Angle

Section AA

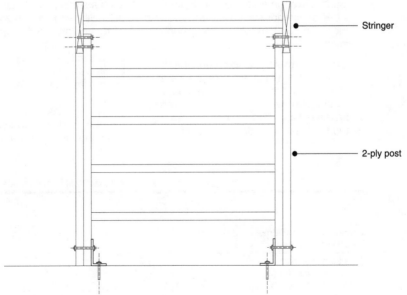

Stringer

2-ply post

5

Stairs and Guards

Premanufactured stairs with housed stringers should rest on top of the lower floor and can be prevented from sliding by fastening a steel angle at the end of each stringer. The end of the stringer may easily be notched so that the angle sits flush with the face of the stringer.

Guards

A guard is a protective barrier that is placed along side the open portion of a stairway, landing or balcony. Its purpose is to prevent accidental falls from one level to another. A guard may be open or closed. Open guards are usually constructed with vertical balusters (spindles or small posts) connected to a top rail, which is usually a handrail. Closed guards may consist of a short solid wall.

Part 9 of the *NBCC* requires that guards be placed around the open sides of all exterior landings or porches and all balconies, mezzanines, galleries or elevated walkways where the height above the lower level exceeds 600mm (2'). The requirements for guards around stairs are as follows:

- Guards are required around all open sides of exterior stairs where the stair is more than 600mm (2') above ground level.

- Guards or walls must surround interior stairs and landings or floors around stairwells where the stair has more than 2 risers. (However, stairs to an unfinished basement in a dwelling unit are permitted to have one unprotected side.)

The *NBCC* also specifies the minimum height for guards which depends on the location of the guard and the type of building. All guards within dwelling units must be at least 900mm (36") high. 900mm (36") is also the minimum required height for guards around:

- Stairs

- Porches, balconies, decks and landing areas with walking surfaces elevated not more than 1800mm above the finished ground level

- Porches, balconies, decks and landing areas serving not more than one dwelling unit

Elsewhere, all required guards, including those installed in commercial buildings, must be 1070mm (42") high.

Where the guard consists of balusters and a rail, the clear space between balusters should be less than 100mm (4") in residential buildings (or any other building where children are likely to be present) and less than 200mm (8") in other types of buildings, such as industrial buildings (where children are unlikely to be present without supervision), and must not facilitate climbing.

Construction Details
Guards must be designed and constructed so that they can resist lateral and vertical loads without breaking or deflecting excessively. The *NBCC* does not provide specific member sizes or connection details, but it gives the minimum loading for which the

Table 5.1
Loads on guards (Part 4 requirements)

Type of guard	Minimum specified horizontal load[1]					Minimum specified vertical load[2]	
	Uniform load		Concentrated load[3]			Uniform load	
	(kN/m)	(lb/ft)	(kN)	(lb)		(kN/m)	(lb/ft)
Grandstands, stadiums, bleachers and arenas	3.0	205	-	-		1.5	103
Access walkways, equipment platforms, contiguous stairs and similar areas[4]	-	-	1.0	225		1.5	103
Other[5]	0.75	51	1.0	225		1.5	103

Notes:
1. Load to be applied inward or outward at the top of every required guard.
2. Load to be applied at the top of every required guard. This load does not need to be applied simultaneously with the horizontal load.
3. The concentrated load is to be applied at any point.
4. These are areas where gathering of many people is improbable.
5. The uniform load or the concentrated load is applied, whichever governs.

guard must be designed. These loads consist of horizontal and vertical loads applied to the top of the guard. (The horizontal and vertical do not need to be considered to act simultaneously.

For buildings designed under Part 9 of the *NBCC,* guards may be sized to resist loads from normal use, or be designed to meet loading requirements set out in Part 4 (Table 5.1).

The balusters or solid panels within the guard must also be capable of withstanding a concentrated severe horizontal load of 0.50 kN (112 lb) applied at any point in the element.

Guards must be constructed so that the balusters or solid panels are well connected to the rail at the top and to the stair or landing at the base. The top rail in turn spans between main posts. These posts must be rigid and strong enough to prevent side-sway.

The main posts in stair guards are called newels. The base of the newel must be securely anchored to the stair or floor

structure so that it is capable of resisting the minimum lateral loading specified by the *NBCC.*

For exterior decks and balconies, the guard usually consists of wood pickets fastened to a top rail. The rail should be at least a 38mm (2" nom.) wood member placed on the flat to provide horizontal bending strength.

To provide a strong and rigid guard, the posts supporting the floor structure should cantilever up above the floor to act as the guard posts (Figures 5.5 and 5.6). The rail should be fastened to the post using bolts and angles. Also, one of the floor joists should be connected to the post.

These connections will assure that the load from the rail is transferred to the post and in turn from the post back to the main structure through the floor. The long term structural integrity of exterior guards must be guaranteed. Because exterior guards are usually exposed to wet conditions, the use of preservative treated wood is recommended.

Figure 5.5
Connection details for balcony guards

Elevation

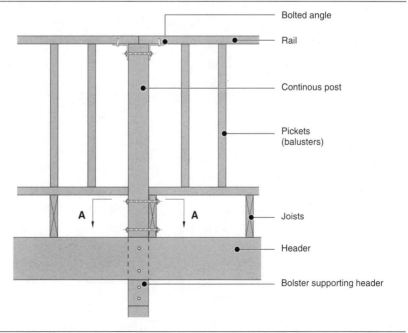

Section AA

Figure 5.6
Alternate connection details for balcony guards

Alternative 1

Elevation

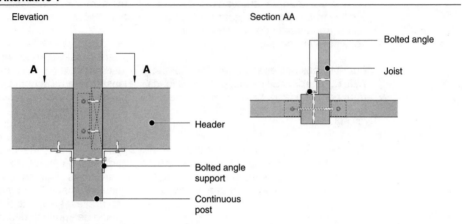

Section AA

Bolted angle

Joist

Header

Bolted angle support

Continuous post

Alternative 2

Elevation

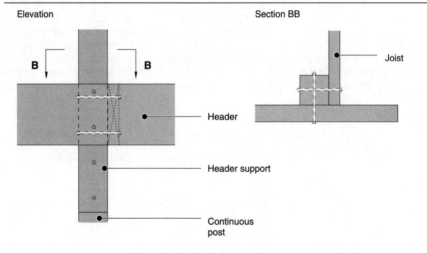

Section BB

Joist

Header

Header support

Continuous post

Elevators for Wood-Frame Construction

Although wood-frame construction is restricted to four stories or less in building height depending on occupancy type, elevator installation in wood buildings is not uncommon, and is in fact becoming more common as the need to extend building access to people of all physical abilities progresses. It would not be unusual in a single storey church building of modern design, for example, to provide elevator access to a basement assembly area.

Once an elevator is installed in a building (even in a one storey building where an elevator is use to travel from the first floor to a basement), the *NBCC* requires that the storeys and rooms or spaces within those storeys served by the elevator be provided with barrier free access.

The code further specifies that, in an unsprinklered building, an elevator installed to provide barrier free access must conform to most of the fire safety requirements specified for the firefighter elevators required for high rise buildings. Otherwise, other means of protecting persons with physical disabilities must be provided such as balconies or refuge areas. These fire safety requirements for elevators relate to the fire separations required around the elevator shaft and the control of smoke movement. These fire separation and fire-resistance rating requirements can be met by using wood-frame construction.

There are no requirements in the *NBCC* for the elevator shaft (vertical service space as it is defined in the *NBCC)* to be constructed of noncombustible materials. However, masonry block or concrete elevator shafts have almost always been used which easily meet the stringent alignment requirements for the safe movement of the elevator car up and down the shaft.

As mentioned in Chapter 3, the framing of wood floors supported at one end by vertical masonry assemblies such as fire walls and elevator shafts, and at the other by wood framing, requires consideration of the shrinkage effects. If an elevator shaft is a noncombustible fire separation, floor joists must be fire cut to allow breakaway of the floor assembly during fire situations, or the floor must be supported independent of the shaft by using posts and ledgers, or wood stud walls for support. Where the joists are fire cut and inset into a masonry wall, they should be set slightly lower than the wood frame supported end so that the floor will be level once equilibrium drying has occurred (refer to Chapter 2 for estimating the elevation differences).

5

References

1. *National Building Code of Canada,*
   Associate Committee on the National
   Building Code, National Research
   Council, Ottawa, ON, 1995

2. *Fire Safety Design in Buildings,*
   Canadian Wood Council, Ottawa, ON,
   1996

Thermal Insulation

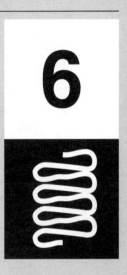

Overcompressing fibreglass batt insulation can significantly reduce the insulating values of assemblies.

Batts should be installed to fit closely into the spaces they will insulate.

Attic spaces above the insulation must be well ventilated to prevent the condensation of escaped moisture.

Installing rigid insulation on the exterior is a way of increasing the thermal resistance of assemblies.

For this sprinkler piping chase lying between parallel chord trusses, a gypsum wallboard liner, vapour barrier and insulation have been installed above the piping to create a warm space for the wet system.

Insulation and barriers to air and moisture movement are essential to ensuring good energy efficiency and building performance.

6.1   General Information

The building envelope consists of several elements necessary to provide comfort to building occupants, and protection for the building fabric. Insulation is the building component which controls temperature directly, and indirectly affects the movement of moisture to and from building spaces.

This chapter deals specifically with the temperature control aspect of the building envelope. (Those aspects of the building envelope that inhibit the movement of moisture and vapour are discussed in Chapter 7.)

Over the past 30 years, rising energy costs and energy conservation concerns have required that the building industry improve the thermal efficiency of new construction.

Prior to the 1980s, the *NBCC* Committee for Energy Conservation produced *Measures for Energy Conservation,* which made recommendations for minimum thermal resistances for building materials. These recommendations were useful for energy minded home builders. However, they were not enforceable under provincial building codes. During the 1970s and 1980s, provincial building codes increased their minimum thermal resistance requirements.

During the 1980s, the federal government began to provide incentives for builders to construct energy efficient homes, and owners of commercial buildings, wishing to reduce operating costs, have also demanded improved levels of thermal efficiency.

The federal government initiated a *Super Energy Efficient Home Program* that sets building standards for house construction. The homes meeting this criteria are called R-2000 homes. Although R-2000 homes and other buildings built to R-2000 requirements exceed minimum standards set by the building codes, in most cases the extra cost of construction can be offset by savings in energy costs.

The purpose of this section is to illustrate proper methods for insulating wood buildings. To do this, the following topics are included:

6.2   Heat Transfer and Insulation

6.3   Insulating Wood Buildings

6

Thermal Insulation

6.2   Heat Transfer and Insulation

Introduction

Heat always moves from a warmer area to a colder area. During the winter, heat is transferred from the interior of a heated building to the exterior. In the summer, heat can be transferred from the exterior to the interior during the day and may move in the other direction at night when it is cooler outside. Heat is transferred by three mechanisms:

- Conduction:
  Conduction occurs in a solid material when the molecules are excited by a heat source on one side of the material. These molecules transmit energy (heat) to the cold side of the material. Conduction occurs primarily through the foundation and framing members in buildings.

- Convection:
  Convection is the movement of air that occurs as heated air becomes less dense and rises, and cooler air is drawn in to fill the space left by the displaced heated air.

- Radiation:
  Radiation occurs in the absence of a medium when one object transfers heat to another object by releasing heat waves. For example, the sun produces radiant energy that heats the earth. Radiation into buildings occurs mainly through glass windows and doors.

Buildings are affected by all three heat transfer mechanisms. Most heat loss occurs by conduction through the building components and by air leakage.

Building assemblies must be designed to resist the flow of air. Air leakage can contribute to heat loss and it can carry water vapour into wall cavities and lead to condensation (Chapter 7).

National Building Code Requirements

The *NBCC* does not specifically define the amount of insulation required. However, many provincial codes specify the amount of thermal resistance (RSI) that the insulation alone or the assembly must have.

Thermal resistance (RSI) is the resistance of an assembly to the transfer of heat and is given in units of $m^2 \cdot °C/W$. The imperial equivalent is R value expressed in units of $ft^2 \cdot h \cdot °F/BTU$.

The *NBCC* requires a vapour barrier on all insulated assemblies to prevent water from diffusing into the assembly. The air barrier is necessary to ensure that moist air does not flow around the vapour barrier and into the assembly. Without these barriers (Chapter 7), moist air could condense in the assembly and lead to deterioration of the wood framing and loss of thermal resistance of the insulation.

Except where the insulation provides the principal resistance to air leakage, thermal insulation shall be installed so that at least one face is in full and continuous contact with an element with low air permeance.

Insulation

The *NBCC* lists several types of acceptable insulating materials such as flexible batt insulation, loose fill insulation, rigid panels, and spray-type insulation. Typical thermal resistance values of these materials are given in Table 6.1.

Flexible Batt Insulation

Flexible batt insulation is made from mineral wool or glass fibre.

This type of insulation will be damaged if it gets wet and therefore flexible batts should be installed after a building is enclosed and weathertight. Batt insulation should fill the cavity. If batt insulation is compressed to fit into a space, its thermal efficiency will be reduced.

6

Thermal Insulation

Table 6.1
Thermal resistance of common building materials

Building material		Thickness		Thermal resistance	
		mm	in.	RSI $m^2 \cdot °C/W$	R $ft^2 \cdot h \cdot °F/BTU$
Insulation materials					
Flexible (mineral wool, glass fibre)	low density	140	5-1/2	2.83	16
	medium density	140	5-1/2	3.30	19
	high density	140	5-1/2	3.93	22.5
Loose fill	glass fibre	100	4	2.00	11
	mineral fibre	100	4	2.30	13
	cellulose fibre	100	4	2.50	12.5
Spray	polyurethane	100	4	4.1	23
	isocyanurate	100	4	3.4	19
	cellulose fibre	100	4	2.4	13.5
Rigid nonstructural	expanded bead polystyrene, Type 1	25	1	0.64	3.5
	expanded bead polystyrene, Type 2	25	1	0.69	4
	extruded polystyrene foam, Type 3	25	1	0.74	4.2
	extruded polystyrene foam, Type 4	25	1	0.88	5
	polyurethane or isocyanurate board	25	1	1.0	5.5
	fibreglass wall sheathing	25	1	0.77	4.5
	glass fibre roof board	25	1	0.69	4
Structural materials					
Softwood lumber (except cedar)		100	4	0.87	5
Cedar logs and lumber		100	4	0.92	5.2
Concrete	2400 kg/m³ (150 lb/ft²)	100	4	0.045	0.3
	1760 kg/m³ (110 lb/ft²)	100	4	0.13	0.7
	480 kg/m³ (30 lb/ft²)	100	4	0.69	4
Concrete block (3 oval core)	sand and gravel	100 / 300	4 / 12	0.12 / 0.22	0.7 / 1.2
	cinder aggregate	100 / 300	4 / 12	0.20 / 0.33	1.1 / 1.9
	lightweight aggregate	100 / 300	4 / 12	0.26 / 0.40	1.5 / 2.3
Common brick	clay or shale	100	4	0.07	0.3
	concrete mix	100	4	0.05	0.2
Face brick (see Cladding)					
Stone (lime or sand)		100	4	0.06	0.3
Steel		100	4	0.002	0.01
Aluminum		100	4	0.00049	0.002
Roofing					
Asphalt roll roofing		Typ.	Typ.	0.026	0.1
Asphalt shingles		Typ.	Typ.	0.078	0.5
Wood shingles		Typ.	Typ.	0.17	1
Built-up membrane (hot-mopped)		Typ.	Typ.	0.058	0.3
Crushed stone (not dried)		100	4	0.055	0.3

| | | Thickness | | Thermal resistance | |
Table 6.1 *(cont'd)* **Thermal resistance of common building materials** — Building material		mm	in.	RSI m²•°C/W	R ft²•h•°F/BTU
Sheathing					
Plywood and OSB		9.5	3/8	0.08	0.5
Insulating fibreboard sheathing		25	1	0.5	2.8
Polyethylene film		0.10	4 mil	neg.	neg.
		0.15	6 mil	neg.	neg.
Sheathing paper		Typ.	Typ.	0.011	0.06
Cladding					
Softwood siding (lapped)	drop (19 x 184mm [1" x 8" nom.])	19	3/4	0.14	0.8
	bevel (12 x 184mm [3/4" x 8" nom.])	12	1/2	0.14	0.8
	bevel (19 x 235mm [1" x 10" nom.])	19	3/4	0.18	1
	plywood	9	3/8	0.10	0.6
	wood shingles	Typ.	Typ.	0.17	1
Fibreboard	medium-density hardboard (panel or lapped)	9.5	1/2	0.10	0.6
	high-density hardboard (tempered service)	9.5	1/2	0.08	0.4
Brick (clay or shale)		100	4	0.074	0.4
Stucco (metal lath)		25	1	0.035	0.2
Metal (clapboard or vertical V-groove)		Typ.	Typ.	0.12	0.6
Interior Finish					
Gypsum wallboard		13	1/2	0.08	0.4
Gypsum plaster		13	1/2	0.018	0.1
Flooring					
Maple or oak		19	3/4	0.12	0.6
Pine or fir		19	3/4	0.17	1
Plywood, OSB		16	5/8	0.14	0.8
Linoleum or tile (resilient)		3	1/8	0.014	0.08
Terrazzo		25	1	0.014	0.08
Carpet	fibrous underlay	Typ.	Typ.	0.37	2
	rubber underlay	Typ.	Typ.	0.23	1.3

6 Thermal Insulation

Loose-Fill Insulation

Loose fill insulation is made from glass fibre or mineral wool fibres that have been chopped into small pieces. It can also be produced from chopped polystyrene or cellulose fibre. Cellulose fibre is made from recycled newsprint that has been treated with fire retardants and other chemicals to prevent deterioration.

Loose-fill insulation is blown into horizontal spaces such as floors or ceilings with special equipment. It must be installed to the density recommended by the manufacturer. Part 9 of the *NBCC* permits the use of loose-fill in spaces **other than horizontal,** only in the following situations:

- Water repellent loose-fill insulation may be used between the **outer and inner wythes** of masonry cavity walls.

- Loose-fill insulation may be added to wood-frame walls of existing buildings (doing this will change the thermal gradient of the wall assembly and therefore, to prevent condensation, the vapour resistance of the wall should be verified before insulating).

- Loose-fill insulation can be used in attic spaces over ceilings sloped not more than 2.5 in 12.

- Blown-in insulation can be used in above-ground wood frame walls of new construction (provisions must be made for inspection, avoiding settlement in the insulation, allowing ease of interior finish application and avoiding use of water in the insulation unless it can be shown that the water will not adversely affect other materials).

When using loose-fill insulation in attic spaces, care must be taken to prevent blockage of the air vents in soffits and the ventilation path between roof rafters. Also, measures are needed to minimize airflow into the insulation near the soffit vents to maintain the thermal performance of the material. A space not less than 63mm (2.5") shall be provided between the top of the insulation and the underside of the roof sheathing.

Rigid Panel Insulation

Rigid panel insulation is made from a variety of materials including polystyrene, polyurethane, polyisocyanurate, phenolic, and rigid glass fibre. Each of these materials has different properties specific to their intended use.

Rigid insulation may react with certain chemicals. Therefore, adhesives and all chemicals in contact with rigid insulation should be approved by the product manufacturer before use. When using adhesives to affix panels, the panels should be glued with a grid pattern to block air convection currents behind the panels.

Water resistance is an important consideration in the choice of rigid insulation. Polyurethane foam is dimensionally unstable under high humidity and freeze/thaw conditions. Therefore, it should not be used for built-up roof systems.

For ground contact applications, low-density (Type I) expanded polystyrene should not be used, however high-density (Type II) expanded polystyrene is acceptable.

Spray Type Insulation

Spray type insulations are becoming more widely used in construction due to their ease of installation and their ability to seal gaps. There are three types available.

- cellulose or chopped fibre insulation, mixed with adhesives and sprayed on to a surface with a special applicator

- isocyanurate foam, made of two-component chemicals mixed with a special application sprayer, used for exterior stud wall cavities, perimeter joists spaces, and around windows and doors

- polyurethane foam, mixed on site or purchased premixed in cans or canisters, often used to insulate and seal around windows and doors.

Foams may be mixed and foamed in a factory, or be foamed in place on site. Foamed-in-place insulation is useful for insulating existing buildings but may not be stable or durable in some environments.

Foams that expand in place must be installed with care to ensure that the foam expands enough to completely fill the cavity, and does not exert undue pressure on large surfaces such as gypsum wallboard finishes.

6.3   Insulating Wood Buildings

Introduction

In wood-frame building systems, a substantial portion of the heat loss occurs from conduction through the framing members, which have a lower thermal resistance than the insulation. This is called thermal bridging. Many of the techniques to improve the thermal resistance of a wall utilize concepts that reduce the effect of thermal bridging through the framed members.

The thermal ratings given in following sections are calculated for the insulation cavities and not the framed members. Thermal bridging through the framed members will tend to reduce the overall thermal efficiency of an assembly.

Wood-Frame Walls

Stud Walls

Wood stud walls are usually insulated by installing flexible batt insulation between studs (Figure 6.1). Polyethylene sheets with sealed joints installed over the studs on the warm side act as both the air and vapour barrier (Chapter 7). In the past, 38 x 89mm (2" x 4" nom.) stud walls were extensively used for residential construction. While larger studs are not usually required structurally, they are often used because of the increased cavity size they provide for insulation.

Figure 6.1
Stud wall with standard sheathing and cladding

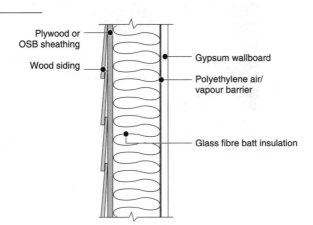

Plywood or OSB sheathing
Wood siding
Gypsum wallboard
Polyethylene air/ vapour barrier
Glass fibre batt insulation

6

Thermal Insulation

Material	Thermal resistance					
	Stud size					
	38 x 89mm (2" x 4" nom.)		38 x 140mm (2" x 6" nom.)		38 x 184mm (2" x 8" nom.)	
	RSI	R	RSI	R	RSI	R
Interior air film	0.12	0.6	0.12	0.6	0.12	0.6
12.7mm (1/2") gypsum wallboard	0.08	0.5	0.08	0.5	0.08	0.5
Air/vapour barrier	0.00	0	0.00	0	0.00	0
Glass fibre batt insulation	2.10	12	3.30	18	4.34	24
7.5mm (5/16") plywood or OSB sheathing	0.06	0.3	0.06	0.3	0.06	0.3
12mm (15/32") beveled softwood siding	0.14	0.8	0.14	0.8	0.14	0.8
Exterior air film	0.03	0.2	0.03	0.2	0.03	0.2
Total	2.53	14.4	3.73	20.4	4.77	26.4

Stud Walls with Exterior Thermal Sheathing

A common way to increase the insulating value of a stud wall is to use external thermal sheathing. The structural sheathing is replaced with rigid or semi-rigid insulation panels (Figure 6.2).

The panels can be nailed to the stud wall using special nails with large plastic washers. The maximum thickness of exterior insulation is limited by its ability to be properly fastened and the ability to fasten strapping or siding to the stud frame.

If large nails are used the siding may split and if the insulation is over-nailed, the insulation may compress. This compressed insulation can expand with time causing the nails to pull through the siding.

When exterior thermal sheathing is used, diagonal bracing must be installed in the wall to add the rigidity usually provided by plywood or OSB sheathing.

Figure 6.2
Stud wall with exterior thermal sheathing

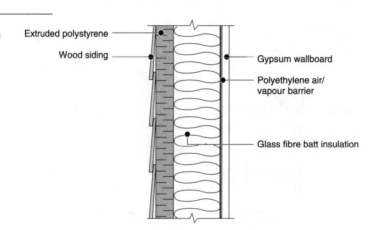

Extruded polystyrene

Wood siding

Gypsum wallboard

Polyethylene air/vapour barrier

Glass fibre batt insulation

Thermal resistance

Material	Stud size					
	38 x 89mm (2" x 4" nom.)		38 x 140mm (2" x 6" nom.)		38 x 184mm (2" x 8" nom.)	
	RSI	R	RSI	R	RSI	R
Interior air film	0.12	0.6	0.12	0.6	0.12	0.6
12.7mm (1/2") gypsum wallboard	0.08	0.5	0.08	0.5	0.08	0.5
Air/vapour barrier	0.00	0	0.00	0	0.00	0
Glass fibre batt insulation	2.10	12	3.30	18	4.34	24
25mm (1") extruded polystyrene (Type 4)	0.88	5	0.88	5	0.88	5
12mm (15/32")beveled softwood siding	0.14	0.8	0.14	0.8	0.14	0.8
Exterior air film	0.03	0.2	0.03	0.2	0.03	0.2
Total	3.35	19.2	4.55	25.1	5.59	31.1

Stud Walls with Interior Strapping

Wood-frame walls can be constructed with strapping on the interior of the studs to create a space for additional insulation (Figure 6.3).

The strapping, usually 38 x 38 or 64mm (2" x 2" or 4" nom.), can be applied vertically or horizontally, but thermal bridging through framed members will be reduced by placing the strapping perpendicular to the stud framing. In this way, the insulation between the strapping covers the studs and the only thermal bridging points occur at the intersections of the studs and straps.

If interior strapping is applied vertically, additional blocking or drywall clips will be required at corners and at intersections of ceilings and walls.

Interior strapping allows the electrical services to be installed in the strapped space so that the vapour barrier will have fewer penetrations and openings.

Figure 6.3
Stud wall with interior strapping

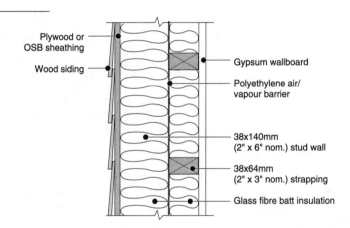

Plywood or OSB sheathing
Wood siding
Gypsum wallboard
Polyethylene air/vapour barrier
38x140mm (2" x 6" nom.) stud wall
38x64mm (2" x 3" nom.) strapping
Glass fibre batt insulation

Material	Thermal resistance	
	RSI	R
Interior air film	0.12	0.7
12.7mm (1/2") gypsum wallboard	0.08	0.5
64mm (2-1/2") glass fibre batt insulation	1.51	8.6
Air/vapour barrier	0.00	0
140mm (5-1/2") glass fibre batt insulation	3.30	18.7
7.5mm (5/16") plywood or OSB sheathing	0.06	0.3
12mm beveled softwood siding	0.14	0.8
Exterior air film	0.03	0.2
Total	5.24	29.8

6

Thermal Insulation

Truss Walls

A truss wall system can provide greater thermal resistance than standard frame walls. It consists of a sheathed loadbearing wall with trusses outside the wall which are supported at the lower end by a ledger (Figure 6.4).

The trusses are made from 38 x 38mm (2" x 2" nom.) or 38 x 64mm (2" x 3" nom.) material and plywood gusset plates. The polyethylene vapour barrier is placed over the wall sheathing and extends from the foundation wall and up over the top of the stud wall. The truss wall is anchored through the vapour barrier into the wall studs and insulation is added between trusses.

Double Stud Walls

The construction of double stud walls can provide much greater thermal resistance than a single wall with strapping or external thermal sheathing (Figure 6.4).

In single-wall construction, the insulation thickness is limited to the wall size, but in the double-wall system, the space between the walls can be increased to provide greater insulation values. Also, the problem of thermal bridging through the wood frame is virtually eliminated as a result of the space between the two walls.

A double-wall system is usually comprised of an exterior loadbearing wall, and a lighter non-loadbearing wall on the inside to support the interior gypsum wallboard. The centre cavity between the double walls is generally 89 or 140mm (4" or 6" nom.) to accommodate an extra RSI of 2.1 or 3.5 (R value of 6 to 20). The batts are installed horizontally in the centre cavity, and vertically between the both sets of studs.

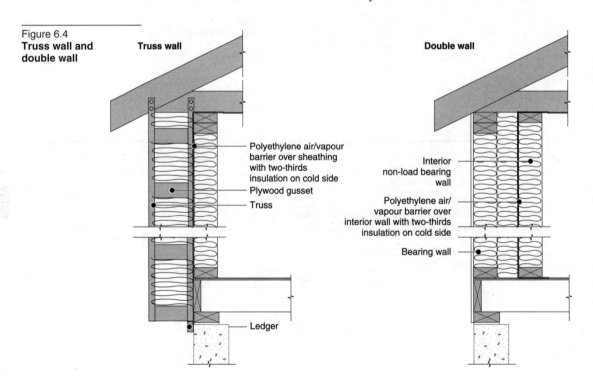

Figure 6.4
Truss wall and double wall

Truss wall

- Polyethylene air/vapour barrier over sheathing with two-thirds insulation on cold side
- Plywood gusset
- Truss
- Ledger

Double wall

- Interior non-load bearing wall
- Polyethylene air/vapour barrier over interior wall with two-thirds insulation on cold side
- Bearing wall

Insulating Floor-Wall Intersections

To provide continuity of insulation at the intersections of floors and walls, batt insulation should be placed inside the header and a rigid foam block used to enclose the space (Figure 6.5).

The rigid foam block can serve as the air and vapour barrier, provided it has a low permeability and the edges are sealed to the floor joists, subfloor and the lower wall.

The use of recessed headers at the foundation wall will allow extra rigid insulation to be placed on the outside of the header (Figure 6.6).

The insulation on the outside of the header must have at least twice the RSI (R) value as the insulation placed between the joists. The polyethylene can be passed under and around the header during assembly to provide a continuous vapour barrier.

Figure 6.5
Insulation of floor-wall intersections

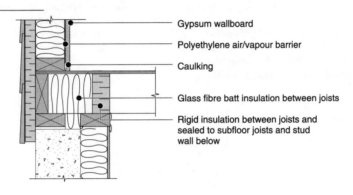

Gypsum wallboard

Polyethylene air/vapour barrier

Caulking

Glass fibre batt insulation between joists

Rigid insulation between joists and sealed to subfloor joists and stud wall below

Figure 6.6
Recessed header

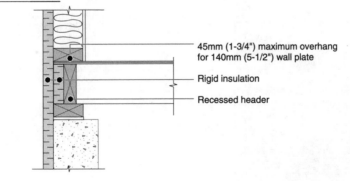

45mm (1-3/4") maximum overhang for 140mm (5-1/2") wall plate

Rigid insulation

Recessed header

6

Thermal Insulation

Foundations

Foundation walls enclosing basements and heated crawl spaces are typically poorly insulated and in the average building, are the largest contributor to heat loss. Foundation walls can be insulated either on the exterior or on the interior.

Specific requirements are provided in the provincial building codes but for energy efficiency, the insulating value of a foundation wall should be at least equivalent to the other walls in the building envelope.

Foundation walls around unheated crawl spaces do not require insulation, but the floor framing between the heated and unheated space must be insulated.

Concrete and Masonry Block Foundation Walls with Exterior Insulation

Foundation walls enclosing heated spaces can be insulated with rigid insulation boards made from polystyrene or glass fibre installed vertically on the exterior of the wall (Figure 6.7).

The above grade portion of the rigid insulation should be fastened to the sill plate or to the foundation wall with an adhesive. If the above grade portion is not covered by the exterior cladding, the exposed insulation should be protected from mechanical damage with flashing and cement parging on wire lath.

Figure 6.7
Concrete foundation with exterior insulation

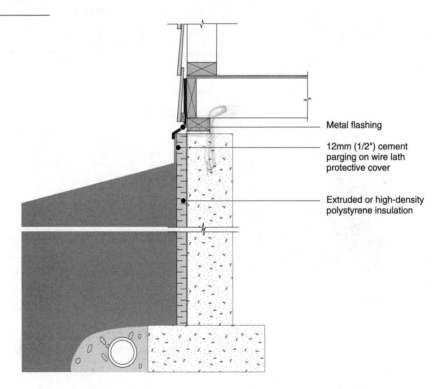

Metal flashing

12mm (1/2") cement parging on wire lath protective cover

Extruded or high-density polystyrene insulation

Material	Thermal resistance	
	RSI	R
Interior air film	0.11	0.6
200mm (8") concrete foundation wall (2400 kg/m^3 [150 lbs/ft^3])	0.09	0.5
64mm (2-1/2") extruded polystyrene (Type 4)	2.25	12.8
Total	2.45	13.9

Uncured concrete foundation dampproofing compounds can react with some foam insulations; therefore, dampproofing should be allowed to cure completely before applying insulation.

Concrete and Masonry Block Foundation Walls with Interior Insulation

Concrete and masonry foundation walls can be insulated on the interior with rigid polystyrene insulation placed between strapping, or 38 x 64 or 89mm (2" x 2-1/2" or 4") frame walls can be installed and insulated with batt insulation (Figure 6.8).

The stud walls can also be built away from the concrete to provide a cavity for additional insulation. To reduce air flow behind the wall, it is advisable to install the batt insulation horizontally within the cavity and vertically between the stud spaces.

A moisture barrier of 0.05mm (2 mil) polyethylene, building paper or asphalt emulsions is required on the inside of the foundation wall below grade level to prevent moisture from migrating through the foundation and into the insulation and wood framing members. Since the foundation is usually colder than the ambient

Figure 6.8
Concrete foundation with interior insulation

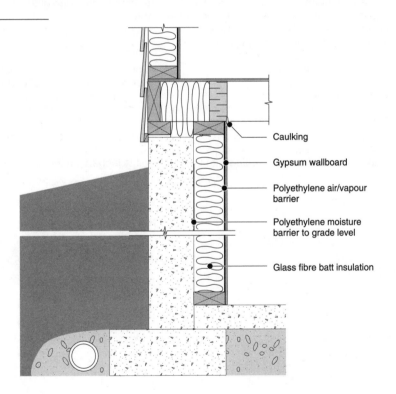

Caulking

Gypsum wallboard

Polyethylene air/vapour barrier

Polyethylene moisture barrier to grade level

Glass fibre batt insulation

6

Thermal Insulation

		Thermal resistance	
Material		RSI	R
Interior air film		0.11	0.6
12.7mm (1/2") gypsum wallboard		0.08	0.5
Air/vapour barrier		0.00	0.0
89mm (3-1/2") glass fibre batt insulation		2.10	12
Moisture barrier		0.00	0.0
200mm (8") concrete foundation wall (2400 kg/m^3 [150 lbs/ft^3])		0.09	0.6
	Total	2.38	13.7

building air temperature, a polyethylene vapour barrier must be installed on the warm side of the insulation to prevent condensation within the assembly.

Permanent Wood Foundations

Permanent wood foundation can be easily and economically insulated by installing glass fibre batt insulation between studs (Figure 6.9). As for above ground conventional framing, polyethylene vapour barrier must be installed on the warm side of the insulation to prevent condensation.

Glass fibre drainage insulation can also be applied over the exterior moisture barrier to increase the RSI (R) value of the wall, improve foundation drainage, and protect the moisture barrier from mechanical damage during backfilling.

Unheated Crawl Spaces

For an unheated crawl space, the main floor framing is insulated as part of the building envelope. Before the batt or rigid insulation is installed between the floor joists, the joints in the subfloor should be sealed with caulk-

ing or adhesive to provide the floor system with an air and vapour barrier. Plywood sheathing and OSB (commonly 15.5mm [5/8"] thick) have a permeability rating that meets the requirements of a Type 2 vapour barrier (Chapter 7).

Where flexible batt insulation is used, it should be held in place by fastening wire mesh to the underside of the joists, and be protected from mechanical damage by a material such as sheathing paper. If loose fill insulation is to be blown into the joist spaces, fibreboard sheathing or other high permeability sheathing should be fastened to the bottom edge of the joists to support the insulation and protect it from moisture. All services that pass through the floor should be sealed.

Unheated crawl spaces must be vented with a minimum area of $0.1m^2$ (1 ft^2) for every $50m^2$ (500 ft^2) of floor area. The vents must be distributed uniformly around the building. The floor in the unheated area must also be covered with a 0.15mm (6 mil) polyethylene moisture barrier with joints lapped a minimum of 100mm (4").

Figure 6.9
**Permanent
wood
foundation**

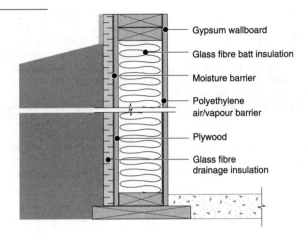

— Gypsum wallboard

— Glass fibre batt insulation

— Moisture barrier

— Polyethylene
    air/vapour barrier

— Plywood

— Glass fibre
    drainage insulation

| | **Thermal resistance** | |
Material	RSI	R
Interior air film	0.11	0.6
12.7mm (1/2") gypsum wallboard	0.08	0.5
Air/vapour barrier	0.00	0.0
140mm (5-1/2") glass fibre batt insulation	3.30	18.7
15.5mm (5/8") plywood or OSB sheathing	0.13	0.8
Moisture barrier	0.00	0.0
25mm (1") glass fibre drainage insulation	0.77	4.4
Total	4.39	25.0

6

Thermal Insulation

Attics and Ceilings

Roofs with Attic Spaces

In most buildings, heat loss through the roof can be kept small since ceilings can be easily insulated using batts or loose fill insulation placed between the ceiling joists to obtain high thermal resistances.

The insulation can cover the ceiling joists provided it does not restrict the air flow to the soffit vents. For this reason, baffles are often used to prevent insulation from blocking the air flow path to the overhangs (Figure 6.10).

Roof spaces must be vented. The unobstructed vent area should be equal to at least 1/300 of the insulated ceiling area. Vents can be placed in the roof, eave, or gable end and must be equally distributed on opposite sides of the building.

The point of weakest thermal resistance in a ceiling is usually at the exterior wall line. This space may not provide room for adequate insulation, and in some cases may cool sufficiently to allow condensation and mildew buildup on the surface of the interior finishes. The amount of insulation

Figure 6.10
Insulation of ceiling wall intersection

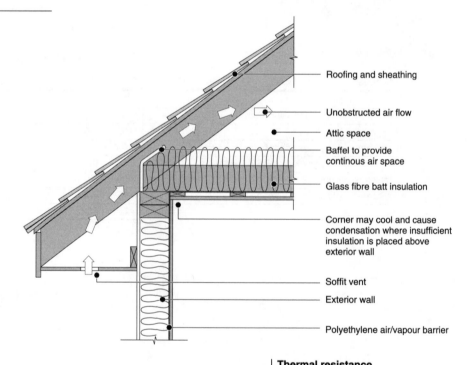

- Roofing and sheathing
- Unobstructed air flow
- Attic space
- Baffel to provide continous air space
- Glass fibre batt insulation
- Corner may cool and cause condensation where insufficient insulation is placed above exterior wall
- Soffit vent
- Exterior wall
- Polyethylene air/vapour barrier

Material	Thermal resistance	
	RSI	R
Interior air film	0.11	0.6
12.7mm (1/2") gypsum wallboard	0.08	0.5
Air/vapour barrier	0.00	0.0
267mm (10-1/2") glass fibre batt insulation	6.30	35.6
Attic air films	0.22	1.2
15.5mm (5/8") plywood or OSB sheathing	0.13	0.7
Asphalt shingles	0.078	0.4
Exterior air film	0.03	0.1
Total	6.95	39.3

that can be placed above the exterior wall is governed by the depth of the rafter or truss. To allow room for extra insulation at the ceiling perimeter, the truss designer can increase the depth of the truss to allow greater insulation thicknesses. Where rafters are used, special measures, such as raising the rafters and supporting them on a ledger board, can provide room for extra insulation (Figure 6.11).

A polyethylene vapour barrier is placed on the warm side of the insulation to prevent warm moist air from entering the insulated attic space. All penetrations of the vapour barrier, including the chimney, plumbing vents, and attic hatch, should be adequately sealed.

Cathedral Ceilings and Low Sloped Roofs

Insulation for cathedral ceilings can be installed on top of the roof using rigid insulation, or can be installed within the joist space using batt insulation. These types of roofs are usually framed using 38 x 235 or 286mm (2" x 10" or 12" nom.) joists with 38 x 38mm (2" x 2") cross purlins, and batt insulation between the joists.

The purlins are placed on top of the joists to provide ventilation above the insulation (Figure 6.12). Wood I-joists or roof trusses can be used to achieve deep assemblies thereby increasing the space available for insulation. Roofs with low slopes can be insulated in the same manner as cathedral ceilings.

When the insulation is placed below the roof sheathing, the *NBCC* requires that cathedral ceilings and roofs with slopes less than 1 in 6 have a minimum unobstructed ventilation area of 1/150 of the insulated ceiling area. The vents must be distributed uniformly to ventilate each roof space.

Figure 6.11
Raised rafters to provide additional ceiling insulation

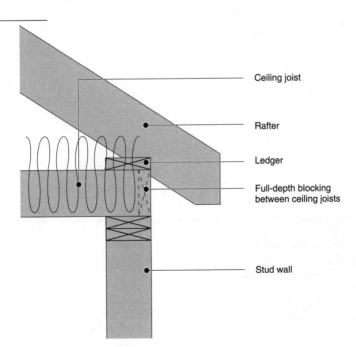

Ceiling joist

Rafter

Ledger

Full-depth blocking between ceiling joists

Stud wall

6

Thermal Insulation

The cross purlins may be omitted if each joist space is individually vented.

A minimum clearance of 63mm (2.5") must be provided between the top of the insulation and the underside of the roof sheathing.

Required vents must be distributed uniformly on opposite sides of the building so that at least 25% of the ventilated area is at the upper part of the roof, and at least 25% is at the lower part of the roof.

Figure 6.12
Cathedral ceiling

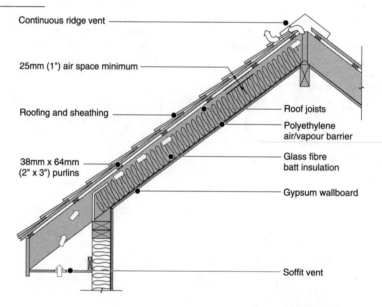

Continuous ridge vent

25mm (1") air space minimum

Roofing and sheathing

38mm x 64mm (2" x 3") purlins

Roof joists

Polyethylene air/vapour barrier

Glass fibre batt insulation

Gypsum wallboard

Soffit vent

Material	Thermal resistance	
	RSI	R
Interior air film	0.11	0.6
12.7mm (1/2") gypsum wallboard	0.08	0.4
Air/vapour barrier	0.00	0.0
178mm (7") glass fibre batt insulation	4.20	24
Enclosed air films	0.22	1.2
15.5mm (5/8") plywood or OSB sheathing	0.13	0.8
Asphalt shingles	0.078	0.4
Exterior air film	0.03	0.15
Total	4.85	27.6

Insulating Post and Beam Timber Construction

When stud walls are used as infills in post and beam construction, these walls will be insulated in the same manner as the frame construction described previously.

Post and beam buildings are usually framed with tongue and grove decking and insulated with rigid insulation (Figure 6.13). Since the interior surface of the deck is exposed, the vapour barrier must be placed on top of the deck, and care must be taken to ensure that enough insulation is present to prevent condensation from occurring at the vapour barrier. For this to

be the case, at least two thirds of the total insulating value of the roof must be above the vapour barrier.

The roofs and walls of a post and beam wood building can also be framed and insulated using prefabricated composite panels (Section 4.2).

The thermal resistance of the panels depends on their thickness and the insulating properties of the materials from which they are made. Vapour diffusion resistance is provided by the panel itself and therefore a separate vapour barrier is not required. An air barrier is provided by sealing the panels at the joints.

Figure 6.13
Built-up roof

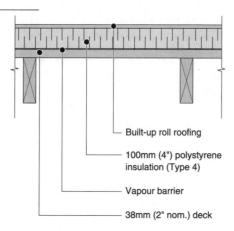

Built-up roll roofing

100mm (4") polystyrene insulation (Type 4)

Vapour barrier

38mm (2" nom.) deck

Material	Thermal resistance	
	RSI	R
Interior air film	0.11	0.6
38mm (1-1/2") wood decking	0.33	1.8
Vapour barrier	0.00	0.0
100mm (4") extruded polystyrene (Type 4)	3.52	20
10mm (3/8") built-up roll roofing	0.058	0.4
Total	4.02	22.8

6

Thermal Insulation

Log Buildings

The thermal resistance of a log building is typically provided by the insulating value of the logs themselves. A log building with a mean log thickness of 200mm (8") has an RSI value of 1.8 (R 10.4). A higher thermal resistance can be obtained by building a stud wall with batt insulation on the inside of the logs.

An adequate seal between logs and around doors and windows is of critical importance in log construction since a continuous air and vapour barrier is not provided. Air leakage significantly increases the heat loss in a log building, and can result in condensation and decay of the logs.

Log buildings must be detailed to allow for the settlement of logs due to shrinkage. Since logs are usually green at the time of installation, a large amount of shrinkage will occur as they dry in service. If no allowance is made for shrinkage, the logs may become suspended at door and window openings and other locations, creating large gaps, chinking failures and other problems. This may allow substantial air leakage through the building assembly and may result in condensation and decay problems.

Log walls are often built with a space between the logs that is filled with flexible synthetic chinking. The chinks (spaces) can be filled with rigid insulation or be foamed in place with a closed-cell spray type foam insulation (Figure 6.14) that will expand to fill any voids within the cavity. The insulating value of the foam and rigid insulation is much higher than that of the logs themselves.

In chinkless construction, tongue and groove or nested joints between logs will reduce air leakage. Various types of sealer strips or gaskets can also be laid along the grooves to provide an air seal.

Figure 6.14
Log sealing techniques

Tongue and groove log joints

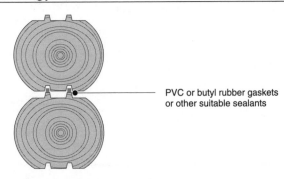

PVC or butyl rubber gaskets
or other suitable sealants

Chinked style logs

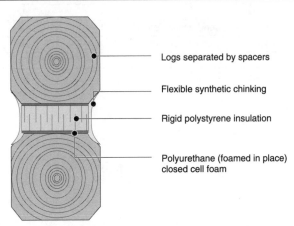

Logs separated by spacers

Flexible synthetic chinking

Rigid polystyrene insulation

Polyurethane (foamed in place)
closed cell foam

Ice Damming

Ice damming occurs due to insufficient attic insulation and air leakage into the roof space. The loss of heat into the attic causes snow on the roof to melt and then refreeze when the meltwater reaches a colder part of the roof.

The accumulation of ice at the eaves and valleys of roofs (ice damming) may prevent melted ice and snow from draining off the roof, and cause the water to back up under the roofing, and leak into the building inte-rior. Ice damming may cause wetting of the insulation in roofs and walls, and damage interior finishes, eaves and gutters. If the problem persists, it may lead to decay of members and costly structural repairs.

To prevent ice damming, the attic must be well ventilated. This will allow the roof to maintain a more uniform temperature by quickly removing any warm air that reaches the attic space. Also, the ceiling must have an adequately sealed air and vapour barrier, and be well insulated to prevent excessive heat loss to the attic.

6

Thermal Insulation

References

1. *National Building Code of Canada,* Associate Committee on the National Building Code, National Research Council, Ottawa, ON, 1995

2. *Canadian Wood-Frame House Construction,* CMHC, Ottawa, ON, 1991

3. *Super Energy Efficient Home Program,* Energy Mines and Resources, Ottawa, ON

Air, Vapour, and Weather Barriers

The application
of furring strips
to create a rain-
screen space
between siding
and sheathing
improves wall
resistance to
infiltration.

The application
of an exterior air
barrier improves
wall perfor-
mance but must
be less perme-
able to the
passage of
moisture than
the interior
vapour barrier.

In this application, furring strips and battens have been applied in readiness for the application of cedar shingles.

Regardless of the siding type to be installed, wall performance is enhanced by the provision of a rainscreen.

Particular attention is required to ensure the continuity of air and vapour barriers around services and partitions.

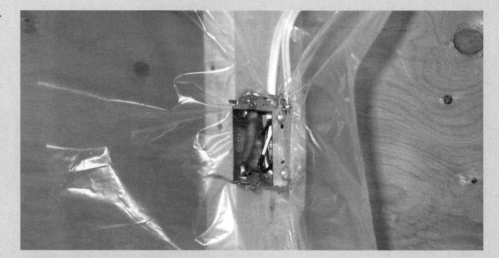

Caulking is required around windows and doors, inside and out to reduce the likelihood of air leakage.

Siding made of western red cedar and other species of Canadian softwoods are attractive weather screen materials.

Cedar shingles or shakes are other weather screen wood materials used for both sidewall and roofing applications.

Composite materials such as this aluminum clad plywood product make durable weather screens.

Left: Factory finished materials such as this OSB product result in low maintenance requirements.

Right: Careful placement of polyethylene and gypsum wallboard result in effective air and vapour barriers.

7.1   General Information

Introduction

A building envelope requires structural strength, a fire resistance rating in some cases, thermal insulation, and it needs to prevent the movement of moisture in both directions between the interior and the exterior.

There are three basic mechanisms by which moisture enters or leaves a building:

- Diffusion:
  Moisture moves from an area of high humidity to an area of lower humidity through porous materials such as gypsum wallboard and sheathing. It is a process which occurs over a large area and a vapour barrier must be provided in the building envelope to reduce moisture movement by diffusion.

- Air leakage:
  Air leakage is the movement of moisture as a result of humid air leaking through the building envelope. Air leakage takes places through gaps and discontinuities in the envelope and has the potential to deposit a large volume of moisture in wall and roof cavities. An effective air barrier is required in the building envelope to prevent moisture movement by means of air leakage.

- Rain penetration:
  Rain penetration is the entry of precipitation into the building envelope. A weather barrier, ideally a rainscreen, and other techniques are used to prevent infiltration.

Increased interest in the energy efficiency of buildings has led to building techniques which alter the way moisture-laden air infiltrates and exfiltrates. Moisture which escaped through building assemblies was not as likely to condense in assemblies because the thermal gradient in building assemblies was different. With high insulation requirements, escaping moisture may condense in building assemblies where it can reduce insulation values and otherwise damage the building fabric.

This chapter deals with the control of moisture movement in buildings. The following major topics are presented:

7.2   Air and Vapour Barriers

7.3   Rainscreen Principle

7.4   Wood Cladding Products

7

Air, Vapour, and Weather Barriers

7.2   Air and Vapour Barriers

Moisture Movement

Air moisture levels are defined by relative humidity. A relative humidity of 100% indicates that the air is holding as much water vapour as possible for a given temperature. A relative humidity between 30 and 50% is the optimum range for comfort. Higher relative humidities may be required, for example to preserve museum artifacts, or in computer rooms to reduce static electricity. Low relative humidities will result in increased static and dust, and some people may experience discomfort.

Warm air is capable of holding more moisture than cold air. Moisture diffuses from the warm, moist side of building components to the colder side where the air retains less moisture.

When warm air is cooled, the decrease in temperature means that the amount of moisture that the air is capable of holding decreases. If the temperature is reduced too far, the air will no longer be capable of holding all of the moisture, and some of the vapour will turn to liquid water and be deposited on the cold surface. This process is called condensation and the temperature at which condensation occurs is called the dew point.

In cold climates, condensation from diffusion usually originates from the inside during the cold months. The reverse may occur in very hot, humid climates where air-conditioning is used extensively.

Exfiltration of warm, moist air by air leakage is the major cause of moisture deposition. It occurs as a result of a pressure differential between the building environment and the outside. Moisture may be carried through the envelope in either direction depending on whether a positive or negative pressure occurs in a building at any given time.

Rain penetration of the building envelope may, of course, occur in both hot and temperate climates.

The *NBCC* requires that all thermally insulated wall, ceiling, and floor assemblies be provided with both a continuous barrier to prevent the leakage of air, and a barrier to prevent the diffusion of water vapour into the building assemblies (Figure 7.1).

The *NBCC* also requires that wall sheathing paper be applied to the exterior of the sheathing to prevent rain penetration. For wood-frame construction, a polyethylene sheet (properly supported and caulked) is usually used to serve as both the air and the vapour barrier.

It is important that cladding and other weather-shield materials not admit water, but also have the permeability to allow the escape of moisture which has bypassed the interior air and vapour barriers.

Sheathing, building paper or wrap, and cladding all allow the transfer of vapour in small quantities. However, as indicated in Chapter 2, it is important to construct with wood products having low moisture contents, and to minimize the amount of rain water trapped in assemblies during construction to ensure that excessive moisture in the wall cavities does not damage the building envelope. High initial moisture content is also generated in buildings as a result of the curing of concrete, and the drying of gypsum wallboard compound and paint.

Vapour Barrier

A vapour barrier is a membrane that restricts the migration of moisture by diffusion from an area of high humidity relative to one of low humidity. A vapour barrier must be located near the warm side of walls and ceilings so that condensation in the cold region of the assembly does not occur.

Vapour barriers are usually placed on the warm side of the insulation to keep water vapour from cooling and condensing within the wall assembly.

Condensation will not usually occur as long as two-thirds of the insulating value of the wall is located outside the vapour barrier. In far northern regions, however, up to 80% of the insulation value may be required outside the vapour barrier. Other vapour barrier locations are permissible provided it can be shown that condensation will not occur.

Direct applied cladding

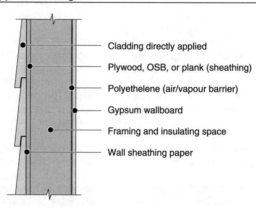

Cladding directly applied

Plywood, OSB, or plank (sheathing)

Polyethelene (air/vapour barrier)

Gypsum wallboard

Framing and insulating space

Wall sheathing paper

Wood clad rainscreen

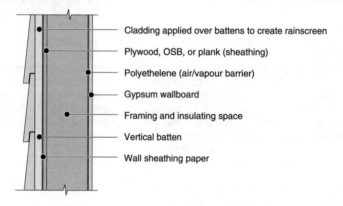

Cladding applied over battens to create rainscreen

Plywood, OSB, or plank (sheathing)

Polyethelene (air/vapour barrier)

Gypsum wallboard

Framing and insulating space

Vertical batten

Wall sheathing paper

Brick veneer rainscreen

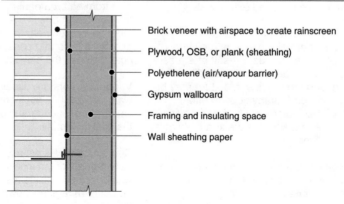

Brick veneer with airspace to create rainscreen

Plywood, OSB, or plank (sheathing)

Polyethelene (air/vapour barrier)

Gypsum wallboard

Framing and insulating space

Wall sheathing paper

Materials such as asphalt impregnated kraft paper, polyethylene, aluminum foil, and paint (two coats of alkyd applied to gypsum wallboard) deter water vapour from penetrating into and through the building envelope by diffusion.

Because diffusion takes place slowly over a large area, small openings in the vapour barrier do not greatly affect moisture movement by diffusion. However, such openings do increase air movement and the mass transport of moisture-laden air through small openings, and are potentially a greater hazard for moisture deposition than diffusion. Where the polyethylene is intended to serve as both the air and vapour barrier, it should be continuous.

A 0.15mm (6 mil) polyethylene membrane is the most commonly used vapour barrier in wood-frame construction. The polyethylene vapour barrier, when properly lapped and sealed, effectively restricts air leakage, in which case the polyethylene sheet is referred to as the air/vapour barrier.

Vapour Barrier Performance Standards

Membrane type vapour barrier materials must conform to the requirements of the following standards:

- CAN/CGSB-51.34-M, *Vapour Barrier, Polyethylene Sheet for Use in Building Construction*

- CAN/CGSB-51.33-M, *Vapour Barrier Sheet, Excluding Polyethylene, for use in Building Construction*

7

Air, Vapour, and Weather Barriers

Table 7.1
Perm rating of building materials

Material		Perm rating [1]
Sheathing (low insulation value)	12.7mm (1/2") foil-faced gypsum board	Negligible
	6.4mm (1/4") plywood	23 – 74
	12.7mm (1/2") gypsum board sheathing	1373
	11mm (7/16") oriented strandboard (OSB)	44
	11mm (7/16") fibreboard sheathing	772 – 2465
	17mm (2/3") wood sheathing	982
Insulation	25mm (1") foil-faced urethane	Negligible
	25mm (1") extruded polystyrene	23 – 92
	25mm (1") urethane foam	69
	25mm (1") phenolic foam	133
	25mm (1") expanded polystyrene (type 2)	86 – 160
	Fibrous insulations	Very high
Membrane Materials	Metal	Negligible
	0.15mm (0.006") polyethylene	1.6 – 5.8
	Breather type sheathing membrane	170 – 1400
	Spun bonded polyolefin film	3646

Notes:

1. Perm ratings are derived from:
   - Bombaru, D., Jutras, R., and Patenaude, A. Air Permeance of Building Materials. Summary report prepared by, AIR-INS Inc. for Canada Mortgage and Housing Corporation, Ottawa, 1988.
   - The Details of Air Barrier Systems for Houses. Ontario New Home Warranty Program, Don Mills, 1993.

2. One metric perm represents one nanogram of water per second per square metre of material under a pressure of one Pascal (1 metric perm = $1ng/(Pa \cdot s \cdot m^2)$).

These materials are rated in terms of their permeability and are grouped into two categories:

- Type 1 – vapour barriers that have a permeability of 15 metric perms or less

- Type 2 – vapour barriers that have a permeability of 45 metric perms or less before aging and 60 metric perms after aging

Any material with a permeability greater than 60 metric perms is not a vapour barrier. The permeability of some common building materials are shown in Table 7.1. The lower the permeability of a material, the more effectively it retards vapour diffusion.

Polyethylene is an example of a Type 1 vapour barrier, and asphalt impregnated kraft paper is an example of a Type 2 vapour barrier. Type 1 vapour barriers are required in wall construction that has exterior sheathing with a high resistance to moisture movement (as is the case with the plywood and OSB sheathings used in wood-frame construction). It is also required where high interior humidities are expected as in the case of a greenhouse or climate-controlled computer room.

Type 2 vapour barriers may be used in low-rise construction where high relative humidity is not expected and where the exterior sheathing does not have a high resistance to moisture movement.

Where OSB or plywood is used over unheated floors (e.g., garages), they can act as vapour barriers. This means that polyethylene sheet, which could trap rain water during construction, is not required. Continuity of the air barrier must be maintained across the floor assembly.

In walls, the normal gap between panels provides sufficient air permeance to allow excess moisture to escape.

Air Barrier

An air barrier is a membrane that restricts air leakage into and out of a building, thereby restricting the movement of moisture into building cavities.

Air sealing is an important factor in the construction of buildings for the following reasons:

- air leakage can be a high proportion of the total heat loss from a building

- air sealing contributes to building comfort by reducing draftiness

- air leakage through walls and roofs transports moisture that condenses on framing members, possibly in sufficient amounts to cause mould growth or other problems

Air leakage in a building occurs wherever there is an opening, hole, or puncture in the building envelope. The frequency and quantity of air coming through these openings will depend on these factors:

- Stack effect:
  the action of warm air rising in a building and causing outward air pressure in the upper storeys and inward air pressure at the base of the building

- Ventilation effect:
  negative air pressure in a building caused by the emission of air by ventilation fans without a supply of replacement air

- Wind effect:
  the positive pressure on the windward side of a building and the negative pressure on the leeward side of a building caused by wind

The quantity of water which can be transported by air leakage is substantial. Suppose an opening caused by an electrical outlet has a net opening area of 6.25cm^2 (1 in^2). During one month, 2600mm^3 (1.1 ft^3) of air would enter the wall cavity under a 10 Pa (0.002 psi) pressure difference (equivalent to a 15 km/h [10 mph] wind). This would amount to approximately

3000 kg (6600 lbs) of air and 14 kg (30 lbs) of water. Even if only 10% of this water condenses out in the cavity, this would mean a deposition of 1.4 kg (3 lbs) of water.

There are several specific locations in frame construction where air leakage is likely to occur. These include: plumbing vents or stacks, electric boxes and services, framing around doors and windows, basement walls at sill plates and headers or band joists, the top of interior partitions and exterior walls, exhaust fans and dryer exhausts, oil fill and vent pipes, supply and return pipes for air conditioning systems and heat pumps, and any other locations where exterior walls and ceilings are traversed by services, vents, and pipes.

Openings such as these allow air to exfiltrate or infiltrate, and must be properly sealed to reduce drafts, reduce heating costs, and to avoid warranty repairs after construction has been completed.

To function properly in the long term, an air barrier must be durable, strong, and continuous. A polyethylene vapour barrier, supported on one side by gypsum wallboard and partially supported on the other side by compressible batt insulation, is subject to flexing as a result of negative wind pressure.

When the polyethylene is 0.15mm (6 mil) in thickness and joints are supported by framing members, caulked, and held tight in place by the application of gypsum wallboard, the membrane is considered to be capable of withstanding negative air pressure, and it constitutes an air/vapour barrier.

Gypsum wallboard is a rigid material capable of withstanding negative wind pressure. When gypsum wallboard is sealed around outlets and openings, and when gaskets are applied between floor and ceiling horizontal framing members, an

Figure 7.2
Air/vapour barrier details

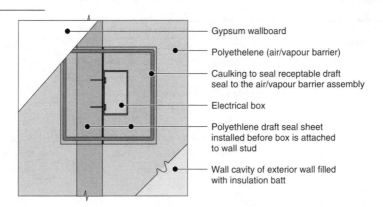

- Gypsum wallboard
- Polyethelene (air/vapour barrier)
- Caulking to seal receptable draft seal to the air/vapour barrier assembly
- Electrical box
- Polyethlene draft seal sheet installed before box is attached to wall stud
- Wall cavity of exterior wall filled with insulation batt

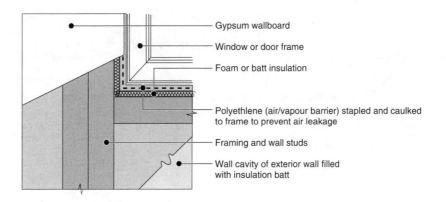

- Gypsum wallboard
- Window or door frame
- Foam or batt insulation
- Polyethlene (air/vapour barrier) stapled and caulked to frame to prevent air leakage
- Framing and wall studs
- Wall cavity of exterior wall filled with insulation batt

air barrier called the airtight drywall approach (ADA) results. A paint coating vapour barrier can be applied to the air barrier gypsum wallboard so that a polyethylene membrane is not required.

Air Barrier Performance Standards

The National Research Council of Canada has devised a classification system for air barrier systems according to air permeability. Air permeability values for common building materials are given in Table 7.2.

In those cases where the air barrier is placed on the envelope exterior, the air barrier must restrict the flow of air but be more permeable than the interior vapour barrier so that moisture which does pass into the building assembly can escape to the exterior.

Air Quality

The installation of a continuous air barrier to stop air leakage in new construction means that building air does not change as often as a result of air leakage to and from a building. Therefore, it is important to provide adequate ventilation.

This may seem contradictory, but the purpose of most buildings is to provide people with a controlled environmental enclosure. Reliance on air leakage to provide ventilation is not a controlled situation, may not be comfortable for occupants, and may lead to building envelop deterioration. So good design provides air tight construction, controlled ventilation, and air change to control air quality. The 1995 *NBCC* contains explicit guidelines for mechanical ventilation requirements for buildings.

Table 7.2
Measured air permeability of building materials

Material		Air permeability[2] L/(s•m^2)
Sheathing (low insulation value)	12.7mm (1/2") foil-faced gypsum board	Negligible
	6.4mm (1/4") plywood	0.0084
	12.7mm (1/2") gypsum board sheathing	0.0091
	11mm (7/16") oriented strandboard (OSB)	0.0108
	11mm (7/16") fibreboard sheathing	0.8285
	17mm (2/3") wood sheathing	High – depends on no. of joints
Insulation	25mm (1") foil-faced urethane	Negligible
	25mm (1") extruded polystyrene	Negligible
	25mm (1") urethane foam	Negligible
	25mm (1") phenolic foam	Negligible
	25mm (1") expanded polystyrene (type 2)	0.0214
	Fibrous insulations	Very high
Membrane Materials	Metal	Negligible
	0.15mm (0.006") polyethylene	Negligible
	Breather type sheathing membrane	0.2706
	Spun bonded polyolefin film	0.9593

Notes:

1. Air permeability values are derived from:
   - Bombaru, D., Jutras, R., and Patenaude, A. Air Permeance of Building Materials. Summary report prepared by, AIR-INS Inc. for Canada Mortgage and Housing Corporation, Ottawa, 1988.
   - The Details of Air Barrier Systems for Houses. Ontario New Home Warranty Program, Don Mills, 1993.

2. Air Permeability is measured at 75 Pa.

Moisture Control Measures

Building moisture levels are controlled by a combination of methods:

- moderating the generation of humidity in buildings

- minimizing mass transport by using air barriers

- minimizing diffusion of moisture by using vapour barriers

- ventilating moisture exceeding the amount required for occupant comfort or building function

One of the most effective methods for controlling moisture damage is to keep indoor relative humidity at moderate levels. In air tight residential occupancies, the moisture generated by cooking, bathing and washing might result in humidity levels which are too high requiring ventilation of moisture laden air. In an office environment, winter heating and the nature of the building might result in humidity levels too dry for occupant comfort, and humidification might be required.

Rain Penetration Barriers

Several building skins may be used to form the weather barrier. These might include a cladding to deflect and shed the majority of water away from the building, wall sheathing paper or wrap to shed any wind driven precipitation which penetrates the cladding, and ideally a cavity between the two creating a rainscreen effect (Section 7.3).

Rain penetration barriers are installed over the structural sheathing to protect the interior components of the wall from exposure to elements (rain, snow, and sun) that may degrade the structural members or reduce the effectiveness of the insulation.

Tar impregnated paper has been typically used for this purpose but recently other materials such as spunbonded polyolefin, polypropylene and perforated polyethylene films have become accepted by the building industry.

Wall sheathing paper or wrap must be tight enough to stop rain penetration but be more permeable to vapour transmission than the vapour barrier located on the warm side of the wall.

Caulks and Sealants

Caulking should not be relied upon as a substitute for good detailing and good construction. It is a means of providing added protection against air infiltration wherever construction joints occur, and especially around windows and doors. The effectiveness of caulking is significantly improved with proper preparation of the surface and the selection of the appropriate caulking compound for the job.

A variety of caulking compounds and sealants are available. Some are appropriate for use both indoors and outdoors, while others have more specialized applications. Interior caulking (Table 7.3) is used for air sealing. When selecting an interior caulking, colour, odour, drying time, durability, and resistance to mould are important characteristics.

Exterior caulking (Table 7.4) is used for weatherproofing rather than air sealing. An exterior product must endure more thermal and environmental stress.

7

Air, Vapour, and Weather Barriers

Table 7.3
Caulks and sealants for interior use

Sealant type (CGSB spec. #)	Typical uses & materials	Joint width and % move-ment	Cost	Life-span, years	Solvent	Advantages	Disadvantages
Oil or resin based (11-GP-6M)	Interior rigid joints	10mm (3/8") 1%	Low	3 to 5	–	Lowest cost	Low perfor-mance, may dry hard, may bleed oils, cannot be painted
Acoustical (19-GP-21M)	Interior unexposed joints, polyethylene sheeting	16mm (5/8") 10%	Low	20	Mineral spirits	Good workability, good sealing properties, adheres to polyethylene	Cannot be painted, difficult to clean, non-hardening, needs support
Acrylic latex (19-GP-21M)	Interior fin-ishes and low-movement joints, except metal	9mm (3/8") 2%	Mod-erate	12+	Water	Good general purpose caulk, low movement fast curing, paintable	Apply above 4.4°C (40°F) only, low moisture resistance, moderate flexibility
Vinyl acrylic latex	Interior fin-ishes, porous surfaces such as wood or concrete	9mm (3/8") 2%	Mod-erate to low	10	Water	Low cost, paintable, (Lower perfor-mance than acrylic latex.)	Apply above 4.4°C (40°F) only, poor flexibility, shrinks, low moisture, sun resistance
Thermoplastic elastomer	Interior air seal and fin-ishes, adheres well to most interior surfaces	12mm (1/2") 4%	Mod-erate	20+	Toluol, Xylol	Good moisture resistance, paintable, minimal odour, clear	Low elasticity, low resistance to water, sun

Source: *Technical Bulletin No. 1, Windows,* The National Energy Conservation Association (NECA), Winnipeg, MB

7

Table 7.4
Caulks and sealants for exterior use

Sealant type (CGSB spec. #)	Typical uses & materials	Joint width and % movement	Cost	Life-span, years	Solvent	Advantages	Disadvantages
Solvent-based acrylic (19-GP-5M)	Widely used, general purpose exterior sealant	19mm (3/4") 7.5%	Mod-erate	15+	Xylol	Excellent adhesion, good resistance to chemicals (cannot be painted)	Should be applied above 4.4°C (40°F), subject to stains cracks before service life
One-part polysulphide	Large joints, masonry and concrete	19 to 24mm (3/4" to 7/8") 12 to 25%	Mod-erate to high	20	Toluol, Xylol	Excellent flexibility and durability, resistance to moisture, paintable	Requires surface priming strong odour during application, toxic to skin
Hypalon	Concrete, metals wood, masonry	15mm (1/2") 12.5%	Mod-erate to high	10 to 20	Mineral spirits	Good elasticity, cures to consistency of rubber, paintable	Should be applied above 10°C (50°F), slow curing, unsuitable for most surfaces
Butyl-based (19-GP-14M)	Exterior metal or masonry sealant non-exposed interior	12mm (1/2") 5 to 10%	Mod-erate	5 to 10	–	Very flexible	High shrinkage, must cure 1 week before painting, low moisture resistance
Silicone (19-GP-18M)	Exterior fin-ishes some interior uses	25mm (1") 12 to 25%	High	20+	Xylol	Excellent performance, good temperature and flexure resistance	Cannot be painted, high cost, may require surface priming, gives off odour when curing
Thermoplastic rubber	Exterior finishes interior finishes	13mm (1/2") 50%+	Mod-erate to high	25	–	Exceptional flexibility, available in range of colours, minimal odour	Lowest service temperature specified as -30°C (-23°F), should be applied above 5°C (16°F)
Polyurethane and pre-polymer Type (CAN2 19.13-M82)	Small exterior and interior joints (walls, floors)	12mm (1/2") 25 to 50%	High	25	Toluol, Xylol	Excellent flexibility and resistance, minimal odour, paintable	High cost, primer may be required, low adhesive to plastics
Two-part polysulphide	Joint filler, high traffic areas, wet areas	20mm (3/4") 25%	Mod-erate to high	20+	Toluol, Xylol	Excellent adhesion, flexibility and durability	Difficult applica-tion from bulk loader, may require surface primer
Transparent removable	Small crack air-sealing, usually interior windows	10mm (3/8") 10%	Low	One winter	–	Low cost, easy application and removal, suitable for most materials	Must reapply each winter, gives off odour while curing, 24 hrs to harden

Source: *Technical Bulletin No. 1, Windows,* The National Energy Conservation Association (NECA), Winnipeg, MB

Moisture Problem Areas

There are certain areas where moisture problems may occur in buildings.

Windows
Condensation problems often occur around windows due to air leakage or conduction through the window frame (Chapter 10). Condensation may be reduced by improving the thermal efficiency of the window, lowering the humidity level in the building, reducing air leakage from around windows, or by increasing the temperature of the window surface by additional heating.

Framing Intersections
Wall to wall and wall to ceiling intersections in buildings may be areas of condensation due to thermal bridging through framed members, discontinuous air seals, and insufficient insulation. Adequate insulation and air barrier installations will prevent this problem.

Attics and Ceilings
Air leakage and diffusion into attics may result in condensation in these spaces on the underside of the roof sheathing and roof framing members. Adequate ventilation of the attic and a continuous air barrier at the ceiling can prevent condensation formations in roof spaces and attics.

Ventilation requirements are generally stated as a ratio of vent area to ceiling area with the added requirement that ventilation be distributed throughout the attic or roof space.

The most effective ventilation employs the stack effect of warm air rising and leaving the attic at the peak while drawing outside air in at the eaves. Continuous vents at the eaves and ridge give optimum air movement through the attic space.

The energy efficiency practice of installing ceiling insulation with thicknesses of 300mm (12") or more requires special considerations to prevent blocking eave vents. One solution is a roof-truss modification to provide added height above the outside wall. This permits extending the full insulation thickness over the top plate of the wall. Another solution is to use rigid pans in each rafter space to prevent insulation from blocking eave vents.

Flat roofs are particularly vulnerable to the accumulation of condensation because they rely primarily on wind pressures for ventilation and are usually vented at the perimeter only. Good air and vapour barrier protection is critical in flat roofs, and it is particularly important to limit air leakage around recessed lighting, vent stacks, and other openings.

A mansard roof with a flat center portion is also susceptible to condensation. Steeply sloped sides permit warm air to rise from all sides, resulting in a stagnant condition in which little moisture escapes from the roof cavity. The potential for problems in this type of roof are particularly critical in a large building, such as an apartment building, where the flat portion is wide. The problem can be alleviated by installing outlet vents near the centre of the roof to allow ventilation of each joist space.

Unventilated roof spaces, both flat and sloped, are successfully used in many commercial applications but may result in moisture problems for residential applications because of higher indoor humidity. The unventilated roof must have materials with the ability to absorb and store moisture passing into it until sun shining on the roof can drive moisture back out of the material and into the building. The system operates best with some vapour resistance on the warm side to reduce the rate of moisture movement into the roof space.

7.3 Rainscreen Principle

Introduction

While vapour barriers protect building assemblies by reducing the diffusion of moisture into assembly cavities, and air barriers reduce the mass transport of moisture into and out of assemblies, a rainscreen equalizes pressure and restricts infiltration of precipitation into the building assembly.

Rain Penetration

Rain penetration can occur where there is a combination of water at the surface of the wall, openings through which it can pass, and a force to move the water through these openings. The elimination of any one of these three conditions could prevent the occurrence of rain penetration. While wide roof overhangs may help to shelter the walls of a low-rise building for most weather conditions, exceptional weather conditions may still cause the walls to be rain wetted. Therefore one of the remaining two conditions must be eliminated to prevent rain penetration.

The face seal approach attempts to eliminate all the openings in the wall through which water can pass. However, the materials used to seal all these openings are exposed to extremes of weather and to movements of the building. Even if the problems of job site inaccuracies and imperfect workmanship can be overcome and a perfect seal achieved, the in-service weather conditions will eventually cause the deterioration and failure of these seals, creating openings in the wall through which water can pass. Unfortunately, these openings can be extremely tiny and difficult to identify, so that even an extensive maintenance program may not keep the building free of openings.

The alternate approach to controlling rain penetration is to eliminate the forces which drive or draw water into the wall. These are:

- Kinetic energy:
  The inertia of wind driven rain forces water into openings.

- Capillary action:
  Due to surface tension, water is drawn into small openings by capillary action.

- Gravity:
  Gravity causes water to move down the face of the wall, into any downward sloped passages, and into the wall.

- Air pressure differences:
  When the pressure on the exterior face of the wall is higher than on the interior of the wall, water can be forced through tiny openings in the wall.

Principle of Pressure Equalization

It is not possible to prevent wind from acting on a building but it is possible to counteract the pressure of the wind by making the pressure difference across the exterior cladding of the wall close to zero. If the pressure difference across the cladding is close to zero, one of the main causes of rain penetration, pressure differential, is eliminated.

When wind acts on the building facade, a positive pressure occurs on the windward side and a negative pressure on the leeward side. If the cavity behind the cladding is vented to the outside, some of the wind blowing on the wall enters the cavity, causing the pressure in the cavity to increase until it equals the exterior pressure.

7

Air, Vapour, and Weather Barriers

The wall sheathing must be capable of resisting this wind pressure and must be relatively airtight for the pressure in the cavity to equalize with the outside. If there are openings in the air barrier, the pressure in the cavity will not equalize and rain penetration may occur.

Rainscreens for Wood-Frame Construction

A rainscreen wall system consists of an exterior cladding, drained and vented to the outside, a cavity behind the cladding, and an air barrier.

For wood-frame walls, the cavity is made by providing furring strips at 400mm (16") centres to which the cladding is attached. The furring strips, from 9.5 to 19mm in thickness (3/8" to 3/4" nom.) may be applied vertically or horizontally depending on the direction in which the cladding is applied. Drain holes are required for horizontally applied furring strips. Insect screening is recommended where the rainscreen is open to the outdoors.

Wood-frame construction employs the rainscreen concept with a variety of cladding systems (Figure 7.1). It is routinely used in combination with brick veneer claddings, and metal, vinyl, wood, or stucco wall finishes would also benefit from this type of construction. In addition to reducing penetration, the rainscreen allows siding to dry faster, and allows moisture escaping the building by diffusion or air leakage to dissipate better.

Drain holes or vertical passages should always be provided in the rain screen cavity in case some precipitation does penetrate the exterior cladding. However, it is still desirable to the overall function of the wall to minimize any penetration of rain.

7.4   Wood Cladding Products

Introduction

There are many wood-structure buildings in service which are clad with non-wood materials such as sheet metal, vinyl, or masonry. Although wood cladding materials such as siding and shingles have in many cases provided long service, there is no doubt that the desire on the part of building owners to keep exterior maintenance to a minimum has resulted in a decrease in the use of wood as an exterior cladding material.

However, the properties that make wood such a versatile material, such as its ease of workability and its appearance qualities, are also applicable to cladding. For this reason, speciality wood manufacturers have been developing wood cladding products which drastically reduce maintenance requirements while retaining the positive attributes of wood building materials.

When wood cladding materials are installed without stain or paint coatings, the wood weathers and acquires a gray patina (colour varies with species). If the wood is installed in such a way that drying between wettings is possible, the wood will last indefinitely. There are many sidewall applied shingle buildings in wet maritime environments, for example, which have endured harsh weather conditions for decades.

Paint technology has had a number of advances which improve the ability of paints to move as dimensional changes to wood and other substrates occur, and to allow moisture gain and escape from wood surfaces. In addition, some wood siding manufacturers have developed products with paint and stain finishes applied under pressure in the factory. A short description of these products and other more conventional wood cladding products follows. More detailed information may also be found in the *Wood Reference Handbook*.

Wood Siding

Several Canadian softwood species are used for siding. The most common are western red cedar, eastern white cedar, jack pine , lodgepole pine, red pine, Douglas fir, and spruce. The species which perform best for siding applications are those which are light weight and have grains best suited for painting or staining.

Western red cedar is a popular siding because of its excellent dimensional stability, natural resistance to decay, workability, attractive weathering tone when left to weather naturally, and its ability to hold coatings and stain.

Wood siding is often installed directly over sheathing and sheathing paper. However, the construction of a windscreen by using furring strips under the siding is recommended.

Grades

For all Canadian softwood species, boards graded as Select Merchantable are recommended for exposed exterior uses where high quality appearance is a requirement. In addition to the Select Merchantable grade, there are two categories commonly used for finish work which are species specific. These are Eastern Red and White Pine, and Western Red Cedar.

For Eastern Red and White Pine, the grading categories suited for exposure are Select (B and Better, C, and D) and Common (1, 2, and 3). Select grade is clear or almost clear depending on the grade level, and Common usually contains knots. For some applications, a knotty appearance is preferred and the 1, 2, and 3 Common grades contain knots which are tight and not subject to loosening and loss during service.

The Western Red Cedar category is available in several grades and grade categories suitable for both exterior and interior applications. It is available dressed or rough, and kiln dried, air dried, or green. The major grade categories, grades, and principal characteristics for siding are shown in Table 7.5.

Sizes

Wood siding is usually produced in random lengths of 1.8 to 5m (6' to 16') and in widths of 89 and 140mm (4" and 6"). Western Red Cedar is also produced in wider widths of 200, 250, and 300mm (8", 10", and 12") and is available in lengths up to 7.2m (24'). Standard thickness are 12.5, 15.9 and 19mm (1/2", 5/8", and 3/4") and other thicknesses are available upon request.

Patterns

The most common siding types are:

- bevel siding:
  boards sawn with one edge thicker than the other

- drop siding:
  patterned upper edge and grooved or lapped lower edge

- vertical siding:
  square-edged boards with battens over the joints or tongue-and-groove boards

Table 7.5
Typical grades for exterior cladding

Grade category	Category description	Grades	Principal characteristics
Finish, Paneling, Ceiling and Drop Siding	This category is usually dressed four sides and kiln dried.	Clear heart	Highest quality for top quality appearance, many pieces are absolutely clear.
		A	Very good appearance but allows some small imperfections.
		B	Good appearance, many pieces have a fine appearance on one side and larger or more numerous growth characteristics on the back side.
Bevel Siding	This category is made by resawing kiln dried surfaced lumber on a bevel to produce two beveled pieces. Most commonly used for exterior siding.	Clear heart	Intended for highest quality applications, exposed width is all heartwood and free from imperfections.
		A	Very good appearance with some small imperfections permitted.
		B	This grade, permitting small imperfections and two or less cutouts, is a good quality siding where a painted surface is required.
		Rustic	This grade has a rough finish on the better side and is used as a sidewall covering where a rustic appearance is desired.
Tight-knotted Stock, Rough or Dressed Knotty Paneling and Sidings	Knots and other markings are the distinguishing characteristics of this grade category.	Select knotty	Good quality siding with a knotty appearance. Knots are tight and small.
		Quality knotty	Larger knots are permitted and some may be loose or unsound.
Knotty Bevel Siding	This is like the preceding grade category except the siding is beveled.	Select knotty	see above
		Quality knotty	see above

Notes:
1. The grades in each of these categories are not stress-graded but are graded according to the appearance of the better face. The reverse side often has characteristics approximately one grade lower than the face.

Nailing patterns (Figure 7.3) should be used which allow the wood siding to shrink and swell without restraint.

Factory Finished Wood Siding

Some sidings are now available pressure treated and pre-stained to increase service life and eliminate the need to finish the siding after installation. This applies to species other than cedar, though some manufacturers are also pre-staining cedar siding.

The stain is applied either during or after the pressure treatment process and may be applied to both the face and back to equalize moisture movement. This finish is durable for many years and can be restained when required. One manufacturer offers a 15-year warranty on the finish which is extendible an additional 15 years if an approved stain is applied during the initial 15-year period.

7

Air, Vapour, and Weather Barriers

Figure 7.3
Nailing patterns for wood siding

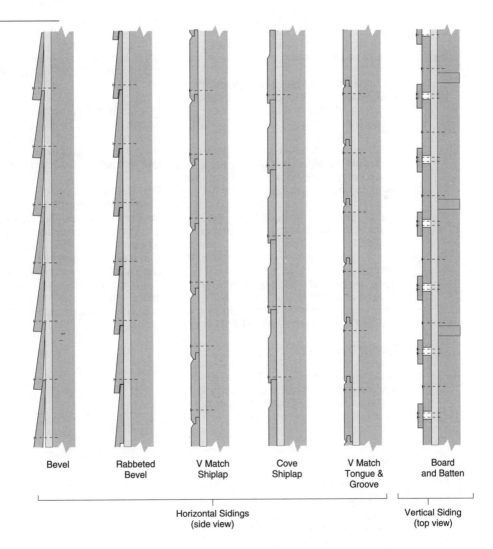

| Bevel | Rabbeted Bevel | V Match Shiplap | Cove Shiplap | V Match Tongue & Groove | Board and Batten |

Horizontal Sidings
(side view)

Vertical Siding
(top view)

Shingles and Shakes

Cedar shingles and shakes have a long history of performance in North America. The patina developed by cedar products with time is the reason why this historic building product is often favoured for the cladding of contemporary buildings.

Shingles are made from eastern white cedar and western red cedar, and shakes are made from western red cedar.

Shingles are manufactured by sawing and therefore have a relatively smooth surface. Shakes are made by splitting the wood along the grain and therefore shakes have at least one face which is striated.

Both products may be used for application to sidewalls and roofs. Selecting between shingles and shakes is based on the appearance desired.

Cedar has a high natural resistance to decay and therefore, for light and moderate exposures, cedar shingles and shakes can be left to weather naturally, can be bleached to accelerate and balance colour change, or can be stained. Again, the choice is dependent on the appearance desired.

Grades

There are several grades of shakes and shingles available (Table 7.6). Grade selection has a bearing on the appearance and durability of the completed installation.

Special Treatments

A surface chemical treatment is desirable for shingles and shakes where conditions conducive to deterioration occur such as combined heat and humidity for consider-able portions of the year, low roof pitch or low-slope applications, or for roofs kept moist by debris, or in close proximity to foliage.

In such cases, clear wood preservatives containing mildew and decay resisting chemicals are applied by brush or spray. Surface treatments are not permanent and should be applied at approximately five-year intervals depending upon the products used.

Shingles and shakes which have been pressure treated with CCA preservative are also available. The pressure treatment is permanent and will extend the service life of the roof. Most CCA-treated shingles and shakes are available with a 30-year warranty.

In areas of low humidity where moss, fungus, and mildew are not potential problems, commercial oil based preservatives will prevent excessive dryness and therefore prolong the natural resilience of cedar.

Fire-Retardant Cedar Shakes and Shingles

No.1 grade Western Red Cedar shingles and shakes are available pressure-impregnated with fire retardants to meet testing standards developed by Underwriters Laboratories and adopted by the National Fire Protection Association. The fire-retardant chemicals used are suited for exterior applications, and provide long-term protection.

Table 7.6 **Grades of cedar shingles and shakes**	Species	Grade	Description
	Western Red Cedar Shingles [1]	No.1 Blue Label	Premium grade of shingles for roofs and sidewalls which are made entirely from heartwood, are 100% clear, and have 100% edge-grain.
		No.2 Red Label	Good grade for many applications with at least 250mm clear on 400mm (10" on 16") shingles, 275mm on 450mm (11" on 18") shingles, and 400mm on 600mm (16" on 24") shingles. Flat grain and limited sapwood are permitted in this grade.
		No.3 Black Label	Utility grade for economy applications and secondary buildings with at least 150mm clear on 400 and 450mm (6" on 16" and 18") shingles, and at least 250mm on 600mm (10" on 24") shingles.
		No.4 Green Label (Undercoursing)	Utility grade for starter course undercoursing.
	Western Red Cedar Shakes [1]	Premium Grade	Best grade of shakes made entirely from heartwood, having 100% edge grain, and defect free. Suited for roof and sidewall applications where high quality appearance is important.
		No.1 (Blue Label)	Good quality shakes made of heartwood but can which can contain up to 3.2mm (1/8") sapwood along one edge and predominantly edge grained. Suited for roof and sidewall applications where high quality appearance is important.
		No.2 Grade (Sidewall or Red Label)	Shakes having good appearance similar to No.1 but flat grain is permitted and restricts use to sidewall applications.
	Eastern White Cedar [2]	A (extra)	The highest grade eastern shingle made from 100% heartwood with no defects, and light brown in colour suited for roofs and sidewalls where a high quality appearance is required.
		B (clear)	A good quality grade made mostly from heartwood. Sound knots not closer than 350mm (7") from the butt are permitted which are not visible for normal exposure distances. Used sidewalls and for roofs having a slope of at least 4/12.
		C (2nd clear)	This grade has a brownish tint and allows some defects. It is used for interior applications and for exterior applications on secondary buildings.
		Clear Wall	This shingle is almost white and contains no or few knots. It is used for interior applications and for secondary buildings for exterior exposure.
		Undercourse	This utility grade frequently contains knots. It is used for undercoursing on double course applications and for shimming in carpentry work.

Notes:
1. Canadian Western red cedar shingles and shakes are graded to CSA 0118.1 *Western Red Cedar Shingles, Handsplit Western Red Cedar Shakes, and Machine Grooved Shakes.*
2. Eastern White Cedar is graded in accordance with CSA 0118.2 *Eastern White Cedar Shingles.*

7

Air, Vapour, and Weather Barriers

Softwood Plywood

For exterior applications such as soffits where only one side is usually exposed to view, G1S is used extensively because the sanded surface has a good appearance when painted or stained.

Medium density overlaid (MDO) plywood is an exterior quality plywood protected with a weather resistant overlay of phenolic or melamine resin and cellulose fibres. MDO plywood has a smooth durable surface ideal for paint coatings which gives a low maintenance finish.

Other specialty grades of plywood are manufactured on special order for use as finish siding. These proprietary products include patterned, overlaid, textured, brushed, embossed, striated, grooved, and pre-finished panels. Special edge treatments may be employed to cover or enhance joints. All plywood edges, exposed or concealed, should be sealed with one or more heavy coats of exterior primer or aluminium-based paint to prevent moisture pick-up and migration.

Oriented Strandboard Panels

Siding products have been introduced which have OSB as a substrate for an exposed face resin coating which imparts colour and simulated wood grain texture to the panels. One manufacturer produces panels with channel groove and plain patterns in panels 1220mm (4') wide by 2.1, 2.4, 2.7, 3.6, and 4.9m (7', 8', 9', 12', and 16') long, and offers a an extended warranty for the substrate if installed according to manufacturer's specifications.

References

1. *Air Sealing: Bulletin 1,* National Energy Conservation Association, Winnipeg, MB

2. *Cladding of Buildings,* A.J. Brookes, Longman Group (FE) Ltd., 1990

3. *Difference Between a Vapour Barrier and an Air Barrier, The,* Building Practice Note No. 54, National Research Council, Ottawa, ON, 1985

4. *Energy Design Update* Vol. 10 No. 6, Cutler Corporation

5. *Moisture Movement and Control in Light-frame Structures,* Gerald E. Sherwood and Anton TenWolde, USDA Forest Service, Madison, WI, 1982

6. *National Building Code of Canada,* Appendix A-9.25, Ottawa, ON, 1995

7. *Study of the Rainscreen Concept Applied to Cladding Systems on Wood-Frame Walls, A,* Morrison Hershfield Limited, Nepean, ON, 1990

8. *Technical Bulletin No. 1, Windows,* The National Energy Conservation Association (NECA), Winnipeg, MB

9. *Testing of Air Barriers, Construction Details,* CMHC Research Project, CMHC, Ottawa, ON, 1991

10. *Testing of Air Barrier Construction Details II,* CMHC Research Project, Morrison Hershfield Limited, Nepean, ON, 1993

11. *Wood Reference Handbook,* Canadian Wood Council, Ottawa, Ontario, 1995

7

Air, Vapour, and Weather Barriers

Sound Control

8

Absorptive material in wood frame assemblies has an effect in reducing sound transmission, but the greatest improvement comes from isolating the gypsum wallboard finishes from the framing so that noise energy is converted into heat energy.

Absorptive material in ceiling and wall assemblies is useful for reducing sound transmission, but again, maximum improvement comes from isolation of components.

The addition of a concrete topping or a gypsum cement slurry topping to a wood frame floor improves the sound isolation properties of the assembly.

8.1 General Information

Controlling the movement of sound between building areas is an important consideration in the design of buildings, particularly in the case of office buildings and multi-unit residential units where privacy is essential.

Wood materials, due to their cellular composition, are in themselves good sound insulators. However, other materials such as fibreglass batt insulation are far better sound insulators than wood.

Wood assemblies can easily be fitted with sound insulating materials and be modified in other ways to provide good sound control between building areas.

This chapter describes the mechanisms of sound movement and the measures which can be taken to minimize it. The following subjects are presented:

8.2   Sound Transmission

8.3   Sound Ratings of Wood Assemblies

8

Sound Control

8.2   Sound Transmission

Introduction

Sound is heard by the ear detecting fluctuations in atmospheric pressure caused by the vibration of air particles. Alternating atmospheric pressure levels produce a sound pressure wave. Sound waves are detected in the ear as pitches that vary for different frequencies or wave lengths.

The unit of measurement for describing the sound pressure level is the decibel (dB). Zero on the decibel scale is arbitrarily set to about the minimum one can hear in a very quiet controlled environment. Background noise is usually at 10 to 50 dB. Normal conversational speech averages about 70 dB, while a cocktail party will approach 85 dB or more. The threshold of pain for the human ear is about 130 dB.

Sound can travel through solid materials as well as air in the form of vibrations. When a sound pressure wave impacts a surface, numerous resonances are produced as the surface vibrates. In this way, sound can be transmitted through building partitions. The best way to reduce sound transmission is to use construction techniques that dampen vibration and convert sound energy into heat of friction.

When a surface is impacted by mechanical means, sound is more readily produced and transmitted. Often footsteps can be heard through floor and ceiling assemblies while voices and other similar noises are blocked. Sound can be categorized into two main types:

• airborne sound

• mechanical contact (impact) sound

Controlling the airborne noise between separate dwelling units is the primary concern of designers, and the basis for the sound control requirements outlined in the National Building Code of Canada (NBCC). The consideration of impact noise is the responsibility of designers and builders, but is not covered by regulation. However, impact noise requirements are being considered for inclusion in future versions of the NBCC.

Sound Transmission Loss

Sound transmission loss is the reduction in noise level resulting from passage through an obstruction. Sound transmission class (STC) is the measure of the effectiveness of a material to attenuate sound. The sound transmission loss caused by a partition or a floor is determined by physical factors such as mass and stiffness.

Ratings for various construction assemblies in the NBCC are based on the American Society for Testing and Materials (ASTM) STC rating system. The method for determining the STC is found in ASTM-E413, Classification for Rating Sound Insulation and the procedures outlined in ASTM-E90, Laboratory Measurement of Airborne Sound Transmission Loss of Building Partitions.

These standards refer to sounds from speech, radio, television, music and similar sources of noise in offices and dwellings, but do not include mechanical contact or impact noises. The ASTM standard advises that the STC system is not intended for noise originating outside a building and does not adequately consider low frequency attenuation such as that generated by local traffic.

For any assembly, the depth of air spaces, the presence or absence of sound absorbing material, and the degree of mechanical coupling between layers critically affect sound transmission losses and therefore the STC. An understanding of these factors can lead to improved design and building performance because small changes in the arrangement of materials can yield large changes in STC with little or no increase in cost.

8

Sound Control

Three interacting physical factors are important in determining whether building occupants are bothered by airborne noise from adjoining spaces. These are:

- the sound transmission losses of party walls or floors

- the level of noise generated in neighbouring occupancies

- the level of background sound in the occupant's space

The last two factors can vary widely. Therefore the designer must select a value of STC that will provide protection for most situations, and accept those cases where annoyance is caused by an unusually noisy neighbour or unusually low background sound levels. If the level of background sound is high enough, intruding sounds will be masked and will not be detectable. On the other hand, if the background noise is excessively high, it can interfere with concentration, relaxation and even conversation.

Experience has shown that, for occupants of multi-family dwellings to enjoy a reasonable degree of acoustical privacy, the effective STC between dwelling units should be at least 55. Values in excess of STC 60 can be achieved with typical building materials by taking particular care in design and construction.

Mass Law

The most important physical property controlling the airborne sound transmission loss through an assembly is the mass per unit area of its component layers. The mass law is a theoretical rule that applies to most materials in certain frequency ranges.

The mass law equation estimates that each time the frequency of measurement or the mass per unit area of a single layer wall is doubled, the transmission loss is increased by about 6 dB. To increase the sound transmission loss of a partition by 12 dB at all frequencies, therefore, the mass per unit area must be increased by a factor of 4. An increase of 18 dB requires an increase by a factor of 8, and so on.

Mass per unit area can be increased by increasing the thickness or by selecting a more dense material. For example, a single layer of cast-in-place concrete 150mm (6") thick gives an STC of about 55. Layers of this weight are generally the practical limit in normal construction.

If a higher STC value than this is necessary, and it often is in high quality construction, it is not economical to continually double the wall or floor thickness to achieve it. Double layer assemblies are a more practical way of getting high STC values without adding excessive weight.

When two layers of material such as gypsum wallboard are glued firmly together, they behave like a single thick layer with an associated lowering of the coincidence frequency.

If the layers are only held together loosely (with screws for example) so that they can slide over each other to some extent during vibration, the coincidence frequency does not move to lower frequencies, and the friction between the layers can introduce some extra energy losses, thereby transforming more noise energy into heat of friction.

Double Layer Assemblies

When lightweight construction and high STC values are desired, double layer construction must be used. Such assemblies can be very effective, but introduce additional effects that must be appreciated if double layer designs are to be successful.

Important factors, in addition to the masses of the component layers, are the depth of the air space, the use of sound absorbing materials within the air spaces, and the rigidity of the mechanical coupling between the layers. The ideal double layer assembly has no rigid mechanical connection between its two surfaces.

Gypsum Wallboard Surfaced Assemblies

The mechanical connection between the layers of gypsum wallboard can be reduced by the use of staggered wood studs, separate rows of wood studs, or a single row of wood studs with resilient metal furring strips to support the wallboard layers independently of the wood studs.

The presence of the sound absorbing insulation material increases the STC anywhere from 3 to 12 STC points, relative to the same wall without sound absorbing material. The amount of increase depends on whether the wall is a single row, staggered, or double stud wall, and whether or not resilient channels are used to attach the gypsum wallboard. Walls with 15.9mm (5/8") gypsum wallboard provide slightly better sound attenuation than those with 12.7mm (1/2") gypsum wallboard by a few STC points.

An STC rating of 60 or more can be obtained if the air space is large enough and gypsum wallboard of adequate thickness is used. Such values have been measured in buildings as well as in laboratories.

The common internal partition used in single family homes having gypsum wallboard attached directly to both sides of the wood studs has an STC rating of about 30. The addition of sound absorbing material in this wall increases its rating by only about 3 points, because the sound energy is transmitted directly from one layer of wallboard to the other through the studs.

The sound absorbing material in the cavity is of much less benefit than it would be if the layers were decoupled, in which case most of the sound would be transmitted through the air in the cavity. Rigid mechanical connections are the acoustical equivalent of an electrical short circuit or a thermal bridge in an insulated wall and should be avoided.

Acoustical Properties of Wood

Wood as a material has good sound attenuation properties. The cellular structure of wood turns sound energy into heat energy due to frictional resistance of the minute interlocking pores. Wood has a higher damping capacity than most materials because of this feature, and as a result, is a preferred material for building components where sound damping is required.

Finished wood surfaces, on the other hand, have a high reflective ability that is comparable to glass, brick, or plaster. Where wood is used as a finished interior surface which must have good sound absorption properties, the wood can be striated or applied in a batten fashion to improve its sound absorption properties.

National Building Code Requirements

The requirements for airborne sound control in Part 9 of the *NBCC* cover the following points:

- dwelling units shall be separated from every other space in a building in which noise may be generated by a construction providing an STC rating of at least 50

- where a dwelling unit is adjacent to an elevator shaft or a refuse chute, the separating construction shall have an STC rating of at least 55

- assemblies with STC ratings of 50 or more require acoustical sealant applied around all openings and junctions of intersecting walls and floors

8

Sound Control

These sound control requirements apply to interior party walls and walls or floors separating dwelling units (Figure 8.1). They do not adequately account for exterior noise such as traffic, particularly that which passes through the weaker sound insulating components such as doors and windows. Where building services pass through assemblies, special care is required to maintain sound isolation by insulating and using acoustical sealants.

The STC sound ratings required by the *NBCC* for various assemblies are based on laboratory test data for sound passage through single partition elements. To verify the performance of a partition in the field, the test ASTM-E336, *Measurement of Airborne Sound Insulation in Buildings,* can be used. The results are generally comparable to the STC ratings resulting from laboratory tests.

The sound transmission between rooms in a building is affected by other factors besides the sound insulating properties in the separate building components. Actual sound transmission between rooms includes leakage through flanking paths, cracks, joints, and weaker sound insulating components such as doors and windows.

A test for actual sound isolation between rooms in a building can be made using ASTM-E597, *Practice for Determining a*

Single-Number Rating of Airborne Sound Isolation for Use in Multiunit Building Specifications. In this test, a specified sound field is produced in the source room that is predominantly above the background noise. Decibel readings are weighted and averaged from the source room and the receiving room using a sound level meter. These weighted source and receiving levels are subtracted and adjusted for proposed room furnishings to produce a normalized sound level difference.

The sound level difference determined by the ASTM-E597 sound isolation test is not identical to the STC rating, and therefore is not enforceable under the *NBCC*. But the test can be useful to measure performance of existing buildings or new buildings for alteration prior to project completion.

Tests for impact sound transmission through floor ceiling assemblies are found in ASTM-E492, *Laboratory Measurement of Impact Sound Transmission Through Floor-Ceiling Assemblies Using the Tapping Machine.* A test method for field measurement of tapping machine impact sound transmission through floor-ceiling assemblies and associated support structures is found in ASTM-E1007, *Field Measurement of Tapping Machine Impact Sound Transmission Through Floor-Ceiling Assemblies and Associated Support Structures.*

Figure 8.1
**Sound control
requirements**

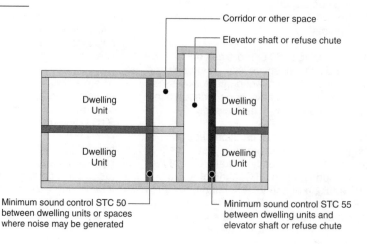

Dwelling Unit

Dwelling Unit

Dwelling Unit

Dwelling Unit

Corridor or other space

Elevator shaft or refuse chute

Minimum sound control STC 50 between dwelling units or spaces where noise may be generated

Minimum sound control STC 55 between dwelling units and elevator shaft or refuse chute

8.3 Sound Ratings of Wood Assemblies

Introduction

Wood frame assemblies can be designed to provide good STC ratings (Figures 8.2 and 8.3). In the 1995 *NBCC*, revisions to the Table on Fire and Sound Resistance on Walls increased the number of listings for wood stud wall assemblies from 15 in 1990 to 165 in the 1995 version. To achieve these specified ratings, the gypsum wallboard layers must be taped and filled. The absorptive material used between framing members to improve STC ratings includes fibre processed from rock, slag, glass or cellulose fibre, and it must fill at least 90% of the wall cavity.

Construction Details

Construction details and recommended construction practice for installing sound insulating partitions are outlined in ASTM E497, *Practice for Installing Sound-Isolating Lightweight Partitions.* This standard includes measures to be taken to prevent conditions that will detract from the sound insulating properties of acoustically rated walls.

8

Sound Control

Figure 8.2
**Sound trans-
mission
classes (STC)
for typical wall
assemblies**
(Source-1995
NBCC)

Section

STC

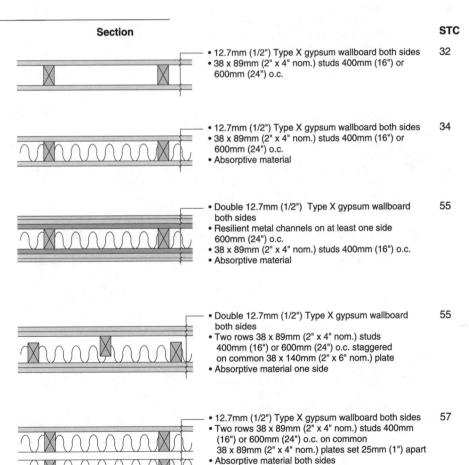

• 12.7mm (1/2") Type X gypsum wallboard both sides   32
• 38 x 89mm (2" x 4" nom.) studs 400mm (16") or
  600mm (24") o.c.

• 12.7mm (1/2") Type X gypsum wallboard both sides   34
• 38 x 89mm (2" x 4" nom.) studs 400mm (16") or
  600mm (24") o.c.
• Absorptive material

• Double 12.7mm (1/2") Type X gypsum wallboard   55
  both sides
• Resilient metal channels on at least one side
  600mm (24") o.c.
• 38 x 89mm (2" x 4" nom.) studs 400mm (16") o.c.
• Absorptive material

• Double 12.7mm (1/2") Type X gypsum wallboard   55
  both sides
• Two rows 38 x 89mm (2" x 4" nom.) studs
  400mm (16") or 600mm (24") o.c. staggered
  on common 38 x 140mm (2" x 6" nom.) plate
• Absorptive material one side

• 12.7mm (1/2") Type X gypsum wallboard both sides   57
• Two rows 38 x 89mm (2" x 4" nom.) studs 400mm
  (16") or 600mm (24") o.c. on common
  38 x 89mm (2" x 4" nom.) plates set 25mm (1") apart
• Absorptive material both sides

Many factors affect the overall performance of a sound barrier including sound leaks, acoustic seals, sound flanking, design oversights and poor workmanship. Many builders increase STC ratings by at least 5 points above the minimum acceptable STC rating to account for these factors.

Acoustical sealants conforming to ASTM C919, *Practice for Use of Sealants in Acoustical Applications,* are required around all openings and joints. This is an important factor in sound barrier construction because even small sound leaks can seriously reduce the effectiveness of the barrier. A wall with an STC rating of 53 when properly sealed, may have an STC rating as low as 29 when not sealed. The most effective sealants have been the non-drying, non-hardening, non-skin-forming types. They can maintain an air tight seal by remaining flexible and adhesive.

Electrical outlets or fixtures in a wall system should not be installed back to back. Back to back installation shortens the sound travel path and increases sound leakage. Outlets and fixtures should be staggered a minimum of 610mm (2') and more where possible (Figure 8.4). Where back to back installations cannot be avoided, heavy caulking will minimize sound transmission. The sound path can also be lengthened by separating back to back installations with material such as sheet lead.

Resilient channels are used to reduce the effect of sound transfer through framed members by damping vibration in the wall sheathing (Figure 8.5). Care must be taken to assure that the sheathing fasteners do not touch the framed members. This type of defect would transmit sound to the framed members. For some wood stud wall arrangements, spacing resilient channels 600mm (24") o.c. instead of 400mm (16") can improve the STC by 2 or 3 points.

Noise can pass an otherwise good sound barrier through open spaces such as crawl spaces, joist spaces, wall spaces, or attic spaces. This is referred to as flanking. To prevent flanking, an adequate sound barrier is required in the flanking space

(Figure 8.6). Flanking can also occur when vibrations are transmitted through framed members, sheathing and subfloor. This type of flanking can be reduced by providing a construction joint in subflooring at the sound barrier.

For floor assemblies, foot impact noise between corridors and adjacent suites or offices can be reduced by making the corridor walls loadbearing, and making the floor joists spanning the corridor simply supported by the corridor walls.

In addition, wood frame floor designs in multi-unit dwellings and offices will benefit acoustically from the use of a 38mm (1-1/2") concrete topping (lightweight or normal weight), or a gypsum cement slurry applied directly over top of the plywood or OSB floor sheathing. For example, a 19mm (3/4") gypsum cement topping can improve a floor assembly STC rating by up to 15%.

When double gypsum wallboard layers are applied to a surface, all joints should be overlapped and wall intersection joints should be staggered. Overlapped joints will increase the sound travel path. This reduces the sound leakage through the cracks and joints.

When staggered studs or double wall construction are used, there should be no mechanical connections or blocking that connect the double wall framing. All plumbing and fixtures should be installed and fastened to one wall system. Proper mechanical installations are important to reduce impact noises that may be created by piping or other mechanical moving parts.

Vibration and impact noises from machinery can be minimized by special mountings. In general, noisy equipment should be properly located to reduce noise transmission. Often sound proofed enclosures are provided for noise generating equipment.

Carpet and underpad act as a cushion to reduce the impact noise generated on a floor due to footsteps.

Figure 8.3
Sound transmission class for typical floor assemblies

Section   **STC**

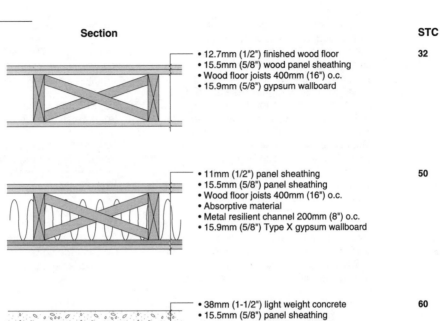

- 12.7mm (1/2") finished wood floor   **32**
- 15.5mm (5/8") wood panel sheathing
- Wood floor joists 400mm (16") o.c.
- 15.9mm (5/8") gypsum wallboard

- 11mm (1/2") panel sheathing   **50**
- 15.5mm (5/8") panel sheathing
- Wood floor joists 400mm (16") o.c.
- Absorptive material
- Metal resilient channel 200mm (8") o.c.
- 15.9mm (5/8") Type X gypsum wallboard

- 38mm (1-1/2") light weight concrete   **60**
- 15.5mm (5/8") panel sheathing
- Wood floor joists 400mm (16") o.c.
- Absorptive material
- Metal resilient channel 200 (8") o.c.
- 15.9mm (5/8") gypsum wallboard

Note:
Panel sheathing may be plywood or OSB

Figure 8.4
Placement of electrical outlets in wall systems

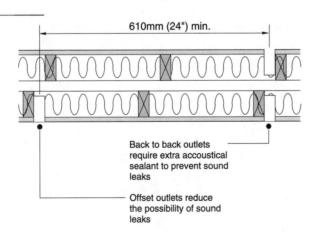

610mm (24") min.

Back to back outlets require extra accoustical sealant to prevent sound leaks

Offset outlets reduce the possibility of sound leaks

8

Sound Control

Windows often represent a weak component of sound insulation on exterior walls (Chapter 10). Double pane windows with an air space are usually provided for sound insulation. Triple pane windows can provide a slightly higher resistance to sound, however the third window pane will develop resonances of its own thereby reducing the overall attenuation. Fixed windows provide more sound insulation than windows that can be opened. Windows should be properly air sealed to minimize sound leaks which affect energy conservation and sound transmission.

Doors are also often weak components of sound insulation and must be properly air sealed to minimize sound leaks. A 45mm (1-3/8") solid core wood door completely sealed with gaskets or weather stripping

can achieve an STC rating of 27.

The following ASTM standards can be used to evaluate a sound rated building assembly in the field.

- ASTM-E336 *Measurement of Airborne Sound Insulation in Buildings*

- ASTM-E597 *Standard Practice for Determining a Single Number Rating of Airborne Sound Isolation for use in Multi-Unit Building Specifications*

- ASTM-E1007 *Test Method for Field Measurement of Tapping Machine Impact Sound Transmission Through Ceiling/Floor Assemblies and Associated Support Structures*

Figure 8.5
Resilient channel fasteners

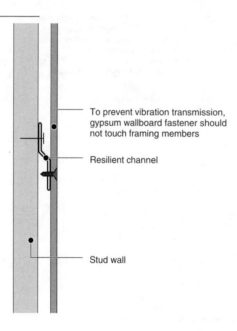

To prevent vibration transmission, gypsum wallboard fastener should not touch framing members

Resilient channel

Stud wall

Figure 8.6
Sound flanking

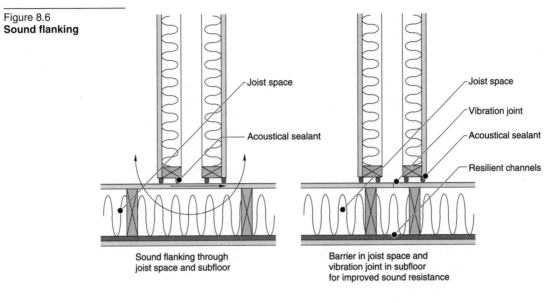

Joist space

Acoustical sealant

Joist space

Vibration joint

Acoustical sealant

Resilient channels

Sound flanking through
joist space and subfloor

Barrier in joist space and
vibration joint in subfloor
for improved sound resistance

8

Sound Control

References

1. *Sound Transmission Loss,* A.C.C.
   Warnock, Canadian Building Digest,
   National Research Council, Ottawa,
   ON, 1985

Fire Protection

9

Penetrations in fire separations must be made in such a way that the integrity of the wall is not affected.

Sprinkler installation can be made in a way that is unobtrusive and in a way that does not detract from aesthetics.

Fire separations must be made continuous above suspended ceilings as in the case of this laboratory in a wood frame building.

Sprinkler heads need not be installed above suspended ceilings if the concealed space contains no exposed combustible construction.

Left: An insulated pocket has been constructed to protect this wet-pipe sprinkler system from freezing.

Right: Exposed wood framing for roof assemblies can be protected by sprinklering thereby waiving the fire-resistance rating requirements.

Electrical service is a major concern for fire safety. Therefore, wiring must be kept back from nailing surfaces, or metal plate protection must be provided between the wire and the sheathing.

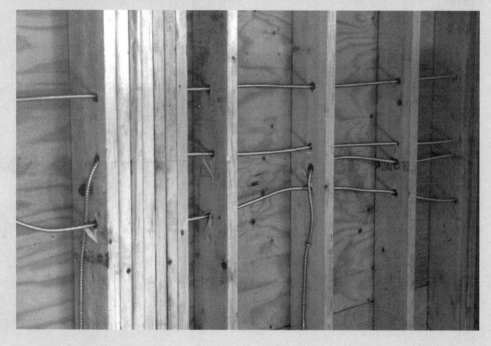

The wood framing abutting this firewall must be supported in such a way that the integrity of the firewall will not be compromised in the event of collapse of the framing in a fire.

Sprinkler systems must be designed so that the required water coverage can be achieved despite obstructions such as open web steel joists or the wood trusses shown here.

Until the full fire-resistance rating of wood assemblies is achieved by final construction, special care is required during construction to protect against fire.

Left: This service bay for piping and other building services is a fire compartment and gypsum wallboard protection must be provided throughout.

Right: Sprinklers must be located not more than 150mm (6") below exposed wood joists.

9.1 General Information

At the present time, the *National Building Code of Canada (NBCC)* and other North American building codes categorize wood buildings as combustible construction.

Despite being termed combustible, construction techniques can give wood-frame construction fire-resistance ratings up to 2 hours.

In addition, the *NBCC* affords post and beam construction meeting certain criteria and thereby qualifying as Heavy Timber construction (Section 4.3), an equivalency to wood-frame construction having a 45-minute fire-resistance rating.

The provision of fire safety in a building is a complex matter; far more complex than the relative combustibility of the main structural materials used in a building. To develop safe code provisions, prevention, suppression, movement of occupants, mobility of occupants, building use, and controlling the fuel are but a few of the factors that must be considered in addition to the combustibility of the structural components.

Some of North America's most disastrous fires, in terms of either loss of life or loss of property, have occurred in buildings which were considered to be of noncombustible or fire resistive construction.

Fire-loss experience shows that building contents play a large role in terms of fuel load and smoke generation potential in a fire. The passive fire protection provided by the fire-resistance ratings on the major floor and wall assemblies in a building, although assuring structural stability in a fire, do not necessarily control the movement of smoke and heat which can have a large impact on the level of safety and property damage resulting from fire.

Sprinklers typically operate very early in a fire thereby quickly controlling the damaging effects. For this reason, the provision of automatic sprinkler protection within a building greatly improves the life safety and property protection prospects of all buildings, including those constructed of noncombustible materials.

Wood buildings must of course meet building code requirements which have already accounted for the nature of wood as a suitable material in assigning maximum permissible building heights and areas. Wood has been used for schools, warehouses, fire stations, apartment buildings, research facilities; virtually all types of buildings. When designed and built to code requirements, these buildings provide the same level of life safety and property protection required for comparably sized buildings constructed of steel or concrete. When sprinkler protection is added, the performance of wood, steel, and concrete buildings in fire situations improves dramatically.

When meeting the area and height limits for the various *NBCC* building categories, wood-frame construction can meet the *NBCC* life safety requirements by making use of wood assemblies (usually protected by gypsum wallboard) which are tested for fire-resistance ratings.

The allowable height and area restrictions can be extended by using firewalls to break a large building area into smaller separate building areas. The recognized positive contribution to both life safety and property protection which comes from the use of automatic sprinkler systems can also be used to increase the permissible height and area of wood buildings.

Extensive discussion and commentary on the complex topic of fire protection for buildings in general and wood buildings in particular is found in the CWC publication *Fire Safety Design in Buildings.* The purpose of this Chapter is to examine specific fire safety requirements necessary in the design, construction, and inspection of wood buildings. The following subjects are addressed:

9.2 Fire Stopping

9.3 Fire-Resistance Ratings

9.4 Service Equipment Openings and Penetrations

9.5 Interior Finish

9.6 Sprinkler Protection

9

Fire Protection

9.2   Fire Stopping

Introduction

Fire stopping is the provision of minor components in building construction, which are typically found in large open concealed spaces, that impede or retard the spread of fire from one area or space to another.

Unlike a fire stop, a fire separation is a complete wall or floor assembly, with or without a fire-resistance rating, that deters the spread of fire within the occupied space of a building. A fire stop may be present in a fire separation. For example, a penetration through a fire separation by a pipe or wire must be fire stopped to deter the passage of smoke and flame through this breach in the fire separation.

In wood-frame construction, dimension lumber is often used as a fire stop between joists or studs, and for larger areas, such as attics or roof spaces, plywood or oriented strandboard (OSB) is used. For penetrations, caulk and other special materials are used to seal small openings.

In some cases, fire stops in wood-frame construction can perform more than one function. For example, the bottom wall plate in a wood stud wall distributes stud loads to the floor platform and also serves as an impediment to the spread of fire from the floor below into the wall cavities on the floor above.

As with other important fire protection features, it is essential to detail the location and composition of fire stops and to verify through inspection their proper installation.

Construction of Fire Stops

The *NBCC* lists generic materials such as gypsum wallboard and dimension lumber which may be used for fire stops, and also provides a standard which may be used for testing proprietary products. The following are permitted types of material for use as fire stops in concealed spaces:

- 12.7mm (1/2") thick gypsum wallboard with joints having continuous support

- 0.38mm (28 gauge) sheet steel with all joints having continuous support

- solid lumber not less than 38mm (2"nom.) thick

- phenolic bonded plywood, oriented strandboard (OSB), or waferboard not less than 12.5mm (1/2") thick with joints having continuous support

- two thicknesses of lumber not less than 19mm (3/4") thick with staggered joints are permitted to be used for fire stopping the width or height of a concealed space that is greater than 38mm (1-1/2") deep

- any other materials which will remain in place and prevent the passage of flames for a period of not less than 15 minutes when subjected to the standard fire exposure in CAN/ULC-S101-M, *Standard Methods of Fire Endurance Tests of Building Construction and Materials*

When openings through these fire stop materials are necessary, the openings must be protected to maintain the integrity of the fire stop. For example, an access door in an attic or crawl space must be protected by using a solid core wood door provided with a self closer and a latch. When the fire stop materials are penetrated by construction elements or service equipment, fire stop materials are required to seal the penetrations. These requirements will be dealt with in more detail in subsequent sections.

9

Fire Protection

Crawl Spaces and Basements

A concealed space below a building is either a crawl space or a basement. The *NBCC* defines the space as a basement if it:

- exceeds 1.8m (5.9') in height

- is used for any occupancy

- is used for the passage of flue pipes

- is used as a plenum in combustible construction

Crawl spaces, if unsprinklered, need to be protected if they exceed certain dimensions and fire stops can be used for this purpose. Basements, on the other hand, must be protected by fire separations which have more structural integrity than is required for fire stops.

Unsprinklered crawl spaces must be separated into compartments by means of fire stopping so that:

- the maximum area of any compartment does not exceed 600m^2 (6450 ft^2)

- the maximum linear dimension does not exceed 30m (98')

Crawl space areas with dimensions which exceed these limits must be provided with a fire stop (Figure 9.1). However, if a crawl space is sprinklered, fire stops are not required regardless of the size of the crawl space.

If the space below a building is a basement, it must either be divided into fire compartments not exceeding 600m^2 (6450 ft^2) by fire separations having a fire-resistance rating of at least 45 minutes, or be fully sprinklered.

Figure 9.1
Fire stopping for crawl spaces

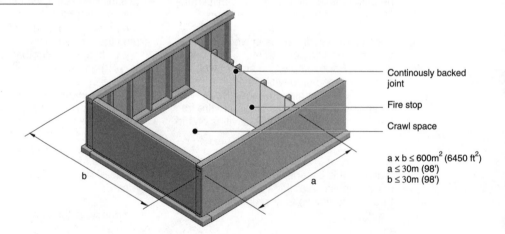

Continuously backed joint

Fire stop

Crawl space

a x b ≤ 600m^2 (6450 ft^2)
a ≤ 30m (98')
b ≤ 30m (98')

Exterior Mansard Style Roofs, Balconies, and Canopies

Mansard roofs, balconies and canopies, by design, may provide a path around the perimeter of a building through which fire can spread. For this reason, fire stopping must be provided in these concealed spaces (Figure 9.2) so that fire cannot bypass the internal fire separations between suites.

If these building features have concealed spaces and are constructed of materials exposed in the concealed space which have a flame-spread rating greater than 25, fire stops must be provided where:

- such features extend across the ends of required interior vertical fire separations

- the maximum dimension in the concealed space exceeds 20m (65')

No fire stopping is required if the concealed space is sprinklered. If the space is sprinklered and unheated, the sprinklers must be on a dry-pipe type system or on an anti-freeze loop connected to a wet-pipe system within the building.

9

Fire Protection

Figure 9.2
Fire stopping for mansard roof

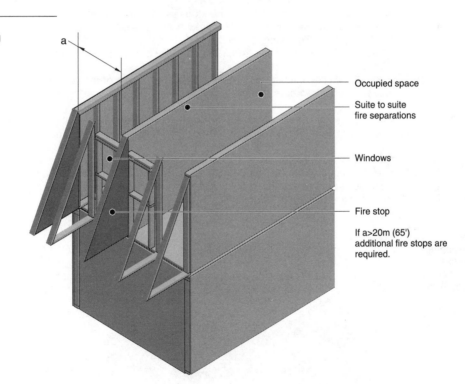

a

Occupied space

Suite to suite fire separations

Windows

Fire stop

If a>20m (65') additional fire stops are required.

Floor, Ceiling, and Roof Assemblies and Attics

Combustible concealed spaces such as large open attic spaces and large open spaces within floor, ceiling, or roof assemblies are required to be fire-stopped if sprinkler protection is not provided within the space (Figure 9.3).

Floors and roofs constructed with solid wood joist or wood I-joist assemblies usually have the ceiling membrane attached directly to the underside of the structural members. The members and the blocking between them usually serve as fire stops in which case no additional fire stopping is required. Fire stopping is required in the direction parallel to the joists if the length of the space exceeds 20m (65').

Where the ceiling is suspended below the floor or ceiling members, creating a large open concealed space, or where open wood trusses or rafters are used, fire stops must be provided in the space. If furring channels are installed to attach the ceiling membrane beneath solid wood joists, it is critical to ensure that fire stopping is also provided in both directions in the small space created by the furring strips.

Such spaces, when unsprinklered or built of materials with flame-spread ratings greater than 25, must be fire-stopped into compartments such that:

- the area of any compartment does not exceed 300m^2 (3230 ft^2)

- the width or length of any compartment does not exceed 20m (65')

If all the exposed structural materials in the concealed space have a flame-spread rating of 25 or less, as does fire-retardant treated wood or wood protected with a ULC listed fire-retardant coating, the dimensions listed previously can be increased to:

- area not more than 600m^2 (6450 ft^2)

- width or length not more than 60m (195')

Fire-retardant treated wood or plywood required to have a flame spread rating of 25 or less must bear a ULC stamp indicating the flame spread rating. If a fire-retardant coating is used to protect the exposed surfaces, the application rates must be specified and be verified during inspection.

Figure 9.3
Fire stopping for unsprin-klered wood truss spaces

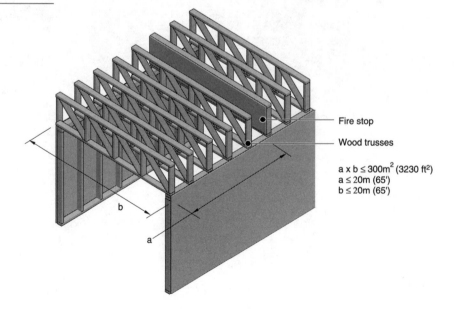

Fire stop

Wood trusses

a x b ≤ 300m^2 (3230 ft^2)
a ≤ 20m (65')
b ≤ 20m (65')

Where a fire stop is installed in an attic having light wood-frame trusses, it is important to ensure that all the joints of the fire stopping material are protected. To accomplish this, each joint must either be located so that it is supported by a truss chord or web, or be protected by a separate batten strip installed on either side of the fire stop material.

As with other combustible concealed spaces, there is no limit on the area of a non-fire-stopped sprinklered ceiling, roof, or attic concealed space of combustible construction.

Coved Ceilings, Dropped Ceilings, Soffits and Stairways

Fire stopping is required at the intersection point of vertical and horizontal spaces in interior coved ceilings, dropped ceilings and soffits (Figure 9.4). For most applications, the fire stopping is provided by the top plate in a stud wall, the end trusses in a floor assembly, or blocking at the end of a floor assembly.

Where these concealed spaces contain construction materials which have flame-spread ratings of more than 25, and are connected to vertical concealed spaces, all interconnections must be fire stopped.

Stair stringers are required to be fire stopped at each floor level and at the end of each run to prevent the spread of fire via the stair stringers.

Wall Fire Stopping

The vertical concealed spaces between the vertical members of a wall assembly can provide a path for smoke and fire to travel undetected vertically through the assembly and must be fire stopped (Figure 9.5). In most wood stud wall applications, fire stopping is provided by the top or bottom plates of the wall assembly.

The use of furring strips or resilient channels which results in a space between the framing and the interior finishes may provide opportunity for fire to travel horizontally in a wall assembly. The airspace in rainscreen construction (Section 7.3) between the cladding and the sheathing of exterior walls may also provide a path for fire spread.

When double studded interior walls are used to provide improved sound isolation between rooms, additional fire stopping is required to prevent fire spread between the two stud cavities.

Fire stops are required at the following locations within concealed spaces in walls or partitions:

- at every floor level

- at every ceiling level where the ceiling forms part of an assembly required to have a fire-resistance rating

- where any horizontal space in a wall assembly (such as that created by using resilient channels to attach gypsum wallboard to the studs) exceeds 20m (65') in length

- where the vertical dimension in the space is more than 3m (10')

9

Fire Protection

Figure 9.4
Fire stopping of dropped and coved ceilings and stairs

Dropped ceiling

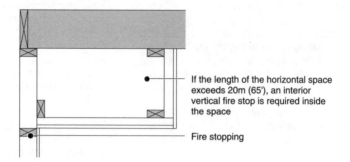

If the length of the horizontal space exceeds 20m (65'), an interior vertical fire stop is required inside the space

Fire stopping

Coved ceiling

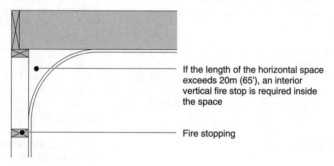

If the length of the horizontal space exceeds 20m (65'), an interior vertical fire stop is required inside the space

Fire stopping

Stair fire stopping

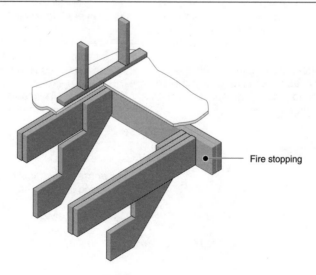

Fire stopping

Figure 9.5
Wall fire stopping

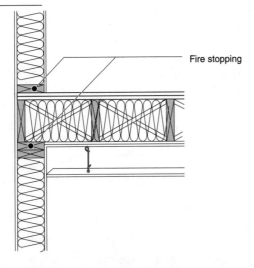

Fire stopping

Fire stops are not required where the wall space:

- has a width not exceeding 25mm (1") and there is only one such space in the cross-section width of the space

- contains no exposed construction materials having flame-spread ratings greater than 25

      – or –

- is filled with insulation

Where a partition extends into a concealed space of a floor assembly, the finished gypsum wallboard or other interior panel finish on the wall assembly (and in some cases the finished wood floor assembly) can act as the fire stop material.

Protection Of Exterior Soffits

In some cases, special protective measures must be used where more than two dwelling units or patient sleeping rooms share a common attic space. (Figure 9.6) This is required to reduce the possibility of fire spreading from a fire in one unit or room to adjacent units or rooms by extending outside via a window or door and up into the attic space through the overhanging soffit.

One alternative is to protect the soffits and fascia within 2.5m (8') of any window or door openings with one of the following:

- noncombustible material at least 0.38mm (0.015") thick and having a melting point 650°C (1200°F) or greater

- plywood at least 11mm (7/16") thick

- oriented strandboard or waferboard at least 12.5mm (1/2") thick

- lumber at least 11mm (7/16") thick

9

Fire Protection

Where used to protect a soffit, these materials must extend at least 1.2m (4') on either side of the opening.

There are several alternatives to providing such protection. One is to completely separate the soffit area from the rest of the roof space by fire stopping. Another alternative is to separate the attic and eave spaces at every two units or rooms.

Figure 9.6
Protection of exterior soffits and attics

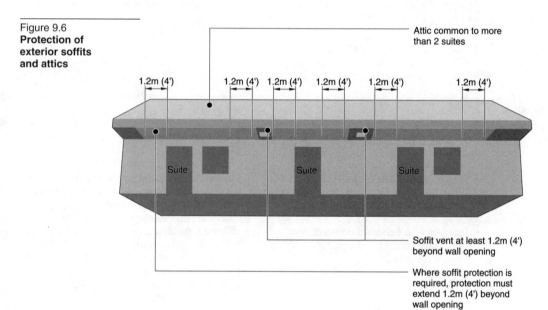

Attic common to more than 2 suites

1.2m (4')   1.2m (4')   1.2m (4')   1.2m (4')   1.2m (4')   1.2m (4')

Suite   Suite   Suite

Soffit vent at least 1.2m (4') beyond wall opening

Where soffit protection is required, protection must extend 1.2m (4') beyond wall opening

9.3   Fire-Resistance Ratings

Introduction

A fire-resistance rating is the time in hours or fraction thereof that a material or assembly of materials will withstand the passage of flame and the transmission of heat when exposed to fire under specified test conditions. However, fire-resistance ratings may also be assigned by extension or interpretation of test results in accordance with the provisions contained in Appendix D of the NBCC.

A fire separation is an assembly that acts as a barrier against the spread of fire. A fire compartment is an enclosed space in a building that is separated from all other parts of the building by enclosing construction which is a fire separation having a required fire-resistance rating (Figure 9.7).

Fire-resistance ratings, fire separations, and fire compartments all contribute to the passive fire safety in a building to provide structural integrity and control fire spread. They are just a few of the many fire safety requirements required for the provision of both active and passive fire protection.

Determining Fire-Resistance Ratings

The fire-resistance rating of an assembly can be determined by test or by extension of data from fire tests. Fire-resistance ratings for tested assemblies must be determined from tests conducted in accordance with CAN/ULC-S101-M *Standard Methods of Fire Endurance Tests of Building Construction and Materials* published by the Underwriter's Laboratories of Canada (ULC).

In all cases, the report for a proprietary fire test specifically describes the materials and construction methods that were used in the actual construction of the assembly that was tested. For a similar assembly constructed in a building to be granted the fire-resistance rating that was achieved in the test, the details of the tested assembly must be duplicated. However, some changes from the original tested assembly are permitted on the basis that the change is not expected to reduce the fire-resistance rating of the assembly.

9

Fire Protection

Figure 9.7
Fire compartments in residential construction

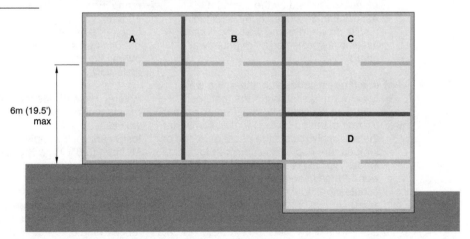

6m (19.5')
max

Notes:
1. All units need to be separated from each other by fire separations having a fire-resistance rating of 1 hour.
2. Floor assemblies in Units A and B need not be constructed as fire separations or have a fire-resistance rating.
3. Floor assemblies within Units C and D need not be constructed as fire separations but must have a fire-resistance rating of at least 45 minutes.
4. Each residential unit is considered to be a separate fire compartment.
5. The 6m (19.5') maximum distance between the lowest floor level and the uppermost floor level does not apply to Part 9 buildings.

Some examples of such changes are the use of larger structural members, closer spacing of supports, addition of insulation in a floor or wall cavity, and the addition of concrete floor toppings over a plywood subfloor. The testing laboratory will often specify in their listings or be in a position to give an opinion on the impact of optional materials for use in a fire-rated assembly. Two documents which are available for further reference in this regard are *Harmathy's Ten Rules of Fire Endurance* which are described in *Fire Safety Design in Buildings* and *Criteria for Use in Extension of Data From Fire Endurance Tests* (ULC Subject C263[e]-M88).

The results of standard fire tests are usually published by the testing laboratory such as the ULC *List of Equipment and Materials Volume III on Fire-Resistance Ratings* or the Warnock Hersey *Certification Listings*.

In some cases, the fire-resistance ratings are also published by the manufacturer of the products tested. For example, the listings contained in *Fire Resistance Design Manual* published by the Gypsum Association describes numerous tests results on wood-frame wall and floor assemblies protected by gypsum wall-board.

In a fire-resistance test, the entire wall, floor, or roof assembly is the test specimen. The assembly is assigned an assembly rating, based on the length of time that the assembly resists the passage of fire or temperature rise while subjected to design loads. Typical fire-resistance ratings for wood-frame assemblies range from 45 minutes to 2 hours.

The other option for assigning fire-resistance ratings involves the extension of data from fire tests. The component additive method found in Appendix D of the *NBCC* is one example of an acceptable approach for assigning fire-resistance ratings on the basis of extension of data from fire tests. Another example is the tables contained in Part 9 of the *NBCC* which describe various wood-frame wall, floor, and roof assemblies and assign them fire and sound transmission ratings on the basis of testing and

historical use in construction.

In applying the component additive method, a wall or floor assembly can be assigned an assembly rating for purposes of determining the fire-resistance rating. When the assembly rating is calculated, a contribution by each component of the assembly to the fire resistance of the assembly, expressed in minutes of time, is added to determine the overall fire-resistance rating of the construction assembly.

The contribution of each element is determined from information listed in tables found in Appendix D of the *NBCC*. These values are based on extensive testing that has been conducted on assemblies using traditional construction materials such as gypsum wallboard, plywood, wood joists and wood trusses. A more extensive discussion on the calculation method can be found in *Fire Safety Design in Buildings*.

Where the component additive method is used, the contribution of each element of the wall, floor or roof assembly is added to determine the assigned fire-resistance rating. For example, the *NBCC* assigns 15.9mm (5/8") Type X gypsum wallboard a time of 40 minutes and wood studs a time of 20 minutes for their contributions to the overall fire-resistance rating of a wall assembly.

Adding these values together gives a fire-resistance rating of 1 hour for a wood stud wall assembly (either loadbearing or non-loadbearing). By applying this same 15.9mm (5/8") Type X gypsum wallboard to a wood truss floor or roof assembly, the fire-resistance rating of either assembly would be 45 minutes, as the *NBCC* assigns a 5 minute value as the contribution of the wood trusses to the fire-resistance rating of a protected assembly.

There is an option for floor and roof assemblies that allows a designer to assign the fire-resistance rating of the assembly on the basis of only the contribution of the ceiling membrane installed on the underside of the structural members. In other words, no credit is given for the contribution of structural members, the membrane on the unexposed (non-fire) side, such as the sub-floor on a floor assembly, or any insulation which may be installed within the floor or roof cavity.

Since only the ceiling membrane is used to determine the fire-resistance rating for the assembly, it is termed a membrane rating. In most cases, this surface membrane is either gypsum wallboard or plaster but in a few cases can also be plywood.

The values assigned to the individual ceiling membranes when calculating a membrane rating are different from what they are when calculating for an assembly rating. This is because the membrane must provide all of the fire resistance and must, by itself, resist the passage of heat and fire for the prescribed fire-resistance rating period.

The treatment of continuity of the fire separation of small openings in the ceiling membrane is different for assembly ratings and membrane ratings.

In summary, the methods by which fire-resistance ratings may be determined are as follows:

- assembly tested in accordance with the standard fire test by a recognized laboratory such as Underwriter's Laboratories of Canada or Warnock Hersey

- assembly or membrane rating determined from the component additive method in Appendix D of the *NBCC*

- assembly or membrane rating contained in Tables A-9.10.3.1.A and A-9.10.3.1.B

Continuity of Fire Separations

It is important to design and construct fire separations which are continuous. The continuity of a fire separation is critical since the fire separation is expected to act as a barrier to the spread of fire. Holes and penetrations in fire separations due to service equipment such as pipes and ducts or improper construction techniques could allow a fire to spread beyond the fire compartment.

Where small vertical openings in a floor assembly are necessary to permit stairs, elevators and other service shafts to travel through the building, the integrity of the fire separation formed by the floor must be maintained by providing vertical fire separations around the shafts. The fire-resistance rating required for the fire separations around these shafts is based on the use of the shaft and the fire-resistance rating required for the floor assembly being penetrated, which can vary from 45 minutes to a 2-hour rating (Figure 9.8).

Continuity is also required to be maintained by protecting openings such as doorways, by installing fire rated doors with self-closing devices, and protecting openings created by heating and ventilation duct-work, by installing fire dampers with fusible links (Figure 9.9).

Where horizontal service spaces or other concealed spaces are located above a vertical fire separation, an approach must be determined for providing continuity for the vertical fire separation. To do this, it is necessary to determine whether the fire-resistance rating of the floor or roof assembly is assigned on the basis of an assembly rating or only on a membrane rating (as explained earlier).

If the horizontal assembly is assigned an assembly rating, the entire assembly is the boundary element of the fire compartment. As a result, the vertical fire separation must extend up through the concealed space to the underside of the sub-floor or roof deck of the horizontal assembly (Figure 9.10)

The membrane rating approach is typically used where the direction of the structural member supporting the floor or roof is perpendicular to the partition and it would be impractical to penetrate the ceiling membrane and extend the partition up to the subfloor or roof deck above, between each joist or truss. But the *NBCC* does not restrict the use of the membrane rating approach to only these instances where the orientation of the structural member is perpendicular to the partitions.

9

Fire Protection

If the membrane rating approach is used, the *NBCC* permits the partition or wall to stop at the underside of the ceiling provided the membrane provides a fire-resistance rating equal to that of the vertical fire separation.

One exception to this is where the fire-resistance rating of the vertical fire separation is only required to be 45 minutes in which case the rating of the ceiling membrane is only required to be 30 minutes.

Figure 9.8
Fire separations for vertical service spaces

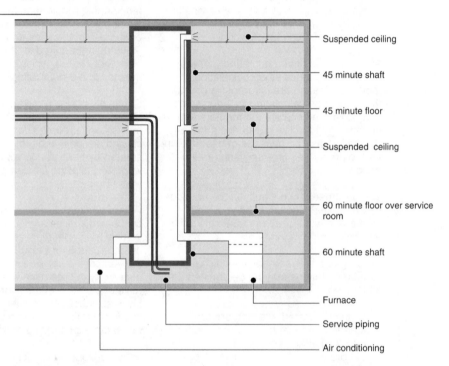

- Suspended ceiling
- 45 minute shaft
- 45 minute floor
- Suspended ceiling
- 60 minute floor over service room
- 60 minute shaft
- Furnace
- Service piping
- Air conditioning

Shaft must provide 60 minute fire separation at bottom and 45 minutes where it passes through the first and second storey and at the top; interior finish of shaft must have flame-spread rating of 25 or less.

Figure 9.9
Protection of openings in fire separations

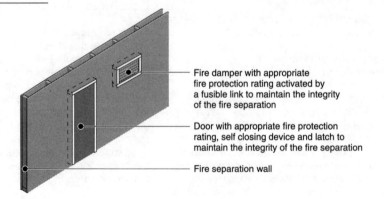

- Fire damper with appropriate fire protection rating activated by a fusible link to maintain the integrity of the fire separation
- Door with appropriate fire protection rating, self closing device and latch to maintain the integrity of the fire separation
- Fire separation wall

Figure 9.10
**Continuity of
vertical fire
separations**

Assembly rating

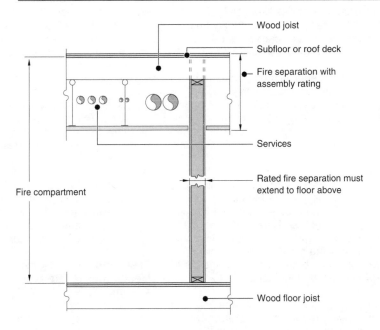

- Wood joist
- Subfloor or roof deck
- Fire separation with assembly rating
- Services
- Rated fire separation must extend to floor above
- Wood floor joist

Fire compartment

Membrane rating

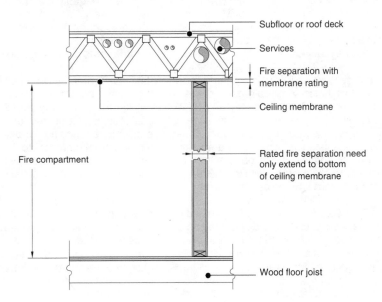

- Subfloor or roof deck
- Services
- Fire separation with membrane rating
- Ceiling membrane
- Rated fire separation need only extend to bottom of ceiling membrane
- Wood floor joist

Fire compartment

9

Fire Protection

Type of Gypsum Wallboard

For tested assemblies listed by ULC, Warnock Hersey or other authority, the type of gypsum wallboard required is specified in the individual listings (Figure 9.11).

In the case of special fire rated material, a manufacturer's stamp should always appear on the gypsum wallboard or on the packaging for the gypsum wallboard. This stamp will list the ULC or other laboratory design numbers for which the gypsum wallboard may be used.

Most fire-rated gypsum wallboard will have a special name such as Fireguard® or Firecode®, and in some cases, a letter designation such as Type C or Type X1. Most fire-rated gypsum wallboard is proprietary in that the material and chemical make-up of the board is specific and confidential for each manufacturer.

Type X gypsum wallboard is commonly used in many fire-rated wood-frame assemblies assigned a fire-resistance rating on the basis of the component additive method or the tables contained in Part 9 of the *NBCC* . Both refer specifically to 12.7mm (1/2") and 15.9mm (5/8") Type X products which allow a designer to assign a fire-resistance rating to an assembly where these products are installed as required.

Type X gypsum wallboard is a generic building product that is specifically defined and described in the CSA Standard CSA A82.27, *Gypsum Board* . It is designated as a fire-rated gypsum wallboard product on the basis of the fire-resistance rating it provides when installed on both sides of a loadbearing wood stud wall assembly with the studs spaced 400mm (16") on centre.

The CSA standard states that a gypsum wallboard product can be designated as Type X if one 15.9mm (5/8") layer applied to both sides of a wood stud wall assembly provides a minimum fire-resistance rating of 1 hour and, one 12.7mm (1/2") layer on both sides provides a minimum fire-resistance rating of 45 minutes.

As for the proprietary gypsum wallboard products, Type X products should carry a stamp or label describing the product as complying to the CSA Standard. For some Type X gypsum wallboard products, the stamp or label is located on the edge of the boards for ease of identification by a building inspector.

For all three methods of assigning fire-resistance ratings, there are options that allow the use of ordinary gypsum products to meet the minimum fire-resistance rating requirements. In the case of proprietary tests, the products specified in the listing must be used. In the case of the ratings from Part 9, the gypsum wallboard must comply with the CSA Standard CSA A82.27, and meet the minimum requirements specified in the standard.

Fasteners for Protective Membranes in Fire-rated Assemblies

The type, spacing and penetration of fasteners used for gypsum wallboard and other protective membranes play an important role in ensuring that an assembly provides adequate fire performance. The gypsum wallboard provides most of the fire resistance for any protected assembly and therefore it is crucial that it remain in place to perform as long as possible.

If it falls off prematurely in a fire situation, the fire will be allowed to spread much quicker than expected based on the assigned fire-resistance rating. As well, early failure of the membrane will expose the structural members to fire at an earlier time than expected, thereby increasing the potential for structural collapse.

If an assembly is assigned a fire-resistance rating on the basis of a test, the type, spacing and depth of penetration of the fasteners used in the test will govern in every case. In fire-rated assemblies assigned a rating on the basis of the component additive method or Part 9, the requirements are described in each document on the minimum depth penetration and maximum spacing of the fasteners.

Figure 9.11
**Example of
ULC listed
wood joist
floor assembly**

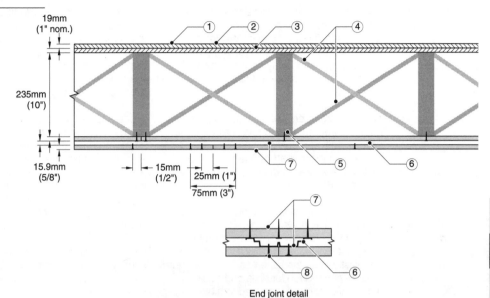

End joint detail

Design No. M503 Unrestrained Assembly Rating: 2h
Combustible Construction
(Finish Rating - 75 minutes)

1. Finish Flooring: 19 x 89mm (1" x 4") T & G flooring laid perpendicular to joists or 15.5mm (5/8")
   select sheathing grade T & G phenolic bonded Douglas fir plywood with face grain perpendicular
   to joists and joints staggered.
2. Building Paper (optional): Commercial sheathing material, 0.25mm (0.10") thick.
3. Sub-flooring: 19 x 140mm (1" x 6") T & G boards laid diagonally to joists or 12.5mm (1/2")
   unsanded sheathing grade phenolic bonded Douglas fir plywood with face grain perpendicular to
   joists and joints staggered.
4. Bridging: 19 x 64mm (1" x 3").
5. Wood Joists: 38 x 235mm (2" x 10") spaced 400mm (16") O.C., fire stopped.
6. Furring Channel: Resilient, formed of 0.5mm (0.021") electrogalvanized steel as shown, spaced
   600mm (24") O.C. perpendicular to joists. Channels overlapped at splice 38mm (1-1/2") and
   fastened to each joist with 63mm (8d) common nails. Minimum clearance of channels to walls,
   20mm (3/4"). Additional pieces 1500mm (60") long placed immediately adjacent to channels at
   end of joints of second layers; ends to extend 150mm (6") beyond each side of end joint.
7. Gypsum Wallboard: (Guide No. 40U18.23). 15.9mm (5/8") thick, 1200mm (48") wide. First layer
   of wallboard installed with long dimension perpendicular to joists and end joints of boards located
   at the joists. Nailed to joists with uncoated 63mm (8d) box nails spaced 180mm (7") O.C. All nails
   located 15mm (1/2") minimum distance from the edges and ends of the board. Second layer of
   wallboard secured to furring channels by 25mm (1") long wallboard screws. Second layer
   installed with long dimension perpendicular to the furring channels and centre line of boards
   located under a joist and so placed that the edge joint of this layer is not in alignment with the end
   joint of the first layer. Secured to furring channels with wallboard screws 300mm (12") O.C. with
   additional screws 75mm (3") from side joints. End joints of wallboard fastened at additional furring
   channels as shown in end-joint detail. All screws located 25mm (1") minimum distance from
   edges of boards.
   ATLANTIC GYPSUM, a division of the Lundrigans-Comstock Limited
   DOMTAR INC.
   GEORGIA PACIFIC CORPORATION
   WESTROC INDUSTRIES LIMITED
8. Wallboard screws: Type S Phillips self-drilling and self-tapping 25mm (1") long.
9. Joint System (not shown): Paper tape embedded in cementitious compound over joints and
   exposed nail heads covered with compound, with edges of compound feathered out.

(Reprinted by permission of Underwriters' Laboratories of Canada)

9

Fire Protection

Generally, for single layer application of gypsum wallboard, the maximum spacing of nails is 180mm (7") on centre for ceilings and 200mm (8") on centre for walls except that both spacings may be increased to 300mm (12") on centre if the nails are installed in pairs.

If screws are used, the spacing is permitted to be 300mm (12") on centre for either walls or ceilings, and for walls with studs spaced not more than 400mm (16") on centre, the screws can be spaced at 400mm (16") on centre.

The depth of penetration of the fastener is as important as the spacing in terms of the ability of the fastener to hold the membrane in place during a fire to provide the required fire resistance to the assembly. The minimum depth of penetration for nails and screws is 20mm (3/4") for walls required to have a fire-resistance rating.

If the fire-resistance rating is assigned on the basis of the component additive method, fastener penetration may need to be greater than for tested assemblies depending on the time assigned to the individual protective membranes by the calculation method. For ceilings, the minimum penetration varies depending upon the fire-resistance rating required for the assembly and ranges from 30 to 60mm (1-1/8" to 2-1/4") for 45 minute to 1-1/2 hour rated assemblies, respectively.

For situations not covered by the requirements of Part 9 or Appendix D of the NBCC, details on fasteners must comply with the requirements of CSA Standard A82.31 Gypsum Board Application. An example would be the requirements for double layer applications of gypsum wallboard.

Size of Structural Members

The issue of substitution of components in fire-rated assemblies was mentioned earlier as being critical for assessing whether or not an assembly has a fire-resistance rating that meets the minimum requirements of the NBCC.

The minimum size of the structural wood member permitted in a fire-rated assembly is also dependent on the source of the fire-resistance rating. The designer must verify that the member sizing is consistent with the fire-resistance rating design, and verify the structural integrity of the assembly.

Since a larger structural member will have more mass than a smaller member of the same material, the larger member can be substituted for a smaller structural member without affecting the fire-resistance rating. However, a smaller structural member cannot be substituted unless alternatives are permitted as specified in the listing or report for the tested assembly.

Listed floor and roof assembly designs specify the minimum sizes required for the floor or roof joists, in almost every case, a minimum depth of 235mm (10" nom.). The maximum depth of wood trusses or wood I-joists assemblies in the listed assemblies varies and is governed by the specific listing.

For assemblies assigned a fire-resistance rating by the Part 9 tables in the NBCC or by using the component additive method, wood joists must be a minimum size of 38 x 89mm (2" x 4" nom.). Metal plate connected wood trusses must have all components meeting these same minimum dimensions.

There is no minimum or maximum depth applied to parallel or pitched chord wood trusses. Trusses with metal webs and wood I-joists cannot be used with the assigned assembly or membrane ratings contained in the Supplement. The maximum spacing of the joists or trusses is typically 400mm (16") on centre unless specifically listed otherwise.

Spacing of Structural Members

The fire-resistance ratings attained by rated assemblies during testing are dependent upon member spacing because of the need for the gypsum wallboard support and fastening to remain intact for a certain length of time. Therefore, it is necessary to ensure that the design and installation of framing members meet the spacing requirements of the fire-rated assembly.

Depending on the source of the design, the members will be required to be at a specific spacing ranging from 300 to 600mm (12" to 24") on centre. The maximum spacings are listed in the test report or the tables contained in Part 9 or Appendix D of the *NBCC*. A closer spacing of the structural members will not usually reduce the assigned fire-resistance rating of the assembly.

Roof and Floor Fire-Resistance Ratings

It is necessary to ensure the continuity of any vertical fire separations required for public corridors or suite separations. As for floors, if an assembly rating is used for the roof, the vertical fire separations are required to penetrate the ceiling gypsum wallboard and extend to the underside of the roof deck. If a membrane rating is used, the vertical fire separations are permitted to end at the ceiling.

When a building is provided with an electrically supervised automatic sprinkler system, the *NBCC* permits the fire-resistance rating for a roof assembly to be waived. This in turn results in no fire-resistance rating being required for the loadbearing elements for the roof including the interior and exterior bearing walls unless a fire-resistance rating is otherwise required for spatial separation or suite separation purposes.

If a heavy timber roof assembly is used, provision of a supervised sprinkler system waives the need to comply with the minimum sizes for heavy timber structural elements such as beams and columns and for minimum roof deck dimensions.

For most unsprinklered residential buildings, no rating is required for the roof assembly. There also is no requirement for fire-resistance ratings on floor assemblies contained within dwelling units when there is no dwelling unit located above another unit. However, the continuity of the vertical fire separations between units and the provision of the required sound transmission ratings in residential construction require attention.

Wall Fire-Resistance Ratings

Walls and partitions are required to have a fire-resistance rating for many applications. These could include any of the following:

- public corridor walls

- walls of exit stairs

- walls of vertical shafts

- loadbearing walls which are supporting a fire-rated assembly

- exterior walls which are required to have a fire-resistance rating to satisfy the spatial separation requirements

Interior walls which are required to have a fire-resistance rating are required to have the same protective membranes, such as gypsum wallboard or plywood, installed on each side of the wood studs. This is required for several reasons. Typically, fire-tested assemblies are tested with symmetrical design with the same membrane on both sides of the wall.

In the case of assemblies assigned a rating on the basis of the component additive method, it is assumed that, except for exterior walls, symmetrical design will occur such that the same membrane will be provided on both sides of the wood studs.

In the Part 9 tables, listings are included of both symmetrical and non-symmetrical wall assemblies. The ratings listed are based on the weakest side being exposed to fire.

This is consistent with the assumption regarding the basic requirements of the *NBCC* for fire-resistance ratings for walls acting as fire separations. If the *NBCC* requires a room to be separated from the remainder of the floor area by a fire separation having a fire-resistance rating of 45 minutes, the fire separation must be designed and protected to provide that rating from either side because a fire can originate on either side.

9

Fire Protection

Special care is required to ensure continuity at jogs and intersections of vertical fire separations (Figure 9.12) which may occur, for example, at locations such as fire hose cabinets. Each face of the gypsum wallboard must be continuous for the entire height and length of the wall.

Vertical shafts for ductwork and elevators are required to be fire-rated by means of a shaft wall. Unless it is tested and listed without protection, both sides of the shaft wall must be taped and finished in the same manner as for interior partitions to provide protection to the fasteners and joints in a fire situation.

In some instances, interior walls or partitions may be required to have a fire-resistance rating where 12.7mm (1/2") regular gypsum wallboard would normally be used. For example, a wall in a residential building may be loadbearing and supporting a fire-rated floor and therefore be required to have a fire-resistance rating. The fire-resistance rating can be achieved with ordinary gypsum wallboard provided the rating is determined on the basis of a fire test, or as described in the tables in Part 9 of the NBCC.

For example, a loadbearing wood stud wall assembly with two layers of 12.7mm (1/2") ordinary gypsum wallboard on both sides is assigned a fire-resistance rating of 45 minutes which could be used to support a floor or roof assembly required to have a 45-minute fire-resistance rating.

If the wall were non-loadbearing, the assigned fire-resistance rating would be 1 hour. With this 1-hour rating, the wall assembly could be used as a suite separation/party wall in multi-storey residential units.

Loadbearing exterior walls are required to have a fire-resistance rating equal to or greater than that required for the assembly supported by the wall. In some cases, such as where the exterior wall supports a roof not required to have a rating, no rating would be required for the exterior wall unless a rating was needed to satisfy spatial separation requirements. Similarly, in post and beam construction where the main structural framing is loadbearing and the wall sections are not, the wood stud wall assembly would not have to have a fire-resistance rating unless required for spatial separation purposes.

The rating and the composition of exterior walls are based on resisting the spread of fire from the interior to the exterior. The NBCC does not require the wall to be rated from the exterior as any fire occurring on the outside of the building is expected to be much less severe than one from the inside. This requirement for the rating of exterior walls, from the inside only, applies to all cases, even when a fire-resistance rating is required for spatial separation purposes.

As such, a fire-resistance rating for an exterior wall is achieved by the use of protective membranes on the inside of the wall (Figure 9.13) in combination with various exterior claddings that are permitted either by the listing, or by the descriptions contained in the tables in Part 9 or in Appendix D of the NBCC.

The assigned ratings will range from 45 minutes to 1 hour depending on the interior membranes and exterior sheathing used. The sidings that are permitted vary and are not governed by the required fire-resistance rating. Where spatial separations are such that noncombustible cladding is required,

Figure 9.12
**Continuity
of wall fire
separation at
wall jogs**

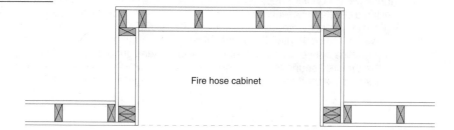

Fire hose cabinet

Figure 9.13
**Fire rated
exterior wall**

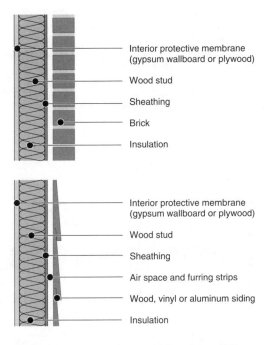

Interior protective membrane
(gypsum wallboard or plywood)

Wood stud

Sheathing

Brick

Insulation

Interior protective membrane
(gypsum wallboard or plywood)

Wood stud

Sheathing

Air space and furring strips

Wood, vinyl or aluminum siding

Insulation

Notes:
1. If the component additive method is used to assign a
   fire-resistance rating, 12.7mm (1/2") Type X gypsum
   wallboard gives a 45 minute rating and 15.9mm (5/8")
   Type X gives a 1 hour rating.

2. Insulation must conform to CSA A101-M, Thermal Insulation,
   Mineral Fibre, for Buildings, and have a mass of not less
   than $1.22kg/m^2$ of the wall surface.

this only affects the exterior finished siding, and not the use of wood studs or the sheathing beneath the siding.

**Fire-Resistance Ratings of
Loadbearing Elements**

Roof and floor assemblies required to have a fire-resistance rating must be supported by other assemblies or building elements having a fire-resistance rating which meets or exceeds the rating of the assembly they support (Figure 9.14) unless the *NBCC* permits mixed construction types.

For mixed construction options, there are provisions that require a combustible floor or roof assembly to have a fire-resistance rating or to be of heavy timber construction. In some cases these assemblies are permitted to be supported by unprotected noncombustible construction such as a steel beam or column. Similarly, a noncombustible floor assembly, such as a mezzanine, that is not required to have a fire-resistance rating in mixed construction can be supported by unrated combustible construction.

If a floor or roof assembly has a certain fire-resistance rating in excess of that required due to the use of components that inherently provide a higher rating, the supporting assemblies do not necessarily have to have the same high rating. The rating for the supporting assemblies is governed by what is required for the floor or roof assembly and not by what is actually provided for the floor or roof assembly. For example, where a floor or roof is required to have a 45-minute fire-resistance rating but is constructed to a rating of 1 hour, the supporting assemblies are permitted to have a 45-minute fire-resistance rating.

9
Fire Protection

The fire-resistance rating required for a supporting element in any storey is based on the fire resistance rating required for the assembly located within the same storey. For example, if the third floor of a three storey building is required to have a 1 hour fire-resistance rating and the second floor is required to have only a 45-minute rating, the loadbearing walls on the first floor supporting the second floor only need to have a fire-resistance rating of 45 minutes even though these walls also provide support for the third floor. The loadbearing walls on the second storey must provide a fire-resistance rating of 1 hour.

Figure 9.14
Support of rated floor and roof assemblies

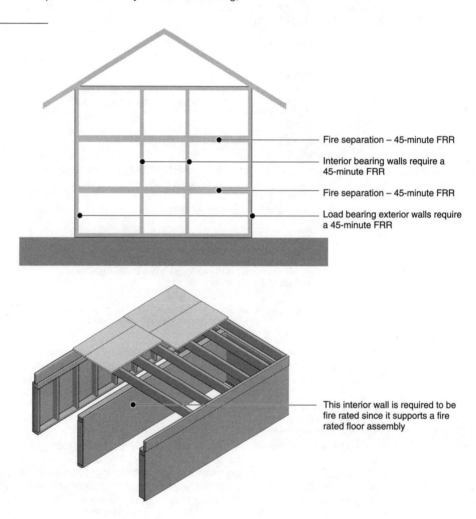

Fire separation – 45-minute FRR

Interior bearing walls require a 45-minute FRR

Fire separation – 45-minute FRR

Load bearing exterior walls require a 45-minute FRR

This interior wall is required to be fire rated since it supports a fire rated floor assembly

Note:
Interior and exterior load bearing walls on the upper storey are not required to be rated if the roof assembly does not require rating.

9.4 Service Equipment Openings and Penetrations

Introduction

Electrical and mechanical services often cross through building fire separations. To maintain the integrity of fire separations, the penetrations must be carefully designed and protection installed to prevent the passage of smoke and flame.

If the assembly being penetrated does not require a fire-resistance rating and the assembly is not a required fire separation, then the requirements described in this section for fire stopping, tight fitting, or protecting openings do not apply.

If the assembly is a fire separation not required to have a fire-resistance rating, only the requirements for tight fitting or fire stopping apply. The limits on outlet boxes, membrane openings and most combustible piping and electrical wires and cables not housed in noncombustible raceways would also not apply.

Conduit and Cables

Under certain conditions, conduits and cables can penetrate fire separations or any other assembly required to have a fire-resistance rating . For example, if wiring or conduit is tightly fitted or fire stopped, the integrity of the fire separation is not considered to be jeopardized (Figure 9.15).

For Part 9 buildings, generic fire stop materials such as mineral wool, gypsum plaster or Portland cement mortar can be used as fire stop materials to maintain the integrity of a fire separation penetrated by conduit or cables. For Part 3 buildings where a fire stop material is required to be used, it must be specifically tested and approved in accordance with ULC Standard CAN4-S115-M, *Standard Method of Fire Test of Firestop Systems*.

9

Fire Protection

Figure 9.15
Protection of floor and ceiling wire and cable penetrations

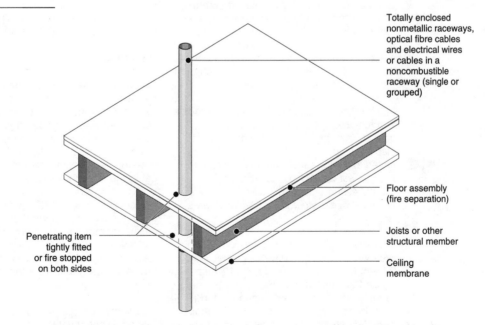

Totally enclosed nonmetallic raceways, optical fibre cables and electrical wires or cables in a noncombustible raceway (single or grouped)

Floor assembly (fire separation)

Joists or other structural member

Ceiling membrane

Penetrating item tightly fitted or fire stopped on both sides

Note:
If the wiring is not enclosed in a noncombustible raceway, the maximum diameter permitted is 25mm (1") with combustible insulation or jacket on the cables unless the assembly was tested with penetrating item.

Electrical wires and cables that are used in combustible construction must meet specific fire-performance criteria when tested in accordance with the vertical flame test specified in CSA Standard C22.2 No. 0.3, *Test Methods for Electrical Wires and Cables* or, if not tested, be enclosed on noncombustible raceways, totally enclosed nonmetallic raceways, masonry walls or concrete slabs.

Test Method for Electrical Wires and Cables

Most electrical wires and cables used in a building of wood-frame construction have combustible insulations or jackets and are not enclosed in a raceway. The *NBCC* contains special provisions for these types of services where wires and cables partly or wholly penetrate an assembly required to have a fire-resistance rating.

Totally enclosed nonmetallic raceways, optical fibre cables, and electrical wires and cables, either singles or grouped, not exceeding an overall diameter of 25mm (1") are permitted to penetrate a fire separation required to have a fire-resistance rating if they are tightly fitted or fire stopped even though they were not part of the test that established the fire-resistance rating of the assembly being penetrated.

In a building designed to Part 3 requirements and required to be of noncombustible construction, this combustible cable must also not char more than 1.5m (5') when tested in conformance with the *Vertical Flame Test-Cables in Cablethrough* in Clause 4.11.4 of the CSA Standard *C22.2 No. 0.3-M Test Method for Electrical wires and Cables.*

If they are not enclosed in noncombustible raceways, wires or cables or groups thereof that exceed the 25mm (1") diameter and that penetrate an assembly required to have a fire-resistance rating must be tested to prove that the fire stop materials and method of installation can maintain the required fire-resistance rating of the assembly.

Electrical Boxes, Receptacles, and Outlets

The penetration of an assembly required to have a fire-resistance rating by electric outlet boxes, switch boxes, light fixtures and similar equipment is addressed by the *NBCC.*

Electrical outlet boxes for switches, plugs or receptacles are permitted to penetrate a membrane in a fire separation if tightly fitted or fire stopped. Where outlet boxes occur on both sides of a fire separation such as in a wall in a residential suite to suite fire separation, the boxes must be offset to minimize the potential of direct fire spread across the wall. While the offset distance is not specified, good practice is to offset the boxes by at least one stud space.

If the outlet box is combustible and penetrates the membrane on a fire separation required to have a fire-resistance rating (Figure 9.16), the installation is required to meet the conditions previously noted and not to constitute an opening in the membrane exceeding 160cm^2 (25 in^2).

Duct Penetrations

There are several wood-frame floor and roof assemblies which are assigned a fire-resistance rating on the basis of a fire test conducted with duct openings present. The specific arrangements regarding size of openings, duct supports, duct material, and fire-stop flaps constructed must be identical to the tested arrangement.

Appendix D of the *NBCC* contains provisions for allowing penetrations of the ceiling membrane on combustible floor and roof assemblies which have been assigned a fire-resistance rating on the basis of the tables in Part 9 or the component additive method.

The duct openings permitted to penetrate these ceilings must lead to ducts constructed of sheet steel. Where the openings exceed 130cm^2 (20 in^2) in area,

Figure 9.16
**Electrical
outlets in fire
separations**

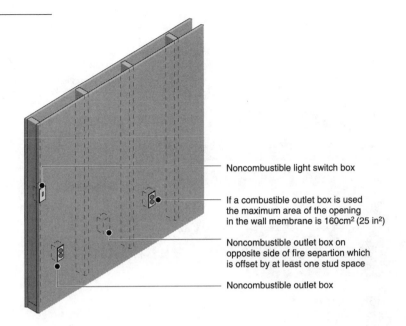

Noncombustible light switch box

If a combustible outlet box is used
the maximum area of the opening
in the wall membrane is 160cm² (25 in²)

Noncombustible outlet box on
opposite side of fire separtion which
is offset by at least one stud space

Noncombustible outlet box

the opening must be protected by a fire-stop flap or thermal protection above the duct. The requirements for this thermal protection and the arrangement of the fire-stop flap are described in Appendix D of the *NBCC*.

There are also limitations described regarding the number of openings and the maximum size of any opening provided in the membrane.

This provision allowing openings in a ceiling membrane leading to ducts also applies to assemblies that are assigned a membrane rating by the tables in Part 9, but it does not apply if the membrane rating is assigned as provided in the Appendix D of the *NBCC*. This further restriction in Appendix D of the *NBCC* is applied because the assigned fire-resistance rating is based totally on the type of ceiling membrane and not the entire assembly.

Pipe Penetrations

Piping that penetrates an assembly required to be a fire separation or an assembly required to have a fire-resistance

rating must be tightly fitted or be fire stopped to maintain the integrity of the fire separation. As well, where penetrating any assembly required to have a fire-resistance rating, the piping, with some exceptions, must be noncombustible or, when combustible, in some cases must have been included as part of the assembly that was tested.

For Part 3 buildings, combustible pipe used for water distribution other than piping for a fire sprinkler system can only penetrate a vertical fire separation if it is fire stopped with a listed fire stop having an F rating, and if the pipe does not exceed 30mm (1-1/4") in diameter (Figure 9.17).

For Part 9 buildings, a similar penetration is permitted to be either tightly fitted or fire stopped with one of the listed generic materials or a listed fire stop material.

Except for sprinkler piping or piping specifically tested and approved for such arrangements, water distribution piping made of combustible material cannot penetrate a horizontal assembly required to be a fire separation or required to have a fire-resistance rating.

Figure 9.17
**Penetrations
by combust-
ible water
distribution
piping**

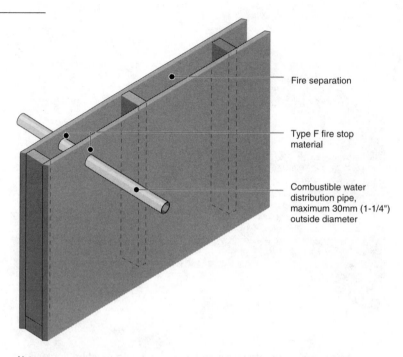

Fire separation

Type F fire stop
material

Combustible water
distribution pipe,
maximum 30mm (1-1/4")
outside diameter

Notes:
For Part 9 building; if the piping is tightly fitted, no fire stopping is required.
The maximum diameter does not apply if the assembly was tested with the piping.

The requirements for fire stop material around piping are somewhat similar to that noted earlier for electrical conduit and wire penetrations, in that for buildings constructed within Part 9 requirements, generic materials are permitted to be used for fire stopping. These include mineral wool, gypsum plaster or Portland cement mortar.

To meet Part 3 requirements, certain pipe penetrations are required to be fire stopped with materials which have passed the fire test in CAN4-S115-M, *Standard Method of Fire Tests of Firestop Systems*.

These fire stops are required to have an F rating to act as a barrier against the passage of flame. If the piping penetrates a firewall or a noncombustible fire separation above a parking garage designed and classified by the code as a separate building, the fire stop material is required to pass the same test and be assigned an FT rating to act as a barrier against the passage of flame, and to meet the temperature transmission criteria of the test.

Combustible sprinkler pipe can penetrate a required vertical or horizontal fire separation only if the fire compartments on both sides of the fire separation are sprinklered (Figures 9.18 and 9.19).

9

Fire Protection

Figure 9.18
Penetrations in vertical fire separation by combustible sprinkler piping

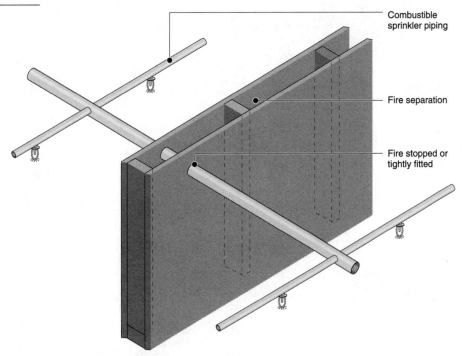

Combustible sprinkler piping

Fire separation

Fire stopped or tightly fitted

Note:
Penetration of a fire separation by combustible sprinkler piping is permitted if both sides of the fire separation are sprinklered.

Figure 9.19
Penetrations in horizontal fire separation by combustible sprinkler piping

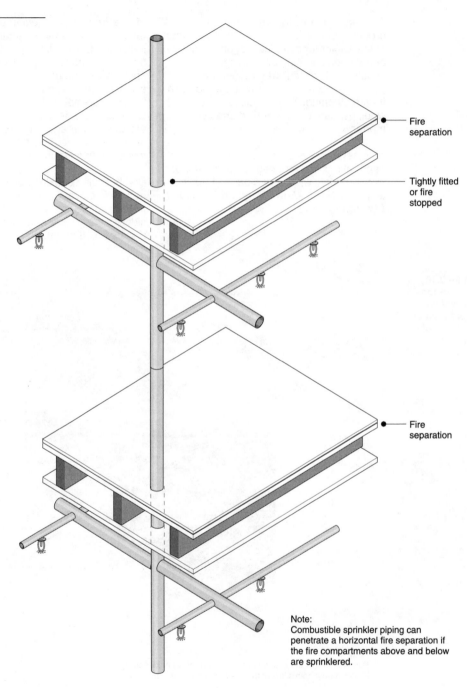

Fire separation

Tightly fitted or fire stopped

Fire separation

Note:
Combustible sprinkler piping can penetrate a horizontal fire separation if the fire compartments above and below are sprinklered.

9.5   Interior Finish

Introduction

In a fire situation, a significant amount of smoke and hot gases are released by the burning contents. These can eventually lead to flashover, a point in time in a fire where all combustible material in the room ignites. The interior finishes in a building, once ignited, can also generate smoke and fire gases and, depending on their flame-spread rating, result in the rapid spread of fire over the interior walls and ceilings.

Interior finish is the material which forms the interior surface of floors, walls, partitions and ceilings of every room, corridor and space. Some typical interior finish materials are:

- paint

- wallpaper

- paneling

- carpeting

- hardwood flooring

- tiles, marble and granite

- skylights

Except as noted later for high buildings, the NBCC requirements govern the use of interior finish materials on the basis of their assigned flame-spread rating so that the fire risk to the occupants of a building is controlled.

The limits on flame-spread rating and smoke-developed classification become more restrictive in areas of a building where the life safety risk is the greatest (such as in exits and public corridors) or where there are institutional occupancies.

The limits on interior finishes, especially for Part 3 buildings, are reduced if the building is provided with automatic sprinkler protection. This is done in recognition of the excellent record which automatic sprinkler systems have for controlling the spread of fire on interior surfaces and thereby controlling the amount of hot fire-gases and smoke produced.

Each of the finish materials listed at the start of this section have unique flame-spread and smoke-generation characteristics. The standard fire test used to assign these fire-test-response characteristics is called the tunnel test because it involves the use of a tunnel shaped furnace which is described in ULC Standard CAN/ULC-S102-M *Standard Method of Test for Surface Burning Characteristics of Building Materials and Assemblies* (refer to *Fire Safety Design in Buildings* for further information).

Code requirements

The *NBCC* does not regulate any finished flooring materials in Part 3 or Part 9 buildings on the basis of either their flame-spread rating or smoke-developed classification except when used in high buildings. Even in high buildings, untreated hardwood flooring is permitted to be used except for exit stairways, certain lobbies and service rooms.

The smoke-developed classification of any interior wall or ceiling finish is not regulated by the *NBCC* except for high buildings.

Most of the *NBCC* requirements for flame spread focus on the exposed surfaces of walls and ceilings, regardless of the thickness of the exposed material. If a material such as plywood is painted or covered with wallpaper or installed beneath another panel finish such as gypsum wallboard, the flame-spread rating limits of the *NBCC* apply to the paint, wallpaper, or gypsum wallboard and not to the plywood material.

In the case of paint or wallpaper, the manufacturer of a product must provide test data on the basis of a test using the finish on a plywood substrate. Depending on the type and thickness of paint or wallpaper used, a flame-spread rating may be able to be assigned on the basis of generic ratings.

The flame-spread rating requirements in Part 3 and Part 9 are generally limits on a surface flame-spread rating. However, if a building is governed by Part 3 and is required to be of noncombustible construction, the flame-spread rating limits also

9

Fire Protection

apply to any material that would be exposed by cutting through the material in any direction. Exceptions to this specific requirement apply for fire-retardant treated wood and heavy timber construction in sprinklered buildings.

This additional requirement for a homogeneous flame-spread rating still would not typically exclude ordinary untreated wood products, including plywood and oriented strandboard (OSB), from being used in large noncombustible buildings.

For most wood products, the natural wood is homogeneous throughout and therefore has the same burning characteristics on any surface that may be exposed. In the case of most plywoods and OSB, since they delaminate during the fire test in the tunnel, the assigned flame-spread rating determined in the test applies to any surface of the materials that may otherwise be exposed.

In both Part 3 and Part 9 buildings, the flame-spread rating requirements generally use 150 as the maximum limit, even in buildings required to be of noncombustible construction.

There are some exceptions. Most doors are permitted to have a flame-spread rating up to 200 except that no limit applies to doors located within a dwelling unit. For exits and public corridors, the flame-spread rating limits on wall and ceiling finishes are reduced to either 75 or 25 depending on the use of the building and whether the material is applied to a wall or a ceiling. Even in these more restrictive cases, there are provisions to permit 10 to 25% of the exposed surfaces to have a flame-spread rating up to 150.

Assigning Flame-Spread Ratings

It has been noted that fire-resistance ratings for wood assemblies can be assigned on a generic basis in lieu of testing. The same principle applies to determining the flame-spread rating of certain generic building materials that may be used as interior finishes for walls, floors and ceilings.

The building code requires a flame-spread rating to be determined on the basis of the average of three tests conducted in accordance with the ULC tunnel test.

Alternatively, the flame-spread rating can be based on the information contained in Appendix D of the *NBCC*.

Different interior finish materials are listed in the *NBCC* (Table 9.1) for which assigned values for flame-spread rating and smoke-developed classification are specified. Except for the noncombustible materials listed, there is a minimum thickness that must be met for each material in order for the assigned ratings to apply. If the thickness of the finish is less than that specified, the rating must be determined on the basis of a standard test.

Lumber having a minimum thickness of 16mm (5/8") is assigned a flame-spread rating of 150. (This is based on an extensive number of tests on different common softwood species.) The value for different plywoods at least 6mm (1/4") thick is also listed as 150 provided there is no cellulose resin overlay on the plywood.

The application of alkyd or latex paint or varnish not more than 1.3mm (1/20") thick, or one layer of cellulosic wallpaper will not affect these assigned values.

However, the values do not apply if shellac or lacquer finishes or other types or thicknesses of paints or wallpaper are used, in which cases, the manufacturer should provide test information for their products.

A number of tested flame-spread ratings for interior finishes are published both by ULC and Warnock Hersey. Many of the fire retardant treatments and coatings available are also published by these organizations.

A number of wood products have flame-spread rating values much less than the 150 which is assigned on a generic basis (Tables 9.2 and 9.3).

In some cases, the flame-spread rating is less than 75 which provides for a much broader application of the material as a finish. However, as noted earlier, most solid wood products can be used extensively in any case because most of them have a flame-spread rating equal to or less than the 150 limit applied to finishes in the majority of rooms and spaces in any building.

As far as specific test results are concerned, the designer should be aware of the differences between the Canadian and US versions of the tunnel test. For many materials such as wood based products and gypsum wallboard, the results of the tests are in essence, identical and the published values from results with either method should be interchangeable.

However, for material which will melt or drip or fall out of place when tested, such as is the case for some foam plastics, the results in the two tests can be significantly different. This is because in the US, all materials, including foam plastics are tested on the ceiling of the tunnel furnace. In Canada, such materials are tested on the floor of the tunnel furnace which results in significantly different assigned flame-spread ratings.

9

Fire Protection

Table 9.1
Assigned flame-spread ratings and smoke developed classifications in NBCC

Materials	Applicable standard	Minimum thickness mm	in.	Unfinished [3] FSR [4]	SDC [4]	Paint or varnish not more than 1.3mm (1/20") thick, cellulosic wallpaper not more than 1 layer FSR [4]	SDC [4]
Hardwood or softwood flooring [3]	–	–	–	300	300		
Gypsum wallboard	CSA A82.27	9.5	3/8	25	50	25	50
Lumber	None	16	5/8	150	300	150	300
Douglas fir plywood [1]	CSA O121	11	7/16	150	100	150	300
		6	1/4	150	100	150	300
Poplar plywood [1]	CSA O153	11	7/16	150	100	150	300
Plywood with spruce face veneer [1]	CSA O151	11	7/16	150	100	150	300
Fibreboard low density	CSA A247	11	7/16	> 150	100	150	300
Hardboard Type 1	CGSB-11.3	9	11/32	150	> 300	[2]	[2]
Standard		6	1/4	150	300	150	300
Particleboard	CAN3-O188.1	12.7	1/2	150	300	[2]	[2]
Waferboard	CAN3-O188.1	–	–	[2]	[2]	[2]	[2]

Notes:
1. The flame-spread ratings and smoke developed classifications shown are for those plywoods without a cellulose resin overlay.
2. Insufficient test information available.
3. Wood flooring unfinished or finished with a spar or urethane varnish coating.
4. FSR – Flame-Spread Rating; SDC – Smoke-Developed Classification
5. Gypsum wallboard complying with the following ASTM standards is also acceptable: ASTM C36, ASTM C442, ASTM C588, ASTM C630 & ASTM C931.
6. Flame-spread ratings and smoke developed classifications for paints and varnish are not applicable to shellac and lacquer.
7. Flame-spread ratings and smoke developed classifications for paints apply only to alkyd and latex paints.

Source: Appendix D, Section D-3, 1995 *NBCC*

Table 9.2
Flame-spread ratings and smoke developed classifications of solid wood products

Species [1]		Flame-spread ratings (FSR)	Smoke-developed classification (SDC)	Source
Birch	Yellow	105 to 110	–	UL [2]
Cedar	Western red	70	–	HPMA [3]
		73	98	CWC [4]
	Pacific coast yellow	78	90	CWC
Fir	Amabilis (pacific silver)	69	58	CWC
Fir	Douglas	70 to 100	–	UL
Hemlock	Western	60 to 75	–	UL
Maple	(flooring)	104	–	CWC
Oak	Red or white	100	100	UL
Pine	Eastern white	85	122	CWC
	Lodgepole	93	210	CWC
	Ponderosa	105 to 230	–	UL
	Red	142	229	CWC
	Western white	75	–	UL
Poplar		170 to 185	–	UL
Spruce	White	65	–	UL
	Sitka	74	74	CWC
	Western	100	–	UL
Walnut		130 to 140	–	UL
Shakes	Western red cedar	69	–	HPMA
Shingles	Western red cedar 12.5mm (1/2" actual)	49	–	HPMA

Notes:
1. Values listed are for lumber, 19mm (1" nom.) thickness, except as noted.
2. UL: Underwriters' Laboratory – UL527, May 1971, Test Report 645197
3. HPMA: Hardwood Plywood Manufacturers Association, Test Reports 202, 203, 335, 337, 592, 596.
4. CWC: Canadian Wood Council – *Fire Safety Design in Buildings*

Table 9.3
Flame-spread ratings for panel products

Product	Thickness mm	in.	Flame-spread rating [1]
Aspen plywood	6.4	1/4	196
Birch plywood	6.4	1/4	115 to 185
	4.8	3/16	170 to 190
	4.0	5/32	160 to 195
Cherry plywood	6.4	1/4	160
Hickory plywood	6.4	1/4	140
Lauan plywood	6.4	1/4	99 to 141
Maple plywood	6.4	1/4	155
Oak plywood	6.4	1/4	125 to 185
Pine plywood	6.4	1/4	120 to 140
Walnut plywood	6.4	1/4	138 to 160

Note:
1. Source: Hardwood Plywood Manufacturers Association

Fire Retardant Treated Wood

Fire retardant treated wood is a wood product that has been impregnated with fire-retardant chemicals under high pressure.

In buildings required to be of noncombustible construction, the *NBCC* requires that the limits on flame spread rating apply to any surface that may be exposed if the material is cut. Although fire retardant treatments typically do not penetrate through the entire thickness of the wood, fire retardant treated wood is exempted from this requirement.

Fire retardant treated wood is a specifically defined term which identifies wood that is pressure impregnated with fire-retardant chemicals and has a flame-spread rating not more than 25.

Surface applied fire-retardant coatings do not impregnate the wood and therefore do not fall under the exemption for fire retardant treated wood when used in buildings required to be of noncombustible construction.

Neither the pressure-impregnated product nor a product coated with fire-retardant chemicals is considered noncombustible within the terms of the *NBCC*. (Some authorities consider any material that has a flame-spread rating of 25 or less to be noncombustible.)

For buildings where combustible construction is permitted, both fire retardant treated or coated wood can be used in locations where the *NBCC* specifies a maximum flame-spread rating of 25.

When coating products are used, the required flame-spread rating can only be provided if the correct number of coatings have been applied as specified by the manufacturer. For this reason, the use of fire-retardant coatings requires diligent inspection of the application.

Fire retardant treated wood, such as plywood or lumber, must have been tested in the tunnel test to merit a flame-spread rating of 25 or less. The same testing requirements apply to fire-retardant coatings that are available today.

Information on both types of products are listed in ULC and Warnock Hersey publications. In the case of fire retardant treated wood products, a label or stamp must be affixed to each piece indicating the assigned flame-spread rating and, in some cases, the smoke developed classifications (Figure 9.20).

9

Fire Protection

Figure 9.20
Label markings for fire retardant treated lumber and plywood

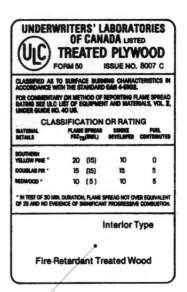

Manufactuer's name, address, and product name

9.6 Sprinkler Protection

Introduction

The installation of an automatic sprinkler system in a building enhances life safety for the building occupants. As well, protection of the property is enhanced to a point where a total loss of the property is highly unlikely except due to some unforeseeable problem. Many reports have been published on fire loss statistics showing a high success rate for sprinkler systems, with most reports approaching 95 to 98%.

The *NBCC* references three installation and design standards for automatic sprinklers published by the National Fire Protection Association (NFPA). The requirements that are discussed in this section are based on these standards:

- NFPA 13 *Standard For the Installation of Sprinkler Systems*

- NFPA 13R *Standard For the Installation of Sprinkler Systems in Residential Occupancies up to Four Stories in Height*

- NFPA 13D *Standard For the Installation of Sprinkler Systems in One- and Two-Family Dwellings and Mobile Homes*

The *NBCC* allows individual design standards to be used for individual types of buildings.

The requirements for sprinklers installed in residential properties differ extensively from those required by NFPA 13 as the residential standards are focused more toward life safety. The scope of 13R and 13D should be checked to determine where the standards can be applied.

The title of NFPA 13R refers to buildings up to four stories in height. This means stories in building height and not number of stories. If a building four stories in height also has a basement, this standard still applies.

If a building is protected with a sprinkler system designed and installed in accordance with whichever of the three referenced standards is applicable, the building is considered to be sprinklered under the *NBCC*. As a result, most of the options for the fire protection requirements that may otherwise be exempted or extended for a sprinklered building, such as increased building area or height, would be permitted.

In view of the excellent fire-loss record in spinklered buildings, many of the fire safety requirements of the *NBCC* are affected if a building is sprinklered. In all cases, the sprinkler system must be electrically supervised. This can result in significant advantages in designing and constructing the building.

- increased travel distance to exits permitted

- the area of unprotected openings in an exterior wall can be increased

- increased heights and areas of a building are permitted

- the need for fire-resistance ratings on roof assemblies and therefore the supports for the assembly are waived

- the need for the fire-resistance ratings on floors and mezzanines and their supports may be reduced or waived

- the access required for firefighting purposes, such as number of streets to be faced, can be reduced

- the use of heavy timbers, including the supports, in buildings of any area up to two storeys in height

The NBCC permits four-storey, sprinklered, wood-frame construction for Group C residential occupancies such as hotels and apartments, Group D occupancies such as offices, Group E occupancies such as retail shops and Group F, Division 2 & 3 occupancies such as factories, sawmills, labs and garages.

9

Fire Protection

In addition to the relaxation of many of the passive fire protection requirements in the *NBCC*, providing sprinkler protection may also result in a lowering of insurance costs especially for high risk occupancies such as Group B institutional and Group F1 industrial occupancies.

Provision of Sprinklers

Where automatic sprinkler protection is required by the *NBCC* to be provided in a building, the referenced standards generally require that the sprinkler protection be provided throughout the building. In a few cases, only a room or floor area may be required to be sprinklered.

If the entire building or floor space is required to be sprinklered, all occupied spaces such as offices, suites, bathrooms and storage rooms must be sprinklered. Concealed spaces within ceilings, shafts and stairwells which contain exposed combustible construction materials must also be sprinklered. (Depending on the type of construction and the occupancy of the building, there are a number of exceptions to this requirement some of which are discussed later.)

Complete automatic sprinkler protection throughout a building is required in most instances since fire-loss experience has shown that, if the fire starts in an unsprinklered occupied area of a sprinklered building, there is a potential for the fire to grow to a point where the severity of the fire exceeds the design capacity of the sprinklers. If a combustible concealed space is unsprinklered, a fire in the space could spread undetected and water from any operating sprinkler will not initially be directed onto the fire.

The balance of this section deals with the rules on positioning and installation of sprinklers and locations where deletion of sprinkler protection is permitted in buildings of wood-frame construction.

NFPA 13 has simplified the spacing, location and positioning rules for sprinklers. Two critical terms related to this are the definitions for obstructed

construction and unobstructed construction. These terms must be used to determine the design and installation requirements for all types of construction.

Specific examples of wood-frame construction such as wood joist, wood truss, wood bar joist, wood I-joist and heavy timber are summarized in the Appendix of the standard as examples of one or the other type of construction.

The rules for clearance to obstructions and distance a sprinkler deflector can be located below a roof, floor, deck or ceiling are also critical. The designer can most easily become familiar with these new provisions by referring to the latest edition of the *Automatic Sprinkler Systems Handbook* published by NFPA.

Concealed Spaces

NFPA 13 requires concealed spaces which are enclosed wholly or partly by exposed combustible construction to be provided with automatic sprinkler protection. If wood structural members are protected by gypsum board within the concealed space, it is not considered exposed combustible construction in the terms of this requirement.

There are situations where it is impractical and in some cases, when applying NFPA 13R and 13D, not necessary to provide sprinkler protection in many concealed spaces. The following describes several situations and conditions under which automatic sprinkler protection is not required.

Although these exceptions can result in many spaces within a wood-frame building being unsprinklered, it is the intent of the *NBCC* that the building is still classified as sprinklered in terms of the requirements and options for fire protection in the building.

For example, although a roof space may be unsprinklered because the ceiling is attached directly to the underside of wood joists, if the sprinkler system is electrically supervised, the fire-resistance rating for the roof assembly can be waived. This principle also applies when sprinkler protection for the roof space is waived in applying NFPA 13R, regardless of the type of roof assembly used on the building.

Double Joist or Stud Spaces

Separate ceiling joists and roof rafters are classified as obstructed construction.

Sprinklers do not have to be located in the space between the joists provided the space does not exceed 150mm (6") (Figure 9.21). Once the space exceeds 150mm (6"), sprinkler protection is required above the lower set of joists. If a ceiling is not installed on the lower set of joists, sprinklers must also be installed below the lower set except when the distance from the sprinkler deflector of the sprinklers on the upper line to the top of the lower set of joists exceeds 457mm (18"), in which case, no sprinklers are required below the lower set of joists.

Figure 9.21
Concealed spaces with double joist obstructions

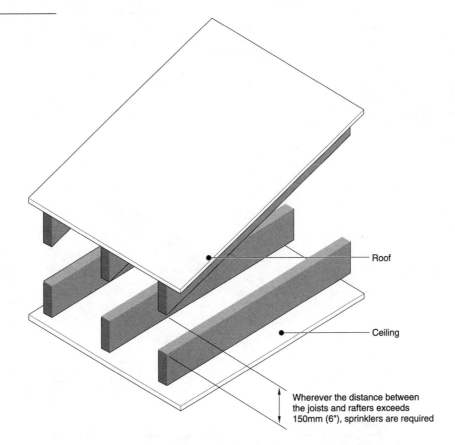

Roof

Ceiling

Wherever the distance between the joists and rafters exceeds 150mm (6"), sprinklers are required

Note:
If a ceiling is not installed below the joists, sprinklers may be required above and below the lower set of joists.

In a wall assembly that has two rows of studs, such as a party wall, no sprinklers are required in the concealed space if the space between the inner faces of the two rows of studs does not exceed 150mm (6").

9

Fire Protection

Wood Bar Joist and Truss Construction

Most wood bar joist and truss construction is considered unobstructed construction (Figure 9.22). With some wood bar joists and wood trusses, the webs could be wide enough for the spaced to be termed obstructed when less than 70% of the cross section area is open.

If wood bar joists are used in the construction of a floor or roof assembly, sprinkler protection is not required in the concealed spaces when the distance is less than 150mm (6") between the roof or floor deck and the ceiling. (Since it is unlikely that the concealed space will be less than the amount specified, suffice it to say that all bar joist spaces must be sprinklered). This applies to wood bar joists which are truss type members having top and bottom chords of wood not deeper than 89mm (4" nom.) and having metal webs for the diagonal and vertical members.

If the depth of the space exceeds this minimum for wood bar joist and in every case for wood trusses, sprinklers must be installed in the space. For these types of construction, the sprinklers in the space are permitted to be spaced on the basis of the requirements for unobstructed construction which allows a protection area per sprinkler of 21m^2 (225 ft^2).

Figure 9.22
Concealed spaces in wood bar joist construction

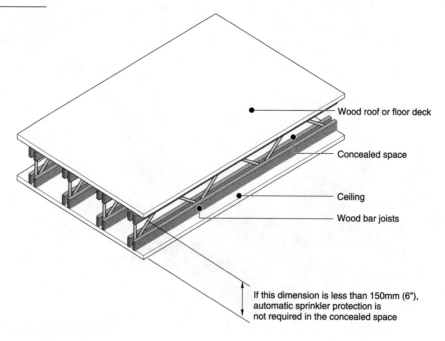

Wood roof or floor deck

Concealed space

Ceiling

Wood bar joists

If this dimension is less than 150mm (6"), automatic sprinkler protection is not required in the concealed space

Note:
If the structural members are wood trusses, sprinkler protection is required in every case (NFPA 13 only).

Wood Joist Construction

Wood joist construction is classified as obstructed construction if there is no ceiling attached or located below the joists. When a ceiling is attached directly to or within 150mm (6") of the underside of the wood joists, the concealed space created is not required to be sprinklered (Figures 9.23 and 9.24).

Sprinklers located below the ceiling would be spaced and positioned on the basis of the requirements for unobstructed construction. If the space were deeper than 150mm (6"), sprinklers in the concealed space would be spaced and positioned on the basis of the requirements for obstructed construction.

An option to sprinklering this space would be to fill the space up to the underside of the joists with noncombustible insulation (Figure 9.26). The insulation acts as a fire stop and as well, limits the available oxygen in the space thereby limiting fire growth.

Figure 9.23
Concealed spaces in wood joist construction

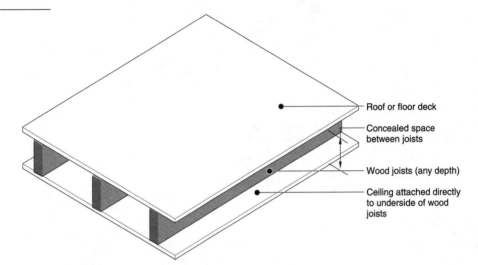

Roof or floor deck

Concealed space between joists

Wood joists (any depth)

Ceiling attached directly to underside of wood joists

9

Fire Protection

Note:
This concealed space is not required to be sprinklered.

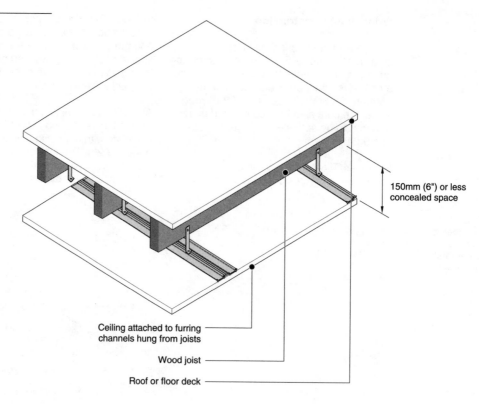

Figure 9.24
Concealed spaces in wood joist construction with dropped ceiling

150mm (6") or less concealed space

Ceiling attached to furring channels hung from joists

Wood joist

Roof or floor deck

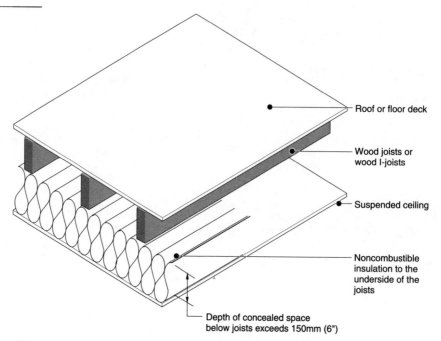

Figure 9.25
Insulated concealed joist spaces for waiving sprinkler protection

Roof or floor deck

Wood joists or wood I-joists

Suspended ceiling

Noncombustible insulation to the underside of the joists

Depth of concealed space below joists exceeds 150mm (6")

Note:
For wood I-joists, sprinklers or insulation are required regardless of depth of space.

Wood I-Joist Construction

Wood I-joist construction is considered by NFPA 13 to be obstructed construction if there is no ceiling attached or located below the joists. If a ceiling is attached directly to the underside of a wood I-joist assembly (Figure 9.26), automatic sprinkler protection is not required in this space if the spaces between the joists are fire stopped into volumes not exceeding 4.53m³ (160 ft³).

The material used for the fire stops for this specific purpose must be material at least equivalent to the webs of the wood I-joists. The sprinklers located below the ceiling are permitted to be spaced and positioned on the basis of the requirements for unobstructed construction. If the ceiling is not directly attached to the joist, the space between the ceiling and the bottom of the joist must be filled with noncombustible insulation (Figure 9.25) or be sprinklered.

Figure 9.26
Concealed spaces in wood I-Joist construction

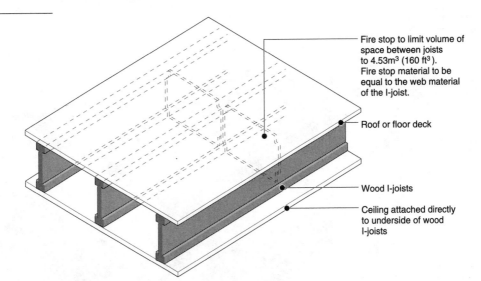

Fire stop to limit volume of space between joists to 4.53m³ (160 ft³). Fire stop material to be equal to the web material of the I-joist.

Roof or floor deck

Wood I-joists

Ceiling attached directly to underside of wood I-joists

Note:
This concealed space is not required to be sprinklered.

9

Fire Protection

Small Isolated Rooms

When there is a small isolated room such as a storage room or washroom whose area does not exceed 4.6m^2 (50 ft^2), the concealed ceiling space over the room is not required to be provided with automatic sprinkler protection (Figure 9.27).

However, automatic sprinkler protection is still required to be provided for the small room. This exception is allowed on the assumption that the walls of the room extend up to the underside of the wood subfloor or deck above thus effectively fire stopping the area above the small isolated room. This exception applies to any type of floor or roof construction.

Figure 9.27
Concealed spaces over small isolated rooms

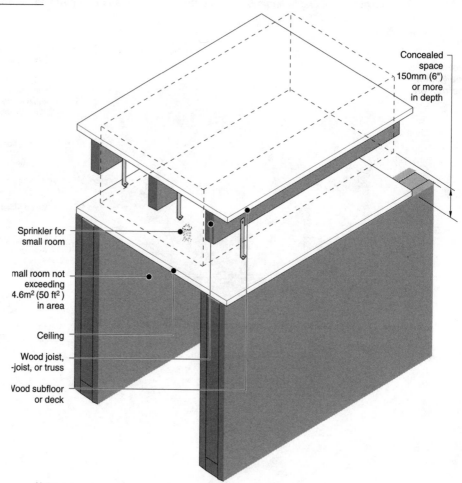

Concealed space 150mm (6") or more in depth

Sprinkler for small room

Small room not exceeding 4.6m^2 (50 ft^2) in area

Ceiling

Wood joist, -joist, or truss

Wood subfloor or deck

Note:
Dotted line indicates concealed space above small room which is not required to be sprinklered.

Attics, Roof Spaces, Floor and Ceiling Spaces, and Crawl Spaces

In buildings protected by a sprinkler system required to conform to NFPA 13, attics and other types of roof or floor spaces are required to be sprinklered unless the concealed space falls within one of the descriptions discussed earlier or the space is totally noncombustible.

In residential buildings protected by a sprinkler system permitted to conform to NFPA 13R and 13D, sprinkler protection is not required for attics, crawl spaces, floor and ceiling spaces, elevator shafts, penthouse equipment rooms, and other spaces that are not used or intended to be used for living purposes or storage. This exception applies regardless of the depth of the space or the type of ceiling that may be installed on the underside of the roof or floor assembly.

Limited Combustible Materials in Concealed Spaces

NFPA 13 does not require automatic sprinkler protection for concealed spaces when all exposed surfaces and construction materials within the space have a flame-spread rating of 25 or less.

This waives the requirements for sprinklering a concealed space if the wood structural components including the exposed deck or sub-floor are fire retardant treated wood. This also recognizes the use of gypsum wallboard as a finish within the space which can conceal all the combustible surfaces thereby negating the need for sprinklers in a concealed space.

Sprinkler Protection in Special Situations

In all three of the NFPA sprinkler standards referenced by the *NBCC*, there are exceptions to the requirements for sprinklers to be installed throughout the building. The previous section discussed examples of concealed spaces in buildings that are not required to be protected under certain cases when applying NFPA 13. This section covers several other special situations where sprinkler protection is not required. In some cases, these exceptions only apply for certain occupancies or for certain rooms or spaces in a building.

9

Fire Protection

Stairways

Sprinklers are required to be installed in all stairways which are of combustible construction (Figure 9.28) even if the stairs are sheathed on the underside with gypsum wallboard.

If the stair shaft and the stairs are of noncombustible construction, automatic sprinklers are only required to be installed at the top of the shaft and under the first landing above the bottom of the shaft (Figure 9.29). If the space under the stairs at the bottom is used for storage then sprinkler protection is required beneath the bottom landing as well.

Where a stair serves both sides of a fire-wall, sprinklers are required to be installed at that landing regardless of the construction of the stair in the shaft (Figure 9.30).

Figure 9.28
Sprinkler protection for combustible stairways

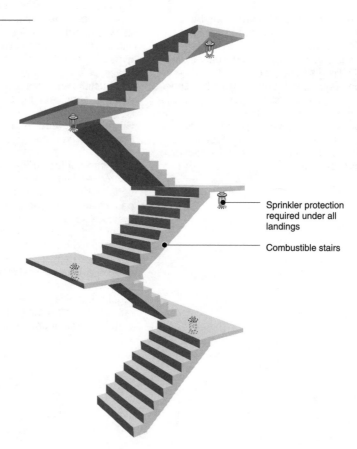

Sprinkler protection required under all landings

Combustible stairs

Note:
Depending on the length of the stairs, sprinklers may also be required on the underside of the stairway.

Figure 9.29
Sprinkler protection for noncombustible stairways

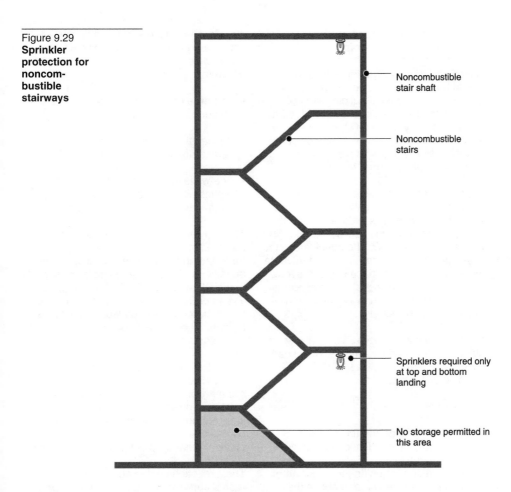

Noncombustible stair shaft

Noncombustible stairs

Sprinklers required only at top and bottom landing

No storage permitted in this area

Figure 9.30
Sprinkler protection for stairways serving two buildings

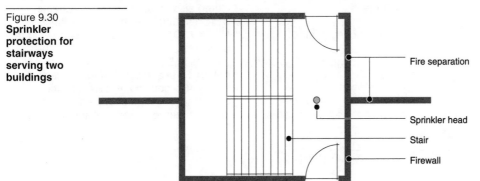

Fire separation

Sprinkler head

Stair

Firewall

Since this exit stair serves both sides of a fire wall, the stair is required to be sprinklered at each landing which serves both sides of the firewall

9

Fire Protection

Small Rooms or Spaces in Residential Construction

Based on fire loss experience in sprin-klered buildings, a number of rooms and spaces in a residential building are not required to be sprinklered. Experience has shown that very few fires start in these locations and any fire which may originate in such a space does not result in a high percentage of injuries or fatalities.

In some cases, the space in question is an area that would be subject to freezing therefore requiring the installation of a dry-pipe sprinkler system. This would result in a delay in operation for the sprinklers in the occupied space. If a separate system were installed just for the space subject to freez-ing, it would increase the cost significantly without necessarily an offsetting increase in the level of life safety.

NFPA 13 does not require automatic sprin-kler protection to be installed in small bath-rooms which are located within any dwelling unit provided the bathroom:

- does not exceed 5.1m^2 (55 ft^2) in area

- has walls and ceiling finished with noncombustible or limited combustible construction with a 15 minute thermal barrier rating including the provision of such finishes behind and above the bathroom fixtures

- is not located in nursing homes

- does not open directly onto public corri-dors or exitways

In addition, automatic sprinkler protection is not required to be provided in clothes closets, linen closets and pantries which are located within dwelling units in hotels and motels when the following conditions are met:

- the area of the room or space does not exceed 2.2m^2 (24 ft^2)

- the least dimension of the room or space does not exceed 0.9m (3 ft)

- the walls and ceiling of the room or space are surfaced with noncombustible or limited combustible materials

The provisions for the use of limited combustible materials as interior finishes for these applications is based upon the definition of limited combustible contained in the Standard, NFPA 220, *Standard on Types of Building Construction.* The use of these materials is intended to reduce the potential fuel for fire growth in the space if a fire should occur.

In addition to the above exceptions, in NFPA 13R, which applies to sprinkler systems for specific residential occupancies up to and including 4 stories in height, sprin-klers are not required in porches, balconies, corridors and stairs which are open to the outside, regardless of the construction type.

The exceptions noted above for small rooms and exterior spaces to be unsprin-klered also apply to sprinkler systems designed and installed in accordance with NFPA 13D. However, the requirement for noncombustible or limited combustible finishes in the unsprinklered bathroom do not apply. In addition to these exceptions, NFPA 13D does not require sprinkler protection in garages, open attached porches, carports and similar structures.

References

1. *Automatic Sprinkler Systems Handbook,* National Fire Protection Association, Quincy, MA, 1991

2. *Criteria for Use in Extension of Data From Fire Endurance Tests,* ULC Subject C263(e)-M88, Underwriters' Laboratories of Canada, Scarborough, ON, 1988

3. *Fire Resistance Design Manual* GA-600-92, Gypsum Association, 13th Edition, Washington, DC, 1992

4. *Gypsum Board Application,* CSA Standard A82.31-M1991, Canadian Standards Association, Toronto, ON

5. *Gypsum Board Products,* CSA A82.27, Canadian Standards Association, Toronto, ON, 1991

6. *List of Equipment and Materials Volume III on Fire-Resistance Ratings,* Underwriters' Laboratories of Canada, Scarborough, ON, 1993

7. *Standard Method of Fire Test of Firestop Systems,* ULC Standard CAN4-S115-M, Underwriters' Laboratories of Canada, Scarborough, ON, 1985

8. *Standard for the Installation of Sprinkler Systems,* NFPA 13, National Fire Protection Association, Quincy, MA, 1996

9. *Standard for the Installation of Sprinkler Systems in One- and Two-Family Dwellings and Mobile Homes,* NFPA 13D, National Fire Protection Association, Quincy, MA, 1996

10. *Standard for the Installation of Sprinkler Systems in Residential Occupancies up to Four Stories in Height,* NFPA 13R, National Fire Protection Association, Quincy, MA, 1996

11. *Standard Method of Test for Surface Burning Characteristics of Building Materials and Assemblies,* ULC Standard CAN/ULC-S102-M88, Underwriters' Laboratories of Canada, Scarborough, ON, 1988

12. *Standard Methods of Fire Endurance Tests of Building Construction and Materials,* CAN/ULC-S101-M89, Underwriters' Laboratories of Canada, Scarborough, ON, 1989

13. *Standard on Types of Building Construction,* NFPA 220, National Fire Protection Association, Quincy, MA, 1995

14. *Ten Rules of Fire Endurance Ratings,* T.Z. Harmathy, Fire Technology, Vol. 1, No. 2, National Fire Protection Association, Quincy, MA, May 1965

15. *Test Methods for Electrical Wires and Cables,* CSA Standard C22.2 No.0.3, Canadian Standards Association, Toronto, ON, 1992

16. *ULC List of Equipment and Materials, Volume I, General,* Underwriters' Laboratories of Canada, Scarborough, ON, 1993

17. *Warnock Hersey's Certification Listings,* Warnock Hersey, Mississauga, ON, 1996

18. *Fire Safety Design in Buildings,* Canadian Wood Council, Ottawa, ON, 1996

9

Fire Protection

Windows
and Doors

Casement windows are often used in combination with fixed windows to provide some ventilation while providing relatively high thermal efficiency for the entire window unit.

Careful fitting and the extension of the weather barrier around the window frame is necessary to reduce the possibility of water infiltration around doors and windows.

Final trim
conceals poly-
ethylene air and
vapour barrier
and batt insula-
tion between
the window
frame and wood
framing.

Left: Sheathing
paper must be
carefully applied
around open-
ings for
windows and
doors.

Right: Trim and
caulking
complete the
installation of an
exterior door.

Where window frames are inserted between columns in post and beam construction, particular care is required in caulking the joint to prevent air infiltration.

Gaps between window frames and framing must be filled with insulation and the polyethylene vapour barrier should span the gap and be caulked and stapled to the window frame.

Doors are often an attractive feature of the building and wood doors can provide an inviting look.

Top left:
Glazing is an important feature of building construction. Proper selection and installation is required to maximize the thermal efficiency.

Top right:
Framing around window and door openings must allow room for proper orientation and be capable of transferring vertical loads around the openings.

Bottom:
Condensation on windows may result from a combination of high humidity and low interior window temperature.

10.1   Windows and Doors

Introduction

Windows and doors are important features of buildings. Access, light, ventilation, and adornment are the attributes provided to building spaces by windows and doors. In addition to these positive features, windows and doors are also a weak link in terms of energy conservation. They are sources of potential significant heat loss, air infiltration and exfiltration, and condensation problems.

There are many types of windows and doors in many price ranges, styles, and modes of operation. The purpose of this chapter is to give basic information about the types of windows and doors, basic principles of heat loss through them, and information about the proper enclosure of a building envelope with these necessary features. Where applicable, particular information is provided for wood windows and doors.

In fire separations, windows and doors are openings which must not compromise the integrity of the fire separation. For information on this subject, refer to Chapter 9.

Window Types

There are five main types of windows (Figure 10.1). Four types are operating windows, meaning they can be opened and closed. The types of operating windows are:

- vertical sliding window

- horizontal sliding window

- awning window

- casement window

The fifth type of window is the fixed window which does not open.

The frames for windows are made of three different materials: wood, metal or vinyl, or a combination of the three. The method of closure and the construction determine how energy efficient the window is.

Vertical Sliding Window
The vertical sliding window is comprised of two glazed windows, one of which is fixed and the other which moves vertically. This is called a single hung window. The sash slides along the tracks in the side jamb of the window unit. In some cases, both of the sashes operate in which case the window is said to be double hung.

Horizontal Sliding Window
The horizontal sliding window operates in the same way as the vertical sliding window, except that it slides along the horizontal plane.

If only one sash opens, the window is single hung. In some cases both sashes open, and the window is said to be double hung.

Awning Window
The awning window is hinged horizontally across the top and swings out at the bottom. It has sliding tracks on either side to guide the operation. A crank apparatus on the side opposite the hinge is used to open and close the window. Newer versions of this type of window pivot on their side to swing out.

From an energy conservation perspective, awning windows are generally more effective than sliding windows. Often they are installed in combination with fixed windows to provide some ventilation capability.

Casement Window
Casement windows open by pivoting in the vertical plane.

Some casement windows pivot from a side-hinge, and recent models usually pivot around their centres. Like the awning window, the casement window is more energy efficient than the sliding window because more pressure can be applied to compress the window to the weather stripping.

Fixed Window
The fixed window, being inoperable, is the most airtight of all window types. It is often used to provide a large window area, but without the air leakage problems of a larger window that opens. The fixed unit is the most secure against forced entry, but cannot function as an emergency exit.

10

Windows and Doors

Figure 10.1
Basic types of windows

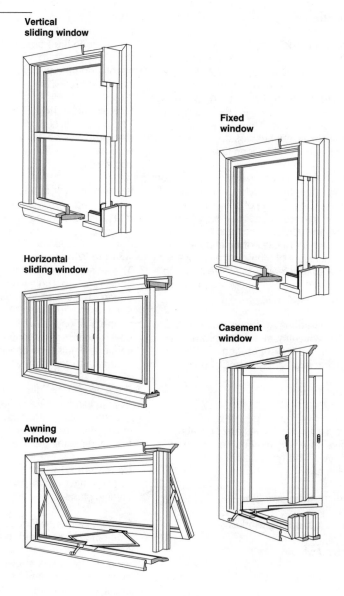

Vertical sliding window

Fixed window

Horizontal sliding window

Casement window

Awning window

Materials for Windows

Wood Windows
Of the materials commonly used for window frames, wood is the best natural insulator. Because wood is susceptible to deterioration as a result of moisture absorption, wood windows may be clad with pre-finished aluminum or vinyl to reduce maintenance requirements.

Metal Windows
Metal is a poor insulator and therefore metal window components conduct heat easily through the window frame making metal windows less energy efficient than wood windows.

To slow the transfer of heat from the interior of the metal frame to the exterior, a thermal break made of a good insulator such as plastic, rubber of wood is required. If there is no thermal break or if it is inefficient, condensation and icing may occur on the interior metal surfaces of the window.

Metal windows are usually prefinished with a baked-on enamel coating which endures a long time before requiring top coating.

Vinyl Windows
Vinyl is a better insulator than metal, but a poorer insulator than wood. Vinyl window components do not require a thermal break and the material is not susceptible to moisture damage or decay.

Combination Windows
Window frames are often constructed from a variety of materials so that the best characteristics of each can be combined to obtain the most energy efficient window.

A common combination window consists of a wood frame and sill, having an extruded aluminum sash and vinyl stop. The vinyl stop functions as a thermal break.

Standards for Windows

CAN/CSA-A440-M90, *Windows* is a single performance-oriented set of technical requirements for windows regardless of the construction material. The standard includes a window classification system, material and design requirements, glazing requirements, performance tests, and installation instructions.

All window designs are evaluated for:

- air leakage

- water leakage

- wind load resistance.

The classification system provides for three levels of performance so that the specifier can select the appropriate level of performance depending on the climatic conditions, height of installation, and type of building. In addition, storm windows and fixed windows have special performance ratings.

Air Leakage
The Canadian window standard rates windows according to their ability to resist air leakage as follows:

- A1 - for use primarily in low-rise residential (buildings of three storeys or less and having an area not exceeding 600m²), industrial, and light commercial use.

- A2 - for use primarily in medium- to high-rise residential, institutional and commercial use.

- A3 - for use in high-performance institutional and commercial applications.

Water Leakage
The Canadian window standard rates windows according to their ability to resist water leakage as follows:

- B1 - moderate climatic conditions

- B2 - severe climatic conditions

- B3 - extreme climatic conditions.

10

Windows and Doors

Wind Load Resistance

The Canadian window standard rates windows according to their ability to resist wind load as C1, C2, and C3. Refer to the standard for details.

Heat Loss Through Windows

Energy in the form of heat always moves from an area with a relatively high temperature to one having a lower temperature.

Like building insulating materials, the thermal efficiency of windows is quantified by the Resistance System International (RSI) value, the metric equivalent of the R-value. Materials that have a greater thermal resistance have a higher RSI value and are better insulators.

Heat transfers through windows by means of conduction, convection, radiation, and air leakage.

Conduction is the transmission of heat through the inner fabric of window materials. Convection is the heat transfer mechanism by which heat is transported by a fluid moving from one area to another. With windows, as warm room air moves down and across the window, it loses some of its heat to the glass and becomes cooler and heavier. The heat gained by the glass will continue to move right through the glass by the process of conduction since the air temperature of the air space of the window is cooler.

Radiation is the transfer of heat by electro-magnetic waves.

Conduction, convection and radiation are heat transfer mechanisms resulting from the transmission of heat from an area of relatively high temperature to one of relatively lower temperature. Air leakage is another type of heat transfer.

Table 10.1 illustrates the percentage of energy losses that are caused by both transmission and air leakage losses in typical Canadian buildings.

Air leakage causes the greatest amounts of heat lost through most windows. The amount of air leakage depends on condition and type (Figure 10.2 and Table 10.2).

Table 10.1
Sources of total annual space heating energy losses (typical values only) [1]

Type of building and location	Transmission losses (% of total losses)					Air exchange (% of total losses) infiltration exfiltration ventilation
	walls	ceilings	windows	doors	basement	
Uninsulated Bungalow						
Vancouver	23	7	6	1	19	46
Saskatoon	33	9	8	1	25	24
Toronto	30	9	8	1	24	30
Halifax	27	8	7	1	23	36
Insulated Bungalow						
Vancouver	19	7	9	1	12	53
Saskatoon	29	11	14	1	16	29
Toronto	26	10	13	1	16	35
Halifax	24	8	10	1	15	42

Notes:
1. Technical Bulletin No. 1, *Windows,* The National Energy Conservation Association (NECA), Winnipeg, MB

Figure 10.2
Air leakage rates for some types of windows

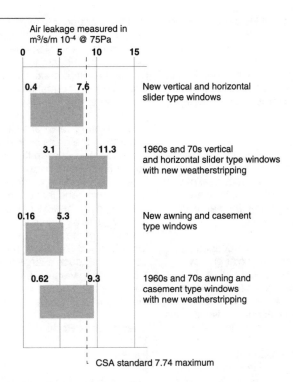

Air leakage measured in m³/s/m 10⁻⁴ @ 75Pa

0   5   10   15

0.4   7.6   New vertical and horizontal slider type windows

3.1   11.3   1960s and 70s vertical and horizontal slider type windows with new weatherstripping

0.16   5.3   New awning and casement type windows

0.62   9.3   1960s and 70s awning and casement type windows with new weatherstripping

CSA standard 7.74 maximum

Table 10.2
Air infiltration test results for windows

Window type	Air leakage rate (m³/s/m) x 10⁻⁴		
	High	Low	Average
Wood casement	5.33	0.16	1.45
Wood horizontal sliding	4.0	0.40	1.90
Wood awning window	4.8	0.34	1.89
Vinyl casement/awning	–	–	0.17

Source:
Technical Bulletin No. 1, *Windows,* The National Energy Conservation Association (NECA), Winnipeg, MB

10

Windows and Doors

The American Society of Heating, Refrigerating and Air-conditioning Engineers reports in its 1981 *Fundamentals Handbook* that windows and doors account for 6 to 22% of the total air leakage in retrofitted buildings. These numbers illustrate the relative importance of heat losses through windows in buildings.

Heat Gain Through Windows

While windows do allow a great deal of heat to escape from buildings, they are also capable of adding heat by means of solar radiation.

The net heat gain of windows, defined as the difference between the solar energy admitted through the window and its conduction heat losses, has been calculated by several agencies. A 1980 National Research Council of Canada study indicates that, in general, over the heating season single-glazed windows are found to be net losers of energy on all orientations, double-glazed are net energy gainers for south, southwest and southeast orientations, and triple-glazed windows extend the positive gains to the east and west orientations.

For south facing windows, a single-glazed window has a net energy gain only in early fall or late spring, a double-glazed window is a net gainer except for December and January for most Canadian locations, and a triple-glazed window has a net energy gain for each month of the heating season.

The full potential of the solar heat gain is usually diminished by partial shielding from curtains and blinds. For maximum thermal efficiency, windows should be shielded at sundown to reduce the speed of heat loss through the window, and the shielding should be removed when the sun is shining. One obvious problem with shielding windows is the increased potential for condensation on the glass, and this should be taken into account when shielding the window.

Windows are poor insulators even if they feature double glass with a thermal break in the frame. A single pane window loses 14 times more heat than an RSI 2.1 (R 12) wall of the same area. The double glass example with thermal break still loses 7.8 times more heat than the same wall.

The insulating value of a window does not come from the glass itself but rather from the air space between the two panes and the air films that cling to the glass. For a typical double pane window, for example, the air space and indoor and outdoor air films account for 96% of the RSI value of a window. The air space alone accounts for over 50% of the total. The panes account for only about 3%. Since the air space accounts for such a large percentage of the insulating value of the window, it becomes important to consider the width of the air space in the design of the window.

Energy Loss Reduction Through the Addition of Panes

The increase in thermal efficiency resulting from additional panes is shown in Table 10.3 (neglecting air leakage).

Replacing a double pane window having a single air space of 19mm (3/4") and a storm spaced 25 to 100mm (1" to 4") from the double window with a triple window having two air spaces of 12.7mm (1/2") results in an increase in energy loss since the RSI value of the triple pane is less than the double pane and storm combination.

However, replacing a double pane window having a single air space of 19mm (3/4") and a storm spaced 25 to 100mm (1" to 4") from the double windows with a triple pane window having two air spaces of 19mm gives only a small improvement in the RSI value of the window.

Table 10.3
Typical thermal resistance of windows [1]

Window type	Metal frame		Wood frame		Improvements (percent) compared to double pane base case	
	RSI	R	RSI	R	Metal frame	Wood frame
Single pane	0.15	0.8	0.17	1.0	–	–
Single pane with storm 25 to 100mm (1" to 4") air space	0.32	1.8	0.34	1.9	–	–
Double pane with 12.7mm (1/2") air space	0.27	1.6	0.34	1.8	base case	base case
Double pane with 19mm (3/4") air space	0.28	1.7	0.36	2.0	3.7	5.8
Double pane with 12.7mm (1/2") air space plus a storm space at 25 to 100mm (1" to 4")	0.44	2.4	0.51	2.8	63	50
Double pane with 19mm (3/4") air space plus a storm space at 25 to 100mm (1" to 4")	0.45	2.6	0.53	3.0	67	56
Triple pane with 12.7mm (1/2") air space	0.40	2.3	0.51	2.8	48	50
Triple pane with 19mm (3/4") air space	0.50	2.8	0.55	3.1	85	62
Triple pane with 12.7mm (1/2") air space plus a storm	0.41	2.3	0.52	2.9	52	53

Note:
1. Metal windows tested incorporate a thermal break.

10

Windows and Doors

The Thermal Resistance of Windows

The total thermal resistance of a window is the sum of its various components arranged in a series. Generally, the more layers there are in the series, the greater the total thermal resistance of the window.

Windows tend to lose heat through the sash, the frame and the glass. The material that each of these parts is made of will affect the heat loss through that part of the window.

Condensation on Windows

There are a number of conditions that can lead to condensation of water vapour on window panes. These include:

- high relative humidity in the building

- low insulating value of the window

- inadequate heating of the interior pane by the heating system

- leaky interior pane causing moist indoor air to strike the exterior pane.

- outdoor temperatures significantly below indoor temperatures.

- interior pane covered by curtains, blinds or other materials causing the temperature of the glass to drop

Condensation on windows usually occurs on the lower surface of glass since that area is always cooler than the upper part of the window due to convection currents of air keeping the upper portion warm. As the air moves down the window, it loses its heat to the glass and by the time it gets to the lower part of the glazing, it can no longer keep that part of the glass warm. Increasing the insulating value of the window can improve the resistance against potential condensation. This can be done by adding a storm window on the exterior or interior of the window.

The temperature and relative humidity at which condensation on windows might occur are shown in Table 10.4.

Whenever storm windows are added, it is important to ensure that the interior window is more resistant to air leakage than the exterior window or condensation problems are likely to occur between the interior and the exterior windows.

Condensation problems on windows can also be caused if the heating system is not keeping the glass area warm enough. Heating systems are designed to be installed along the interior perimeter of the house at the baseboards. This to ensure that the walls and windows (usually the coldest surface in the entire house) are kept warm and above the dew point of the air contained in the house. If the heating system is not allowed to blanket the walls

Table 10.4
Condensation conditions for glazing

Glazing system	Predicted temperature of inboard pane of glass		Indoor relative humidity to cause condensation
	°C	°F	
Single glazing 3mm (1/8") glass	-6	20	15%
Double glazing with 12mm (1/2") air space	8	47	45%
Low-e double glazing with 12mm (1/2") air space	11	52	53%
Triple glazing with 12mm (1/2") air space	11.5	53	55%
Low-e triple glazing with 12mm (1/2") air space	12	54	57%

Note:
1. Based on an indoor temperature of 20°C (70°F) and an outdoor temperature of -18°C (0°F) with a 25 kph (15 mph) wind.

and windows with warm air due to the placement of furniture, curtains, blinds, or any other obstacle, there is a good possibility that condensation will occur on the windows and perhaps even on extreme corners of the walls.

Condensation can also occur if some rooms are kept cooler than others, or if the temperature of the whole building is relatively low as might occur with a very low thermostat setting. Windows are designed with the assumption that the room air temperature of the living space is at or above 21°C (70°F). As the temperature of the air in the building is reduced, the surface temperature of the glass is also reduced since there is less heat available to the glass to keep it warm. Under these circumstances condensation is likely to occur even at low relative humidity levels in the house.

Condensation is one of the most annoying problems associated with windows, and is potentially one of the most serious causes of eventual window deterioration. It reduces visibility through the window, and can stain window parts, curtains and interior finishing. If the condition is allowed to persist, condensation can produce window mould, and can rot untreated wooden windows and their framing. Vinyl and aluminum windows are more resistant to rot, but if not suitably designed, are more prone to sash and frame condensation than wood is.

A shading coefficient describes how much infrared energy (heat) is transmitted by a glazing system. The amount of heat that can pass through a single pane of ordinary float glass is the benchmark when it comes to quantifying a window's shading ability. A clear single pane of glass has a rating of 1. Other glazing systems are compared to this standard and are numerically rated according to how much heat they allow to pass through. For example, clear double-glazing allows about 85% as much heat to pass through as does clear single-pane glass, so its shading coefficient is 0.85. Table 10.5 shows the relative cost of windows with differing thermal efficiencies.

A recent technological advance in glazing and window manufacture is the addition of a coating to the surfaces to reduce the amount of energy transmitted. So called low-e coatings reflect heat, while allowing the passage of visible light. Double-pane low-e glazings typically have a shading coefficient of 0.65, but some are lower. Low-e coatings require an airspace to work effectively and therefore they are used with multiple-pane windows. The coatings allow short-wave solar energy to pass through the glass into the living space where it is absorbed by floors, walls and furnishings. The energy is transformed and reradiated from these interior surfaces as long-wave (heat) energy. When the long-wave energy tries to escape through the low-e coated glass, about 90% of the reradiated heat is blocked.

10

Windows and Doors

Table 10.5 **Thermal efficiency and relative cost of windows**	Glazing system	Approximate R-value	Approximate relative cost
	Single glazing	1	.9
	Double glazing	1.5 to 2.0	1
	Triple glazing	2.5 to 3.0	1.15
	Low-e double glazing	3.0	1.1
	Low-e double glazing with argon fill	4.5	1.1
	Double glazing with low-e plastic interpanes	4.5	1.2
	Double glazing with low-e plastic interpane and argon fill	5.0	1.25

Note:
1. These approximate R-values are dependent upon the type of glass, the use of low-e coatings and the thickness of the interpane air space.

Manufacturers offer low-e windows having either coated glass or a coated plastic film suspended between the panes of glass in a window. In cold climates, low-e coatings reflect exterior heat away from the house in the summertime and retain heat during winter.

Several window manufacturers use argon gas between the panes in combination with low-e glass to further boost the thermal efficiency of double and triple pane windows.

Exterior Doors

Like windows, the energy efficiency of doors is determined by the types and thicknesses of materials used.

Exterior doors are usually constructed of either wood or metal, and have insulated cores. They can also have window panes for visibility or raised wood panels to add visual interest.

Many doors are made of a metal skin supported at its perimeter by a wood frame and packed with an insulation material at its core to increase thermal resistance.

The total thermal resistance of a door is dependent upon the various resistances of the materials from which it is constructed. The resistance for, say, a solid wooden door having the same thickness throughout, is determined using the same method as for windows. In some doors, the material and thickness of material varies across the total surface area of the door. As a result the resistance is not consistent for the total surface area. The RSI of this type of door is determined using a different method than that used to determine the RSI for solid core doors or windows.

Like windows, the thermal resistance of doors benefits from both an interior and exterior air film.

With windows, heat flows through a series of layers such as two panes of glass and the airspace between them. Resistance is consistent across the total area of the window. A typical wood panel door has two areas of construction: solid wood 44mm (1-3/4") thick over 50% of the total area, and 12.7mm (1/2") wood panels over the remaining 50% of this area.

The total thermal resistance of the door takes these percentages of the door surface into account as well as the resistance of each area.

The overall resistance of a door of solid wood, 44mm (1-3/4") thick with no panels is RSI = 0.57 (R 3.3).

The overall resistance of the same door with panels thinner than the rest of the door might be in the range of RSI = 0.4 (R 2.3). Therefore, the thinner wood panels lower the total resistance of the door.

Installation of Windows and Doors

Blocking installed at mid-height of a door frame between the wall studs, for two stud spaces on either side of the rough opening increases the stiffness and resistance to forced entry. However, if a rigid sheathing material such as plywood or oriented strandboard is nailed securely to the framing on both sides of the rough opening, this measure is not necessary.

To limit air leakage beneath the door sill, two parallel beads of caulking should be placed on the subfloor beneath the sill before its installation. Ensure that the top of the sill slopes downward toward the exterior and that it overhangs the exterior finish. The nosing of the sill should form a drip. If the sill is not designed to sit flat on the subfloor but is canted to the exterior, ensure that it is well supported along its entire length. The gap between the sill and the subfloor or subsill should be filled with insulation and the junction of the underside of the sill and the exterior finish caulked to prevent the entry of rain and snow. An air barrier is required at the interior to limit air leakage. This can be accomplished by caulking the junctions of the subfloor, sill, and moulding.

Rough openings for windows and doors should be made about 12.7mm (1/2") larger than the frame dimensions on the top and on both sides. This gap will compensate for slightly out-of-square rough openings and will provide space to insulate around the unit.

Leaving all temporary bracing in place, level the sill and block it into place with wood shims. Ensure that the unit is square and plumb.

Insert shims at regular intervals around the frame and at the locations of locks so that they contact the window or door frame across its entire width. If the pressure is not equal across the width of the frame, the frame may be distorted. Shims should not be installed between the head of the frame and the lintel unless so required by the design of the window (refer to the manu-facturer's instructions). Any deflection of the lintel transmits loads to the window or patio door frame and could affect service.

Figure 10.3
Sealing around window frame

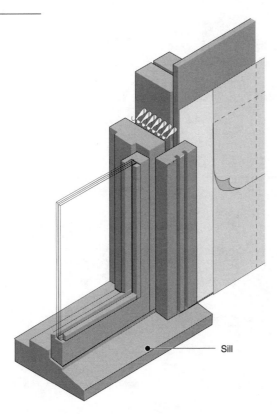

Sill

10

Windows and Doors

If insulation is to be installed on the exterior side of the wall framing, install wood furring of the same thickness as the insulation around the perimeter of the window frame (Figure 10.4). This will allow secure fastening of the exterior wall finish where it meets a window or patio door frame.

Continuity of Insulation, Air Barrier, and Vapour Barrier

Fill the space between the frame and the rough opening completely with an insulation material, such as glass fibre or mineral fibre. Single-component, polymeric foam insulation is available in aerosol containers and is very effective in reducing air leakage, but care should be taken to install the material exactly as the product's instructions direct. Most of these products are polyurethane foam which expands to many times its original volume during the curing process.

The leakage of moisture-laden air into the space between the door frame and the jack stud should be avoided. In cold weather, moisture will condense out of the air and remain in the space, wetting the insulation, the door frame, the trim and the building framing. Besides increasing heat loss, condensation can lead to the growth of mould, rotting of wood, paint failure, and the corrosion of fasteners.

Figure 10.4
Exterior sealing of openings for exterior rigid insulation

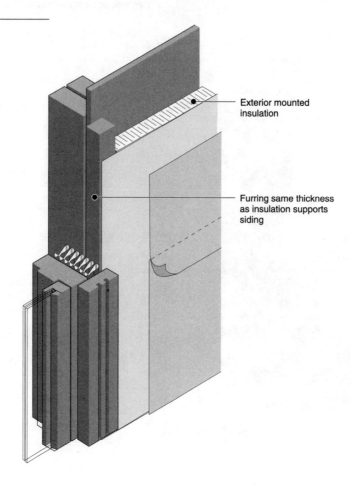

Exterior mounted insulation

Furring same thickness as insulation supports siding

Air leakage can be prevented in the area surrounding the window and door frame by installing a tightly fitting preformed foamed plastic gasket in the space or by ensuring that the vapour barrier material (usually polyethylene) is continuous and sealed tightly to the window or door frame (Figure 10.5).

This can be accomplished by applying a bead of caulking to the edge of the frame and compressing the polyethylene sheet between the frame and the interior trim. As the trim is not installed until some time

after the vapour barrier material, caulking should be applied at the finishing stage.

Before installing windows or doors, ensure continuity of the sheathing paper by fastening a strip of a breather-type sheathing paper over the sheathing or exterior-mounted insulation around the rough opening. Some recommend that the paper be returned around the opening to cover the edge of the sheathing and the framing members. Allow a sufficient width of paper to overlap the wall sheathing paper by at least 100mm (4").

Figure 10.5
Continuity of vapour barrier around openings

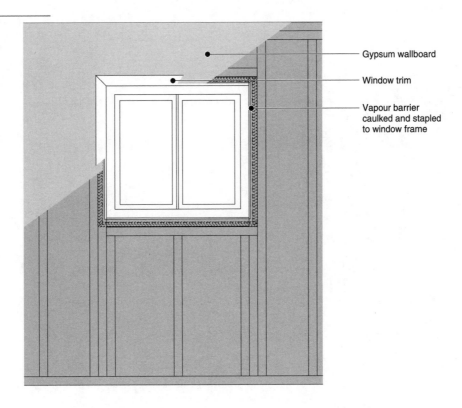

Gypsum wallboard

Window trim

Vapour barrier caulked and stapled to window frame

10

Windows and Doors

Checklist for
New Construction

11.1   General Information

To ensure quality is achieved in a project, good design must be followed by competent site inspection during construction. Information on good design practices for wood buildings was given in previous chapters.

This chapter is a checklist of verifications and procedures to be followed by the inspector. Where appropriate, reference is made to pertinent page and figure references, and in some cases, to other CWC publications. Some figures are provided showing how commonly encountered construction errors should be corrected. Topics are presented in the same order in which they occur in the book, as follows:

11.2   Wood Building Products

11.3   Wood-Frame Construction

11.4   Post and Beam Construction

11.5   Stairs and Guards

11.6   Thermal Insulation

11.7   Air, Vapour, and Weather Barriers

11.8   Sound Control

11.9   Fire Protection

11.10 Windows and Doors

Proper storage of wood materials is an important aspect of quality construction.

11.2   Wood Building Products

Lumber and timber
(Section 2.3)

Species
Engineering properties vary with species. For critical members, supply of specific species will affect performance. Check the grade stamp to verify species. S-P-F is the most common Canadian species and the most commonly used in construction.

Grade
Verify that the grade of material supplied meets the project requirements.

Moisture
Installing dry lumber will reduce the incidence of shrinkage and consequent repair of drywall popping. Grade stamp should indicate either S-Dry (19% MC or less) or S-Grn (>19% MC) at time of surfacing. In either case, at the time of installation, the *NBCC* requires that lumber be 19% MC or less. Verify the moisture content of large consignments of lumber using a moisture meter.

Due to larger dimensions, timber cannot be kiln dried and therefore is often delivered to the site in green condition. To minimize shrinkage, order timber as far in advance as possible and after installation, let drying take place slowly by minimizing exposure to space heaters.

Storage
Store lumber and timber on level supports and under protective cover.

Glulam (Section 2.3)

Verify species, appearance grade, stress grade, and sizes upon receipt of material.

Store and install glulam with factory wrap intact as much as possible. Ensure metal connectors exposed during early stages of construction are coated so that rust stains are not transferred to the wood members.

At the time of erection, check that single-span bending members (f-E grade) are installed right side up.

Trusses (Sections 2.3, 3.3)

Handle trusses so that they are not stressed in their weak axis.

Visually inspect trusses to verify symmetrical plate location.

Store trusses flat and be careful when shifting from the flat to the upright position. Use spreader bars positioned so that the trusses remain straight while they are being lifted.

Wood I-joists, LVL, PSL
(Section 2.3)

Verify dimensions of these engineered products. Verify that the products delivered to the site have engineering values meeting or exceeding those specified.

Store these products under cover.

Panel products
(Section 2.3)

Verify grade and thickness of plywood and OSB panels delivered to the site. Store these products in the dry and take care to protect panel edges, particularly those with tongue and groove edges.

11

Checklist for New Construction

Residential wood-frame construction can be engineered to suit commercial applications.

11.3   Wood-Frame Construction

Floor Framing

Sheathing (Section 2.4)
Verify thickness and grade of sheathing material. Ensure a 3mm (1/8") gap is left between panels to allow for expansion (some tongue and groove panels are shaped to provide this gap automatically). Ensure floor panels are installed right side up and fasteners, gluing, and cross-bracing is done in accordance with the drawings and specifications.

Beam bearing
Check to ensure the beam bearing area on supporting walls and columns is the bearing area specified in the drawings. If a beam is not quite long enough to have adequate bearing areas, crushing of the wood in this region of the beam could result. To rectify the situation of inadequate bearing, the beam can either be replaced or the bearing length can be increased (Figure 11.1).

Figure 11.1
Correction for inadequate beam bearing

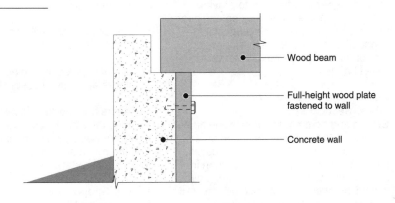

Wood beam

Full-height wood plate fastened to wall

Concrete wall

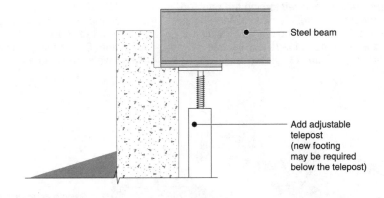

Steel beam

Add adjustable telepost (new footing may be required below the telepost)

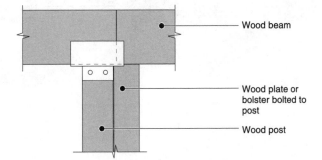

Wood beam

Wood plate or bolster bolted to post

Wood post

11

✓

Checklist for New Construction

Lateral support of beams (Sections 3.3 and 3.4)

Where the drawings indicate a requirement for lateral support of beams by joists or purlins, ensure that a good fit and connection is provided.

Proper size of beam and joist hangers (Section 3.4)

Check drawings and specifications to ensure proper sizes (capacity and fit) of beam and joist hangers are installed. It may be necessary to request the contractor or hanger manufacturer to provide design information sealed by an engineer to verify the suitability of a particular connection. Verify that the number and size of nails required have been used to install hangers.

Cutting and notching of joists (Section 3.3)

Cutting and notching of lumber and timber should only be done as indicated on the drawings. For wood I-joists and trusses, field cuts should only be made when in accordance with the manufacturer's directions. Damaged joists should be repaired by rerouting the electrical or plumbing services and then reinforcing the affected members by fastening new full-length joists alongside. It is also possible to install a header to transfer loads to adjacent members (Figure 11.2).

Proper installation of wood I-joists (Section 3.4)

Check for:

- cut or notched flanges

- incorrectly cut or located web holes

- missing web stiffeners at points of bearing

- lack of rim joists, blocking or cripples between joists supports below load bearing walls

- lack of blocking between cantilever joists at the support

- lack of cripples, filler blocks or backer blocks at points of concentrated loading

Stiffeners and blocking must be added if they are missing. Cut flanges and incorrectly cut webs require engineered repairs and the manufacturer should be consulted for recommendations.

Proper Support for Loadbearing Walls and Posts (Section 3.3)

Loadbearing walls and posts carry vertical loads from the floors and roofs down to the foundation. Check that load paths for load bearing walls and columns are continuous.

Figure 11.2
Correcting excessive joist notching

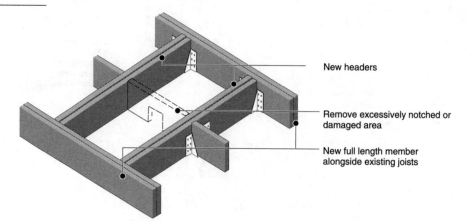

New headers

Remove excessively notched or damaged area

New full length member alongside existing joists

Loadbearing walls must line up over bearing walls on the lower level or be offset by no more than established allowable limits (Figure 3.10). Where the offset is larger, the floor joists must be reinforced to carry the additional load. Solid blocking should also be provided between joists in the floor space between bearing walls.

Posts must also be lined up over supporting posts or walls in the level below. Where a post does not have adequate support, the floor joists must be reinforced or a beam should be added below the post. Solid blocking should always be added between joists underneath posts (Figure 11.3).

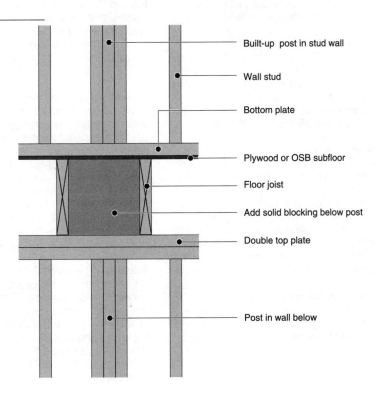

Figure 11.3
Correcting inadequate support for built-up post

Built-up post in stud wall

Wall stud

Bottom plate

Plywood or OSB subfloor

Floor joist

Add solid blocking below post

Double top plate

Post in wall below

11

✓

Checklist for New Construction

Wall Framing (Section 3.3)

Foundation Connection
Ensure diameter, spacing, and embedment of sill anchors, and the presence of specified washers. For engineered shearwalls, ensure that specified hold-down devices are provided. All nuts on anchor bolts and hold-down devices should be tight (and have washers) before walls are enclosed.

Top Plates
Cutting top plates of walls to allow plumbing or ductwork to pass from one level to another weakens the wall. Where this has occurred, the top plates should be tied together using steel straps running along the face of the plates (Figure 11.4).

Bracing
Ensure that walls are adequately braced during erection to withstand wind loads.

Shearwall Construction
Verify panel thickness, blocking requirements, framing species, and nail size and spacing at the outset. Ensure that, where required, hold-down devices are provided and are continuous across floor interfaces.

Diaphragm Construction
Verify panel thickness, blocking requirements, framing species, and nail size and spacing at the outset.

Roof Framing

Ceiling Ties for Rafters (Section 3.3)
Ensure that rafters are adequately tied to ceiling joists to prevent outward movement of the exterior walls.

Raised Rafters (Section 6.3)
Rafters that have been raised above the level of the wall plate to make room for extra insulation require full depth blocking between the joists to prevent rotation at the support (Figure 11.5).

Joists and Girders With Tapered End Cuts
Where the ends of ceiling joists or girders are to be tapered to match the profile of a pitched roof (Figure 11.6), ensure the length and depth of cut are within acceptable limits.

Tapered beams that are overstressed should be replaced or the length of bearing can be increased by fastening a ledger strip or providing other support inside the wall.

Sheathing (Section 3.3)
Ensure a 3mm (1/8") gap is left between panels to allow for expansion (some tongue and groove panels are shaped to provide this gap automatically). Verify thickness and grade of sheathing material. Ensure the specified fastening is used and that edge blocking or H-clips are installed if specified.

Figure 11.4
Repair of cut top plates

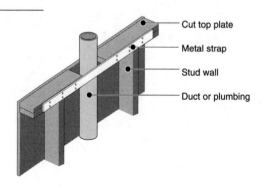

Cut top plate

Metal strap

Stud wall

Duct or plumbing

Figure 11.5
Blocking of raised rafters

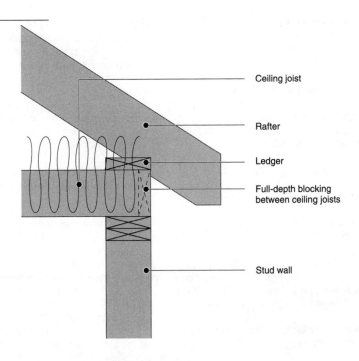

Ceiling joist

Rafter

Ledger

Full-depth blocking between ceiling joists

Stud wall

Figure 11.6
Acceptable taper cut for joists

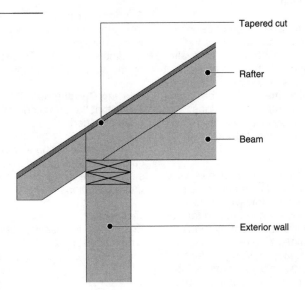

Tapered cut

Rafter

Beam

Exterior wall

Prefabricated Wood Trusses (Section 3.3)

Fabrication

Verify that the trusses have been fabricated in accordance with the shop drawings. This can be done by comparing the materials and the construction details indicated on the shop drawings with the trusses and checking for:

- correct member arrangement

- correct size and grade of lumber

- complete penetration of the truss plates into the wood

- correct size and gauge of truss plates by examining the identification symbols which must be present on plates wider than 76mm (3")

- use of S-Dry lumber if so specified on the shop drawings

- proper placement of plates

In cases where trusses have not been fabricated in accordance with the shop drawings, their suitability should be evaluated by an engineer. If the problem is serious, the trusses may have to be reinforced or new ones may have to be supplied. Reinforcing for connections generally consists of nailed plywood gussets which must be designed by an engineer.

Connector plates are fabricated in various thicknesses. Most joints are connected with 20-gauge plates. However, splices, heel joints, and joints on long-span trusses with wide on-centre spacing may require heavier gauge material to develop the necessary load capacity. Verifying that these heavier gauge plates were used is an extremely important part of the inspection.

Erection

Ensure that all trusses have been installed correctly and in the proper location as shown on the truss layout drawing by checking:

- temporary bracing which is the contractor's responsibility to provide in accordance with recommended practice of the Truss Plate Institute of Canada

- permanent bracing installed as indicated on the truss shop drawings

- permanent bracing must be anchored to walls or roof sheathing using diagonal braces (Figure 3.37)

Proper Orientation

Ensure that parallel chord trusses are installed right side up.

Girder Trusses

Check that multiple truss members, such as girders, are properly tied together as specified on the engineering drawings.

Sectional Trusses

Verify that long or very high trusses which have been delivered in sections are assembled using the field splice indicated on the structural drawings.

Bearing Conditions

Verify that the specified bearing length has been provided.

Interior partitions should not become casual bearings unless the truss and the structure are designed to accommodate these conditions.

Connection

Ensure that trusses are fastened to their supports as specified.

Permanent Wood Foundations

Drainage Layer (Section 3.3)
Ensure that the drainage system below and around the PWF is built according to drawings and specifications.

Proper Materials
Ensure that all of the lumber and plywood is marked to indicate that the material was produced by a certified treating plant and that it meets the CSA Standard for permanent wood foundations.

Cutting of PWF Studs
PWF studs should not be notched but may be cut to length in which case the treated ends should be placed down.

Framing at PWF Stair Openings
Ensure that the framing of stair openings within 1.2m (4') of a foundation sidewall and 1.8m (6') of a foundation end wall is strengthened to provide resistance to lateral earth pressure (Figure 11.7).

Fastening
Ensure that specified nail sizes and spacings are provided.

Framing Straps
Ensure that framing straps are installed to fasten the top of the foundation wall to the floor and are properly secured to studs and headers.

Wall Stability During Backfilling
Ensure that the floor system is in place before backfill commences. Place backfill in stages on all sides so that the lateral pressure is equal on all sides.

Moisture Protection
Ensure that the joints between the plywood sheathing are caulked and that the polyethylene moisture barrier is free from rips and tears that may allow moisture to collect against the plywood sheathing.

Detailed Inspections
Refer to *Permanent Wood Foudations* for detailed inspection information.

Figure 11.7
Strengthening of PWF stair openings

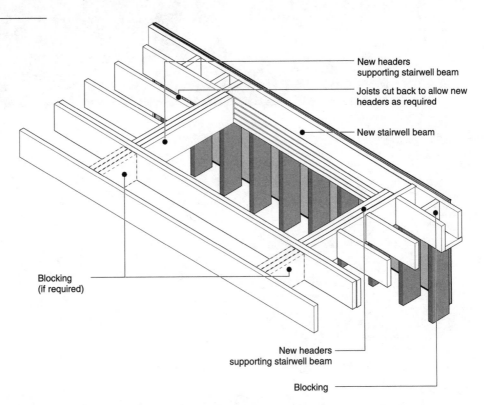

New headers supporting stairwell beam

Joists cut back to allow new headers as required

New stairwell beam

Blocking (if required)

New headers supporting stairwell beam

Blocking

11

✓

Checklist for New Construction

Large loads and large members are typical of post and beam and arch construction. Careful inspection of the elements is required.

11.4 Post and Beam Construction

Timber

Checking and Splitting (Section 2.3)

Some checking is to be expected. Verify that checks and splits do not exceed the limits outlined in the NLGA grading rules. If the defects exceed these limits, the member capacity should be evaluated and the member reinforced if required.

Glulam

Checking (Section 12.3)

Small checks should not affect strength but may affect the appearance of the member. If small checks are undesirable, they may be filled with wood filler after they have stabilized, and the surface refinished as required. The presence of end checks face extending deeper than 10 to 20% of the width of the member should be evaluated by an engineer.

Glulam Delamination (Section 12.3)

Delamination is a separation of the laminations through the glue. Even in a small area, delamination can be quite serious since it may indicate the presence of poorly bonded laminations. It is recommended that all delaminations in glulam be evaluated by a qualified timber engineer.

Seasoning checks in glulam are often found adjacent to the glue lines because of differential shrinkage between laminations. A check may be distinguished from delamination by the presence of wood fibres on both faces of the separation. If glue is present on both surfaces of the opening, delamination has occurred.

Proper Orientation (Section 2.3)

Ensure that f-E grade glulam beams are correctly oriented. The top edge should have a factory mark to indicate the correct direction of installation. If an f-E grade beam is installed upside down its strength will be reduced by about 50%. Therefore, the beam will have to be reoriented or be reinforced.

Plank Decking (Section 2.4)

The moisture content of decking should be checked prior to installation to ensure that it is about 15% or less. The use of higher moisture content material may cause the tongue and groove joints to become loose and result in gaps between the deck members.

Ensure that the specified installation patterns, especially for the controlled random pattern, are followed by the installer.

Bracing (Section 4.6)

Post and beam construction requires temporary bracing to ensure stability during construction. Ensure temporary bracing is adequate to withstand seasonal weather conditions.

Steel rod cross-bracing should be inspected for tightness.

Connections (Section 4.4)

Bolts

Check that the tolerances for connections is acceptable. Bolts should be checked for tightness.

Split Rings or Shear Plates

Before final tightening is done, check with a feeler gauge between members to ensure all split rings and shear plates have been installed.

Glulam Rivet Orientation

Ensure that glulam rivets are installed with the long axis of the head oriented parallel to the grain.

11

✓

Checklist for New Construction

The safe move-
ment of people
in normal and
emergency situ-
ations is an
important
consideration in
the develop-
ment of building
codes.

11.5 Stairs and Guards

Proper Support for Stair Stringers (Section 5.1)

Stair stringers should be supported at the top by a header and at the bottom by the floor. Both ends of each stringer should be adequately secured.

Stringers that are poorly fastened should have the top end connected to the header with nailed or bolted angles, or be supported by posts.

At the bottom, the stringers should be secured with a kicker plate or with angles fastened to the floor or slab (Figures 5.3 and 5.4).

Proper Guard Construction (Section 5.1)

Guards must be constructed so that the clear space between balusters is less than 100mm (4") in residential buildings or buildings where children are likely to be present, and less than 200mm (8") in other buildings. Where the space is too large, extra balusters must be added.

Construction of guards should be inspected closely. Guards should have rigid vertical support members installed with anchorages sufficient to prevent the railing from moving sideways. The rail, balusters and anchorages must be capable of supporting the loads prescribed in Part 4 of the 1995 *NBCC*.

11

✓

Checklist for New Construction

Increasing
energy costs
are resulting in
buildings with
increasing
levels of insula-
tion.

11.6   Thermal Insulation

Batt Insulation (Section 6.2)

Ensure that batt insulation is kept dry during installation. Batt insulation should fill the cavity without cramming.

Loose Fill Insulation (Section 6.2)

Verify that loose fill insulation is installed to the density recommended by the manufacturer and only in those locations indicated in the contract documents.

Ensure that insulation does not block air vents in the soffits and the ventilation path between roof rafters.

Rigid Panel Insulation (Section 6.2)

Adhesives and all chemicals in contact with rigid insulation should be approved by the product manufacturer before use. When using adhesives to affix panels with adhesive, apply the beads in a grid pattern to block air convection currents behind the panels.

Verify that the rigid insulation provided is the type specified.

Spray Type Insulation (Section 6.2)

Verify installation procedure to ensure that spray type insulations completely fill the cavity without causing bulging of sheathing and finish panels.

Thermal Bridging (Section 6.3)

Ensure that details shown on the drawings are installed in areas where framing interrupts the normal provision of RSI (R) value such as at wall intersection.

Where special measures such as external thermal sheathing or double walls have been specified to prevent thermal bridging, ensure that the construction meets the intent of the design.

Attics and Ceilings

Roofs with Attic Spaces (Section 6.3)

Ensure that the ventilation specified is provided. Ensure that there is insulation and ventilation at the exterior walls to prevent ice damming.

Cathedral Ceilings and Low Sloped Roofs (Section 6.3)

When the insulation is placed below the roof sheathing, ensure cross purlins not less than 38 x 38mm are applied to the top of the roof joists. The cross purlins may be omitted if each joist space is individually vented.

A minimum clearance of 63mm (2.5") must be provided between the top of the insulation and the underside of the roof sheathing.

Required vents must be distributed uniformly on opposite sides of the building so that at least 25% of the ventilated area is at the upper part of the roof, and at least 25% is at the lower part of the roof.

Ventilation (Section 6.3)

Ensure that the required ventilation is provided to the attic space and that soffit vents are unobstructed.

11

Checklist for New Construction

Attention to detail is required to ensure that air, vapour, and weather barriers provide the protection required

11.7   Air, Vapour, and Weather Barriers

Air/Vapour Barriers
(Section 7.2)

Where a polyethylene membrane is used as an air/vapour barrier, verify:

- pre-installation of polyethylene barrier strips above and around partition walls to provide continuity for the ceiling air/vapour barrier and behind electrical boxes and around windows and doors for continuity of the wall air/vapour barrier

- monitor installation of the polyethylene barrier sheet, caulk joints, and repair tears

Weather Barriers
(Section 7.2)

Apply the specified wall sheathing paper or wrap as soon as possible after sheathing to provide a degree of protection to the framing from precipitation. Ensure the method of attachment is adequate for the severe conditions prior to the installation of cladding.

Rainscreen (Section 7.3)

If a rainscreen has been specified, verify the spacing of furring strips and the provision of drain holes where the furring strips are to be installed horizontally.

Wood Cladding Products
(Section 7.4)

Wood Siding
Verify the grade and type of siding supplied to the site and examine for moisture content. Ensure major defects falling outside the limits of the grade are trimmed. Encourage the application of stain before installation to avoid unfinished strips from showing if shrinkage occurs. Ensure proper overlap and drip notching around window and door sills to shed water away from the siding.

Ensure that the nailing pattern used will allow dimensional change without splitting the siding.

Install prefinished wood siding in accordance with the specifications so that the manufacturer's warranty will be enforceable.

Shingles and Shakes
Verify shingle and shake grade and exposure length for each application with the specifications.

Softwood Plywood
Verify grade and surface texture. Ensure protection of end grain by painting or with batten strips.

Oriented Strandboard
Panels
Apply prefinished OSB panels and siding in accordance with the specifications so that the manufacturer's warranty will be enforceable.

11

✓

Checklist for New Construction

Sound control is important in many types of occupancies. Wood-frame construction is well suited to the provision of effective and lightweight sound control measures.

11.8   Sound Control

STC Rating (Section 8.2)

Verify the STC ratings required for various assemblies and ensure that construction meets the requirements especially for fastenings. Verify installation of sound absorbing isolation, double assemblies, and staggering of wood studs.

Penetrations (Section 8.3)

Where building services pass through assemblies, ensure that sound isolation is provided by insulating and using acoustical sealants.

Testing (Section 8.2)

To verify the performance of a partition in the field, the ASTM-E336 test can be used. The results are comparable to the STC ratings resulting from laboratory tests.

Wood-Frame Assemblies (Section 8.3)

To ensure the specified STC rating is constructed, verify that:

- the absorptive material, if specified, fills at least three-quarters of the wall cavity

- gypsum wallboard is taped and patched

- where gypsum wallboard is doubled, joints are staggered

Electrical Outlets (Pg. 285)

Check to ensure that electrical outlets or fixtures are not installed back to back. They should be staggered a minimum of 610mm (2') and more where possible.

Resilient Channels (Section 8.3)

Where resilient channels have been specified to reduce the effect of sound transfer through framed members by damping vibration in the wall sheathing, ensure that the gypsum wallboard fasteners do not touch the framing members.

Impact Noise (Section 8.2)

Where specified, ensure there is discontinuity in joists which span corridors and living or office areas.

Double Walls (Section 8.3)

Where a double frame wall has been specified, ensure that there is no mechanical connection or blocking that connects the double wall framing (plumbing and fixtures should be installed and fastened to only one side).

11

✓

Checklist for New Construction

Many types of buildings, including this fire station, can be built of wood while meeting the same requirements for life safety demanded of noncombustible materials.

11.9   Fire Protection

Fire Stopping (Section 9.2)

Materials
Verify that fire stops are adequate by checking:

- thickness and type of material

- correct support of fire stop materials

- protection of openings through fire separations

- protection of openings through assemblies required to have a fire-resistance rating

Locations
Check particularly for fire stops in:

- crawl spaces

- exterior mansard style roofs, soffits, balconies and canopies

- concealed spaces such as floor, ceiling and roof assemblies and attics

- coved ceilings, dropped ceilings, soffits and stairways

Walls
Ensure fire stops are provided at the following locations within concealed spaces in walls or partitions:

- at every floor level

- at every ceiling level where the ceiling forms part of an assembly required to have a fire-resistance rating

- where the horizontal dimension in the space exceeds 20m (65')

- where the maximum vertical dimension in the space is more than 3m (10')

Fire-Resistance Ratings (Section 9.3)

Type
Ascertain from the drawings whether fire-resistance ratings for floor, wall and roof assemblies have been designed on the basis of test rated assemblies or the component additive method using generic materials.

Tested Assemblies
Where the projects documents specify tested assemblies, ensure that the specified ratings are provided by checking:

- spacing and size of studs, joists or trusses

- type and thickness of gypsum wallboard

- suitability of the gypsum wallboard by examining the manufacturer's stamp indicating the ULC or other testing agency's assemblies for which the panels are suited

- fastener type and spacing and taping and patching of gypsum wallboard

Component Additive Assemblies
Where the component additive method or Part 9 tables have been used to provide fire-resistance ratings, ensure that the material thicknesses and types are those specified, and know whether or not the fire-resistance rating is an assembly rating or a membrane rating so that small openings are properly treated.

Continuity (Section 9.4)
Check to ensure that fire separations are continuous. Check to ensure that the fire separation cannot be bypassed. Ensure that holes and penetrations in fire separations due to service equipment such as pipes and ducts or improper construction are fire stopped with the appropriate materials.

11

Checklist for New Construction

Ensure that openings such as doorways are protected by the proper operation of fire rated doors with self-closing devices, and openings for heating and ventilating ductwork by fire dampers with fusible links.

Where electric outlet boxes occur on both sides of a fire separation such as in a wall in a residential suite to suite fire separation, ensure that the boxes are offset at least one stud space.

Ensure that piping that penetrates an assembly required to have a fire-resistance rating is tightly fitted or fire stopped to maintain the integrity of the fire separation. As well, the piping, with some exceptions, must be noncombustible or, if combustible, must have been included as part of the assembly that was tested.

Interior Finish (Section 9.5)

Flame-Spread Rating

Where the specifications restrict the material used for interior finish on the basis of flame-spread, check stamps or labels to ensure the material supplied to the site meets the design requirements.

Fire-Retardant Treated Wood

Where fire-retardant treated wood or plywood has been specified for areas where the maximum flame-spread rating permitted is 25, verify the ULC or other label on the product certifying its suitability for such applications.

Fire Retardant Coatings

The required flame-spread rating can only be provided if the correct number of coatings have been applied as specified by the manufacturer. Check for surface preparation, application temperature, and amount of coating actually used to ensure the prescribed degree of protection is provided.

Sprinkler Protection
(Section 9.6)

Provision of Sprinklers
Where automatic sprinkler protection has been specified for a building, ensure that all areas are serviced with sprinklers.

Concealed Spaces
Ensure that concealed spaces which are enclosed wholly or partly by exposed combustible construction are provided with sprinklers. Sprinklers may not be required when spaces are within certain limits, when the space is filled with insulation, for small isolated rooms of a certain size, in spaces where the flame-spread rating of the materials is 25 or less, or in certain areas of living units.

Placement
Ensure that sprinklers are located in such a way that each sprinkler head is capable of a full area of distribution of water.

Ensure that sprinklers located in open spaces between trusses or open web steel joists meet the requirements of NFPA 13 in terms of minimizing spray disruption from the chords and webs of structural members.

11

Checklist for New Construction

Windows and doors brighten and decorate living and work spaces. Proper installation is important especially for service and energy conservation.

11.10   Windows and Doors

**Windows and Doors
(Section 10.1)**

Verify:

- delivery to the site of the windows and doors specified

- careful storage and handling of units

- proper framing around openings for windows and doors

- proper vapour and air sealing around windows and doors

11

✓

Checklist for New Construction

Inspection, Repair, and Upgrading of Existing Structures

Beam overload has caused a collapse. To repair this failure, the joists will be supported, and the broken beam will be replaced with a new one.

Leakage around a roof drain has caused deterioration of some wood members. The leakage must be stopped to arrest decay, and splices applied to damaged members to strengthen them.

Poor placement of truss plates during fabrication is resulting in a gradual failure of this truss system. This type of deficiency should have been noticed during construction inspection. Repair of the trusses after the fact will involve the adding of plywood gusset plates engineered to provide the required strength.

The collapse of an adjacent building has caused a portion of these trusses to fail. Repair will include spliced top chords, new webs, and the use of plywood gusset plates to restore load transfer between webs and chords.

This is a tension failure in the web of a rod-and-block truss. Repair will involve shoring the truss to realign it, and repairing the failed area with epoxies.

A glueline failure in the bottom laminations of a glulam beam should be assessed by an engineer. Repair will be made by inserting epoxy coated dowels and drill holes will be concealed with wood plugs.

Contact with the ground has resulted in decay of the base of the exterior arch supports. Repair *(below)* required the removal of unsound wood, raising the foundation height above ground, and the provision of adequate drainage.

Inadequate initial bolt tightening and shrinkage have caused this split-ring connection to open and lose capacity. To restore capacity, the bolt should be tightened while the load on the connection is temporarily eased.

A hairline crack in this beam indicates a tension failure. Repair may be effected by the addition of splice plates designed to transfer load around the failed area of the beam.

LVL splice plates have been used to reinforce a failed beam, and connectors have been added to the column to support the wider beam.

Tension rods or angles have been used to strengthen inadequately designed truss members.

12.1   General Information

There are many examples in North America of wood buildings which remain in good condition after many decades and even centuries of service. In places like Scandinavia and Japan, there are examples of wood buildings which have endured for several centuries. This long service can be attributed to good designs matching the service conditions imposed on a building.

As for all building materials, problems can develop as a result of poor design details which do not suit original or revised service conditions imposed on a wood building such as structural overloading, or long term water infiltration leading to a decrease in structural integrity.

This chapter is of course not intended to depict wood as a problem prone structural material. Indeed, the ease with which wood can be worked facilitates any repairs if they are required. Rather, this chapter recognizes that some wood buildings will at some time require repair and therefore it is important for designers and inspectors to recognize problems and know how to alleviate them.

This is particularly true for buildings which are being renovated or extended, or where the occupancy of a building is going to result in increased loading conditions on the structural components.

12.2 Inspection

12.3 Repair and Upgrading

12

Inspection & Repair

12.2 Inspection

Introduction

All types of buildings should be inspected regularly if long term performance is to be ensured, and if expensive and extensive repairs are to be avoided. It will usually be cost beneficial to expend money on inspection and minor repair than to wait until problems become major before taking action.

When serviceability declines to the point where building problems are recognized by occupants or users, problems will be evidenced by such deficiencies as sagging floors, cracks in structural members or walls, or water leakage.

The recommended sequence for undertaking an inspection of a wood building which has been in service for a period of time is as follows:

- examine the exterior

- make a general inspection of the interior

- make a detailed inspection of the members and connections

Exterior Inspection

An examination of the general appearance and alignment of the building exterior can indicate the presence of structural problems. The following in particular should be checked:

- Examine the walls and eaves for plumb and straightness. If the walls on opposite sides of the building are leaning in the same direction, it may mean that the building is inadequately braced, and has moved due to wind or earthquake loading.

- The ridge of gable roofs should be examined for straightness and flat roofs should be checked for areas of ponding or sagging. Localized sagging may indicate the framing has failed or settled in the area of the sag. Although ponding may not result in breaching of the roof

membrane, it may result in loading conditions that overstress the roof structure, thereby compounding the ponding situation.

- Look for cracks in foundation walls, masonry walls, and brick veneer. Cracks may indicate settlement of the foundation and consequent dislocation of wood members and joints.

Identification of alignment problems on walls or roofs from the exterior will give an indication of areas of a building requiring special scrutiny during a detailed interior inspection.

General Inspection of Framing and Members

Using information from the exterior inspection as a starting point, a general inspection should be made of the interior seeking indications of structural distress or deterioration such as the following:

- sloping floors and cracked walls may indicate settlement of the foundations or local crushing of wood members at bearing points due to overstress or deterioration

- beams that have been shored are likely broken or overloaded

- sagging beams or trusses indicate overloading

- water staining or discolouration of the roof framing and framing around drains or plumbing fixtures may indicate water leakage and possibly the presence of decay

- deposits of wood shavings or sawdust may indicate that carpenter ants have nested in the wood framing

- small mud-like tubes, known as shelter tubes, running up a wall or along the face of wood members indicates the presence of termites

12

Inspection & Repair

Detailed Inspection

After assessing the general condition of a building, a detailed inspection of the framing members and connections should be made by examining the members and connections from close range. All areas of potential distress or deterioration should be evaluated.

When a building is changed to a new use, the floor loading may change and the load-carrying capacity of the structure must be assessed. Or, if damage to a member has taken place and the adequacy of the member must be reviewed, several factors must be examined in addition to the actual condition:

- Species:
  Different engineering properties, based on testing, are assigned to different species groups and therefore it is important to establish the wood species of the members under review. For older buildings, grade stamps will not be present. The inspector will have to identify the species in use by obtaining a small sample and referring to a wood technology reference book or seeking assistance from a wood technologist.

- Grade:
  Unless indicated by a grade stamp, grade cannot be determined except by a licensed lumber grader. Provincial grading associations can be contacted for the name of an individual who can make an *in situ* evaluation of lumber grades.

- Size and arrangement of members:
  The size and spacing of members must be determined to determine the distributed loading. Even if drawings are available, the structure should be sampled to see if it was constructed as indicated by the drawings.

- Condition:
  Members must be inspected to determine the amount of intact wood fibre remaining for supporting loads.

- Connections:
  Connections, particularly those in areas where dislocation is known to have taken place, must be inspected. Corrosion of the connectors, enlargement of bolt holes, and crushing or splitting of the lumber in the vicinity of the connection are conditions which should be checked.

The determination of the foregoing factors is of course simplified where framing is accessible from attics or crawl spaces. Where framing is concealed on both sides, a representative sample of the framing must be uncovered so that the variables controlling structural adequacy can be determined.

The following sections describe some problems which may be encountered and suggestions for rectifying them.

Decayed Members

Wood that is exposed to wet conditions may decay unless it has been treated with a preservative. Following are some areas where decay would most likely occur:

- In attics, condensation and subsequent decay can result from inadequate venting or vapour barriers. Decay of wood members in crawl spaces may be caused by inadequate venting or drainage.

- Wood beams, joists, or columns that are embedded or abutting masonry or concrete, especially near grade level, are areas of potential decay. High moisture content due to lack of ventilation or moisture absorption through the masonry or concrete can cause this deterioration.

- Unprotected beams or arch legs that extend outside the building are exposed to wetting and should be checked regularly. Areas of exposed end grain and connections that can hold water should be checked carefully, since these locations are extremely susceptible to decay.

- Water staining or discolourations of wood finishes on roof decks and around drains or plumbing fixtures can indicate the presence of leaks and possible deterioration. Areas where roofing has been replaced may indicate areas of past leakage and therefore the interior of the building at such locations should be examined for evidence of deterioration.

Any water stained members or members in high decay hazard areas as described above should be checked for decay. This may be done as follows:

- To check for surface decay, a sharp instrument should be used to pry the surface fibres. If they break brashly (a sharp cross break) without splintering, the wood is likely decayed.

- To check for internal decay, strike a member along its length with a hammer at regular intervals. A solid ring indicates that the wood is dry and sound, while a hollow or dead sound may indicate an internal rot pocket. After sounding, suspect areas of the member should be drilled using a small diameter auger bit. When the drill hits decayed wood, the shavings will be discoloured and wet. If the decay is old, it may be dry and powdery. In addition, the rate of penetration of the drill in decayed wood will be much greater than for sound wood.

- When a decay pocket is found, the full extent of the decay should be determined by coring a number of areas.

- The moisture content of the wood should be checked with a moisture meter. If the moisture content exceeds 20%, the decay is active.

To determine whether a member requires reinforcement, the load on the member must be compared to the load-carrying capacity of the remaining sound wood. At the ends of beams and the bases of columns, loss of up to 20% of the cross-section can usually be tolerated. At the mid-span of beams, however, a loss of 10% may be serious. In any case, analysis of member stress in relation to cross-section remaining should be made.

Typical repairs for decayed members are outlined in Section 12.3. In addition to undertaking repair, measures must be taken to ensure that further decay is prevented. Either the source of excess moisture must be found and halted, or the member must be replaced with wood material, namely preservative treated wood, which can tolerate high moisture conditions.

Carpenter Ant Damage

Carpenter ants are 7 to 20mm (1/4" to 3/4") long and black to red-brown in colour. They can cause severe structural damage to wood in service. Carpenter ants do not feed on wood, but they use it as a nest for the colony. Carpenter ant damage is usually not seen on the surface of the wood, since the ants generally gain access to the member through checks or other openings which results in large galleries close to the surface that are smooth walled and contain frass (wood debris). This wood material is not digested by the ants, but it is deposited outside the entrance to the nest. The discovery of these wood particles is the best indication of ant infestation.

If carpenter ants are discovered in a building, they can be eliminated by the use of an insecticide such as diazon, applied by a registered pesticide applicator. Slow acting ant bait formulations may also be effective in the control of ants, since they can be carried back to the nest and eventually eliminate the colony.

Carpenter ants prefer moist or wet wood that has softened by decay, or low density woods for their nests. The extent of structural damage may be determined by drilling and sounding members that are suspected of damage. Proper flashing and separation of untreated wood material away from the ground are measures that will reduce the incidence of infestation from the outset.

12

Inspection & Repair

Termite Damage

Only a few locations in Canada, such as southwestern Ontario, are warm enough to support termites.

Termites can attack sound, or decayed wood of all species. Active infestations will contain worker termites which are usually 5 to 7mm (3/16" to 1/4") long, white, and soft bodied. Termites usually travel in shelter tubes that they make from wood and soil. These passageways may be visible on the surface of wood members, foundation walls, or other locations, and are a certain indication of termite activity. However, in many cases these tubes are concealed in cracks or within wall cavities of masonry block foundation walls.

Termites leave no external sign of damage, and therefore infestation may not be detected until failure occurs, or by accident when renovation or other work is done. Their characteristic galleries are irregular in nature and are partially packed with mud and wood particles.

Since termites return to the soil colony frequently, the treatment of infested buildings commonly involves soil fumigation with an insecticide such as chlordane or aldrin applied by a registered pesticide applicator. The soil outside the structure and beneath basement and crawl spaces is treated by injecting the emulsion into holes. Other areas such as the hollows of concrete block foundations are also treated since the insects may gain access to the building framing through these locations.

Removal of all wood in soil contact should always accompany any treatment to eliminate the pathways of termite activity.

Evaluation of structural damage to wood members involves sounding and drilling to determine the amount of sound wood remaining using the same procedures described for Decayed Members (Pg. 404).

Fire Damaged Members

Large members damaged by fire have a layer of char at the surface and a core of solid wood. The thickness of the char layer will vary with severity. Unless the char layer is very thin, an engineer should evaluate the load-carrying capacity of the remaining sound wood. If the member is no longer adequate for the applied loads, reinforcement or replacement will be required.

To determine the amount of solid wood remaining, the char layer must be scraped away and the size of the unburnt core measured. Since the wood within 6mm (1/4") of the char layer has lost tensile strength due to exposure to high temperatures, the effective load-carrying section is considered to be the unburnt core less 6mm (1/4") (Figure 12.1).

Fire damaged glulam should be inspected by qualified personnel since it is important to determine which laminations have been damaged by fire. Loss of the high strength bottom lamination can result in a serious loss of load-carrying capacity. Also, the effect of the fire on the gluelines must also be evaluated.

Figure 12.1
Fire damage of wood members

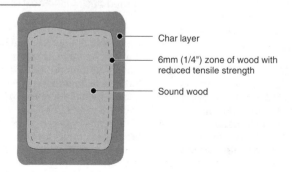

Char layer

6mm (1/4") zone of wood with reduced tensile strength

Sound wood

Checks and Splits in Sawn Timber

Checks and splits in existing sawn timbers should be related to the limits outlined in the National Lumber Grades Authority (NLGA) grading rules. If checks and splits exceed these limits, reinforcement will be necessary unless an analysis of the load-carrying capacity indicates that the defects are tolerable.

Checks and splits usually occur in the first year after the timber is installed and do not increase after this time period has elapsed.

Checking and Delamination in Glulam

Checking is generally only a problem at the ends of a beam, and small surface checks are usually not critical structurally. However, where the depth of the check exceeds 10 to 20% of the width of the beam, an engineer should investigate the load-carrying capacity.

Delaminations are much more serious than checks since they may indicate the presence of inadequate or deteriorated glue bonds between laminations. Although all Canadian glulam must be manufactured using waterproof glues, there may be some deficient glulam members originating from the 1960s which do not meet present standards for waterproof glues.

If weakening of the gluebonds is suspected, the shear strength of the gluebonds should be verified by testing circular plugs cut from the suspect area of the member. Delamination of glulam should be evaluated by a qualified timber engineer.

Radial Tension Failures in Curved Glulam

Splitting and checking along the haunches in glulam pitched tapered beams or tudor arches may indicate that the member has failed in radial tension (Figure 12.2). Radial tension (tensile stresses perpendicular to the grain) occurs in curved members when loaded so that the curvature of the member decreases.

When radial tension failures are discovered, the capacity of the arch or beam should be analyzed by a qualified timber engineer.

Alignment of Trusses and Arches

Arches and trusses should be visually examined to ensure they are plumb and straight. Any misalignment of the top chord of trusses should be taken seriously since it indicates that the top chords are inadequately braced and in the process of buckling. With arches, waviness of either the top or bottom edge could indicate buckling.

Trusses should be examined for sag. This may be done visually by looking along the bottom edge of the member. For large trusses, the amount of sag may be quantified by measuring the difference in elevation between the end of the truss and the centreline with a surveyor's level. Excessive sag often indicates that a member or connection has failed.

Mechanical Damage to Columns

Mechanical damage to columns in areas of vehicular traffic may result from impact by forklifts or other mechanical equipment. As a result, the columns may be reduced in cross-sectional area. A loss of up to 20% in the lower portion may be tolerable. However, measures should be taken to protect the column from further damage by building up the section, and providing a protective covering.

Sagging or Broken Beams

Beams should be examined for sag. This may be done by looking along the length of the member at the bottom edge. When the beam is not loaded, sag should not be noticeable by eye. Noticeable sag may indicate that the beam has been or is overloaded.

Beams that have broken in flexure have cracks perpendicular to the grain in the middle third of the span (Figure 12.3). A beam with a long split at one end may

12

Inspection & Repair

Figure 12.2
Radial tension failures in curved glulam

Arch

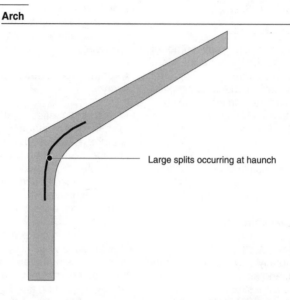

Large splits occurring at haunch

Pitched-tapered beam

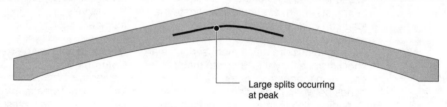

Large splits occurring at peak

Figure 12.3
Broken beams

Bending failure

Bending failure

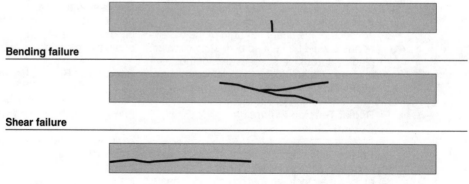

Shear failure

Shear failure at notch

have failed in shear. In this case the split will be at mid depth and the top and bottom portions of the beam will be displaced slightly.

Sagging or broken beams should be shored immediately, and reinforced as soon as possible.

Excessive Notches in Beams and Purlins

Unauthorized notches or holes may have been made in wood members to accommodate services and duct work. Notches at the mid-span of beams cause a serious reduction in capacity and the member should be reinforced. Holes less than 1/4 of the depth of the member are generally acceptable if they are located at mid depth.

Purlins are sometimes notched near the bearing, and as a result develop long splits in the members (Figure 12.3). The splits should be considered as shear failures and should be reinforced. Notches in purlins greater than 1/4 of the depth cause a serious reduction in shear strength and the beam should be reinforced.

Shear Failures at Heel Connections of Rod-and-Block Trusses

Heavy timber rod-and-block trusses were often built with the bottom chord notched to accommodate the top chord at the heel. This notch is the main connection for the transfer of load from the top to the bottom chord in these old types of structures. The thrust from the top chord caused the block of wood beyond the notch to shear off the bottom chord (Figure 12.4) which causes the truss to sag and could lead to a total failure.

Where this shear damage to the bottom chord has occurred, the truss should be shored immediately, and the connection reinforced as soon as possible.

Broken Truss Members

Bottom chord members and tension web members may break due to overstress. Often the failure will occur through the connection where the area of the member is reduced due to the fastener holes. This will cause the truss to sag and could lead to a complete collapse. Therefore, trusses with broken webs or bottom chords should be shored immediately and repaired as soon as possible.

Figure 12.4
Rod-and-block trusses – shear failure at heel connection

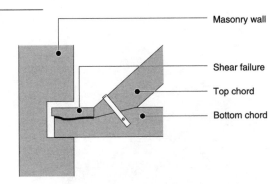

Masonry wall

Shear failure

Top chord

Bottom chord

12

Inspection & Repair

Connection Failures

Connections may fail by crushing of the wood around the bolt or connector. This will cause the joint to relax. This type of failure may be hidden by the side plates; however, the displacement of the side plate is often noticeable since the colour of the wood below the plate will be different than the exposed wood.

Plug failures occur in shear plate and split ring connections that have been over-stressed in tension. In a typical plug failure, the wood around the connector shears off along the grain and protrudes from the end of the member. The plug may be an I or T shape (Figure 12.5). Connections with plug failures should be reinforced as soon as possible.

Splits Through Connections

Splits which pass directly through a fastener or line of fasteners can seriously reduce the capacity of a tension connection. Splits between fastener groups are not usually a problem.

The load-carrying capacity of split connections should be checked by an engineer, and should be reinforced if required.

Gaps at Connections

Gaps between wood members at connections can occur in a number of locations in heavy timber trusses.

In old rod-and-block trusses, gaps are sometimes found between the ends of compression webs and the chord member (Figure 12.6). These may occur if the truss has sagged or if the truss members have experienced significant shrinkage. These web members require full bearing for the truss to be effective; therefore, the truss should be shored and the rods and connections should be tightened, or alternatively, the gaps can be shimmed.

Gaps are sometimes observed between truss chord members at a splice. Gaps between top chord members should be shimmed to bring the member ends into full bearing, unless there are sufficient fasteners to transfer the compressive force. Gaps between bottom chord members are acceptable, but the openings must be inspected for the presence of plug failures.

Gaps can also occur between the faces of web and chord members in trusses. These gaps can seriously reduce the capacity of the connection, particularly where split rings or shear plates are used.

Figure 12.5
Plug failure in a timber-connected joint

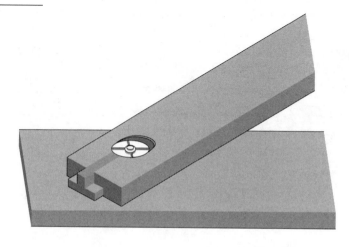

Figure 12.6
**Gaps in rod-
and-block
timber trusses**

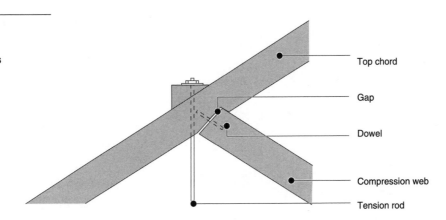

Top chord

Gap

Dowel

Compression web

Tension rod

Often the gap is due to shrinkage, and can be rectified by tightening the bolts. However, if the gap is due to improper grooving for the shear plate or split ring, tightening will not close the gap. In this case, the connection will have to be reinforced unless an analysis indicates that the connection has sufficient load-carrying capacity despite the gap.

Missing Fasteners and Incorrect Connector Installation

Sometimes fasteners are omitted from connections or they are incorrectly installed during erection. This condition may not be noticed until excessive deflection occurs or until the connections are checked during an inspection.

The absence of split rings and shear plates may not be readily noticed since they are not visible on the exterior of the connection. A feeler gauge can usually be used to probe between the two members to determine if the connectors are present. If the members are too closely mated for a feeler gauge, a small diameter drill hole drilled along the member intersection can be used to detect the presence of the rings and plates.

Fasteners can also be installed incorrectly. For example, in some instances, timber connectors have been installed beneath the washers instead of between the two pieces being joined, or glulam rivets have been installed incorrectly with the long axis of the head perpendicular to the grain (the head should always be parallel to the grain).

Missing fasteners should be installed, or the joint should be reinforced. Reinforcement is usually necessary for incorrectly installed rivets, split rings or shear plates. Bolted connections should be always be checked for tightness and tightened where necessary.

12

Inspection & Repair

12.3   Repair and Upgrading

Introduction

The repair and upgrading of defective or deteriorated wood components and connections should be engineered. The following suggestions for repairs should be confirmed by an engineer to suit particular applications. A number of the details may be used to increase existing wood framing or members for heavier loadings.

Defective Beams

Beams that are broken, deteriorated, or undersized may be reinforced by adding new members (Figure 12.7). The new members may be structural composite lumber (LVL and PSL), lumber, or steel plates or channels. The new members should be bolted to the existing beam at regular intervals and be connected to the supports at each end. Where the beam connects to a column, new support brackets or bolsters may be required to support the larger width of the augmented members. Where the beam frames into a masonry or concrete wall, the wall pocket may be widened to accommodate the new members.

Prior to adding the new members, the existing beam should be jacked back into its proper position.

Figure 12.7
Repair for broken bending members

Elevation

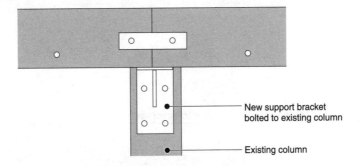

New support bracket bolted to existing column

Existing column

Plan view

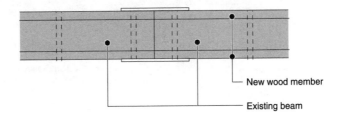

New wood member

Existing beam

Checked or Delaminated Glulam

Where reinforcing is necessary, checked or delaminated beams may be reinforced by using shear dowels secured by epoxy adhesive, or by the addition of riveted side plates (Figure 12.8).

To effect this repair, holes are drilled vertically in the beam and the shear dowels are inserted into the holes which have been liberally coated with epoxy. The dowels may be added from the top or the bottom of the beam. When installed in an area of a member where appearance is important, the holes may be covered with a wood plug to match the appearance of the glulam.

The riveted side plate repair consists of fastening steel plates into the sides of the defective beam with glulam rivets. The plates are oriented diagonally and the beam, in combination with the plates, is then considered to behave like a truss.

Figure 12.8
Shear reinforcement of checked or delaminated glulam beams

Epoxy dowel shear reinforcement

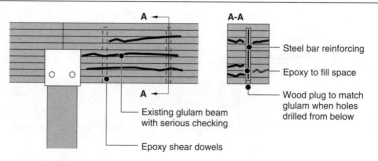

Steel bar reinforcing

Epoxy to fill space

Wood plug to match glulam when holes drilled from below

Existing glulam beam with serious checking

Epoxy shear dowels

Riveted side plate shear reinforcement

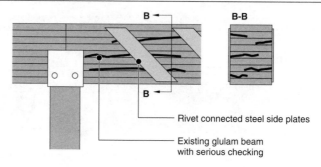

Rivet connected steel side plates

Existing glulam beam with serious checking

Radial Tension Cracks in Glulam

This problem can be repaired by installing bolts with spring washers at one end (Figure 12.9) vertically through the member. The spring washers allow the wood to expand or contract with changes in moisture content without loosening the bolts. The bolts are countersunk into the member, and the visible holes may be covered with wood plugs to match the appearance of the existing glulam.

Figure 12.9
Repair of radial tension failures

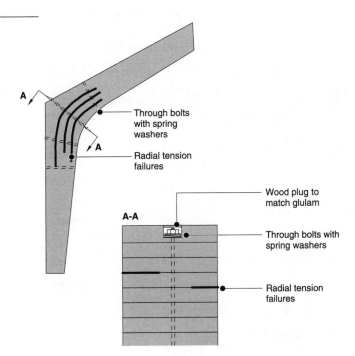

Through bolts with spring washers

Radial tension failures

Wood plug to match glulam

A-A

Through bolts with spring washers

Radial tension failures

12

Inspection & Repair

Decayed Column Bases

Columns with serious deterioration at the base may be repaired by cutting off the decayed area and supporting the cut end on a new steel base (Figure 12.10). A bed of epoxy grout should be added below the column to assure level bearing. Prior to carrying out the repairs, the truss or beam on top of the column must be shored.

Figure 12.10
**Repair for
decayed
column end**

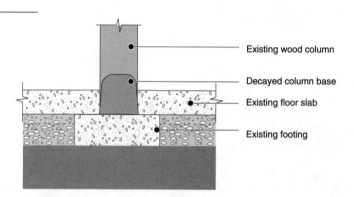

Existing wood column

Decayed column base

Existing floor slab

Existing footing

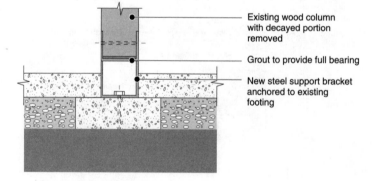

Existing wood column
with decayed portion
removed

Grout to provide full bearing

New steel support bracket
anchored to existing
footing

Decayed Arch Legs

Legs of arches that extend through the exterior walls are very susceptible to decay and insect attack. If the decay is confined to a small area at the base, it is possible to excavate the decay and fill the void with epoxy grout.

Where the decay or insect damage extends up the leg, it should be reinforced by adding new wood or steel members to each side of the arch (Figure 12.11). The upper end of the new members are connected to the existing sound wood by means of shear plates or split rings. The lower end of the new member is supported on the existing concrete pier.

In addition, the leg should be protected from the weather with flashing, and greater clearance from the ground should be provided by adding a drainage well around the pier.

Figure 12.11
Repair for decay at arch heels

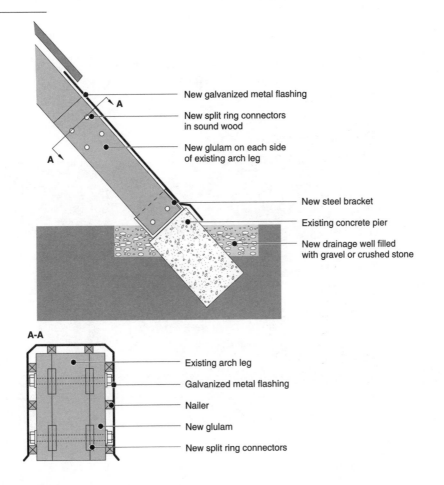

New galvanized metal flashing

New split ring connectors in sound wood

New glulam on each side of existing arch leg

New steel bracket

Existing concrete pier

New drainage well filled with gravel or crushed stone

A-A

Existing arch leg

Galvanized metal flashing

Nailer

New glulam

New split ring connectors

12

Inspection & Repair

Overstressed or Defective Heavy Truss Connections

Glulam gussets may be used to reinforce the connections of heavy trusses that have pairs of webs connected to the face of the chord (Figure 12.12). The glulam gusset is inserted between the web members and must be the same size as the chord. New shear plates are used to connect the existing webs to the new glulam gusset. The gusset is clamped to the existing chord with steel rods and bearing plates. Brackets are also fastened at either end of the new gusset.

Defective Tension Webs

Tension webs in trusses can be replaced with a new member or can be reinforced by adding steel rods on each side of the truss. The rods are fastened to bearing plates above the top chord and below the bottom chord (Figure 12.13).

Figure 12.12
Reinforcement of over-stressed connections

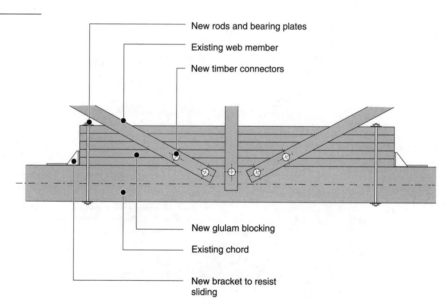

New rods and bearing plates

Existing web member

New timber connectors

New glulam blocking

Existing chord

New bracket to resist sliding

Figure 12.13
Reinforcement for broken tension web or failed connection

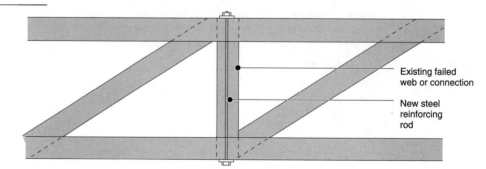

Existing failed web or connection

New steel reinforcing rod

Overstressed Trusses

Heavy trusses with overstressed bottom chords can be reinforced by adding post tension strands (Figure 12.14). The strands are connected to a bearing plate at the ends of the top chord and wrap around two bottom chord panel points. The strand is pulled from one end until the desired level of tension is attained. The tension causes an upward force at the bottom chord panel points, which partially relieves the stress in the bottom chord and reduces the load on the connections at the end panels.

Figure 12.14
Repair of timber trusses by post-tensioning

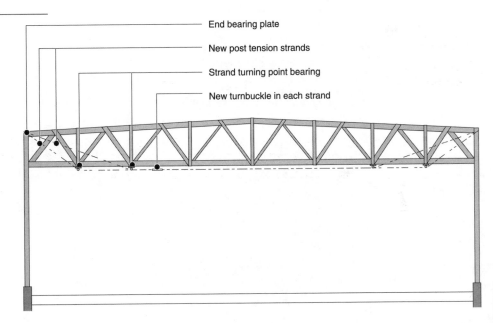

End bearing plate

New post tension strands

Strand turning point bearing

New turnbuckle in each strand

References

1. *New Life for Old Dwellings,* Gerald E.
   Sherwood, Forest Products Laboratory,
   US Department of Agriculture, 1975

2. *Reinforcement of Structural Wood
   Members,* T. Szabo, Eastern Forest
   Products Laboratory, Ottawa, ON, 1975

3. *Restoration of Existing Buildings –
   Arena Structures,*
   Canadian Society of Civil Engineers
   Ontario Chapter, 1977

4. *Structural Repair of Deteriorated
   Timber,* Paul Stumes,
   Association for Preservation
   Technology, Ottawa, ON, 1979

5. *Structural Uses of Wood in Adverse
   Environments,* Robert W. Meyer and
   Robert M. Kellogg,
   Society of Wood Science and
   Technology, Van Nostrand Reinhold,
   Scarborough, ON, 1982

Appendix

Information Sources

There are many specialist groups in Canada and the United States which offer technical information and assistance on the use of wood and wood products in building construction.

If you have a technical enquiry and are not sure who to contact, call the Canadian Wood Council.

Architectural Woodwork

Architectural Woodwork Manufacturers Association of Canada (AWMAC)
P.O. Box 5244
High River, AB T1V 1M4
Telephone: (403)652-3666
Fax: (403)652-7384

Construction Information

National Research Council
Institute for Research in Construction
Montreal Road, Building M-24
Ottawa, ON K1A 0R6
Telephone: (613) 993-2607
Fax: (613) 941-0822
(*Also* Canadian Construction Materials Centre)

Housing Information

Canada Mortgage and Housing Corporation
700 Montreal Road
Ottawa, ON K1A 0P7
Telephone: (613) 748-2000
Fax: (613) 748-6192

Doors, Windows, Mouldings

Canadian Window and Door Manufacturers Association
27 Goulburn Avenue
Ottawa, ON K1N 8C7
Telephone: (613) 233-6205
Fax: (613) 233-1929

L'Association provinciale de l'industrie de bois d'œuvre du Québec, Inc.
2095 Jean-Talon sud, bureau 220
Ste-Foy, QC J1N 4L8
Telephone: (418) 688-1256
Fax: (418) 688-2460

Fire Standards

Underwriters' Laboratories of Canada (ULC)
7 Crouse Road
Scarborough, ON M1R 3A9
Telephone: (416) 757-3611
Fax: (416) 757-9540

Lumber

American Forest & Paper Association
800, 111 – 19th street NW
Washington, DC 20036
Telephone: (202) 463-2700
Fax: (202) 463-2785

Canadian Lumbermen's Association
27 Goulburn Avenue
Ottawa, ON K1N 8C7
Telephone: (613) 233-6205
Fax: (613) 233-1929

Cariboo Lumber Manufacturers Association(CLMA)
205 - 197 Second Avenue North
Williams Lake, BC V2G 1Z5
Telephone: (250) 392-7778
Fax: (250) 392-4691

Central Forest Products Association Inc. (CFPA)
P.O. Box 1169
Hudson Bay, SK S0E 0Y0
Telephone: (306) 865-2595
Fax: (306) 865-3302

Coast Forest & Lumber Association
1100, 555 Burrard Street
Vancouver, BC V7X 1S7
Telephone: (604) 891-1237
Fax: (604) 682-8641

Interior Lumber Manufacturers Association (ILMA)
360 - 1855 Kirschner Road
Kelowna, BC V1Y 4N7
Telephone: (250) 860-9663
Fax: (250) 860-0009

L'Association des manufacturiers de bois de sciage du Québec (Québec Lumber Manufacturers Association)
200 – 5055 boulevard Hamel ouest
Québec, QC G2E 2G6
Telephone: (418) 872-5610
Fax: (418) 872-3062

Northern Forest Products Association
400, 1488 Fourth Avenue
Prince George, BC V2L 4Y2
Telephone: (604) 564-5136
Fax: (604) 564-3588

Maritime Lumber Bureau (MLB)
(Bureau du bois de sciage des Maritimes)
P.O. Box 459
Amherst, NS B4H 4A1
Telephone: (902) 667-3889
Fax: (902) 667-0401

Ontario Lumber Manufacturers
Association(LMA)
(Association des manufacturiers de bois de
sciage de l'Ontario)
325 - 55 University Avenue
P.O. Box 8
Toronto, ON M5J 2H7
Telephone: (416) 367-9717
Fax: (416) 362-3641

Lumber Grading

Canadian Lumber Standards
Accreditation Board (CLS)
406 - First Capital Place
960 Quayside Drive
New Westminster, BC V3M 6G2
Telephone: (604) 524-2338
Fax: (604) 524-6932

National Lumber Grades Authority (NLGA)
406 - First Capital Place
960 Quayside Drive
New Westminster, BC V3M 6G2
Telephone: (604) 524-2393
Fax: (604) 524-2893

Lumber, Plywood, Consumer Information

Council of Forest Industries of British
Columbia (COFI)
1200 - 555 Burrard Street
Vancouver, BC V7X 1S7
Telephone: (604) 684-0211
Fax: (604) 687-4930

Material and Design Standards

Canadian Standards Association (CSA)
178 Rexdale Boulevard
Etobicoke, ON M9W 1R3
Telephone: (416) 747-4000
Fax: (416) 747-4149

American Society for Testing and
Materials (ASTM)
100 Barr Harbour Drive
West Conshocken, PA 19428
Telephone: (610) 832-9500
Fax: (610) 832-9555

OSB, Waferboard

Structural Board Association (SBA)
412 - 45 Sheppard Avenue East
Willowdale, ON M2N 5W9
Telephone: (416) 730-9090
Fax: (416) 730-9013

Particleboard

Composite Panel Association
4612 St-Catherine Street West
Westmount, QC H3Z 1S3
Telephone: (514) 989-1002
Fax: (514) 989-9318

Plywood (hardwood)

Canadian Hardwood Plywood
Association (CHPA)
27 Goulburn Avenue
Ottawa, ON K1N 8C7
Telephone: (613) 233-6205
Fax: (613) 233-1929

Plywood (softwood)

Canadian Plywood Association (CanPly)
735 West 15th Street
North Vancouver, BC V7M 1T2
Telephone: (604) 981-4190
Fax: (604) 985-0342

Residential Building

Canadian Home Builders Association
(CHBA)
200 - 150 Laurier Avenue West
Ottawa, ON K1P 5J4
Telephone: (613) 230-3060
Fax: (613) 232-4635

Shingles and Shakes

B.C. Shake and Shingle Association
9414-A 288 Street
Maple Ridge, BC V2X 8Y6
Telephone: (604) 462-8961
Fax: (604) 462-9386

Cedar Shake & Shingle Bureau
515 - 116th Ave. NE
Suite 275
Bellevue, WA 98004
Telephone: (425) 453-1323
Fax: (425) 455-1314

Treated Wood, Certification and Inspection

Canadian Wood Preservers Bureau
c/o CITW
200-2430 Don Reid Drive
Ottawa, ON K1H 8P5
Telephone: (613)737-4337

Treated Wood, Consumer Information

Canadian Institute of Treated Wood (CITW)
(Institut Canadien des bois traités)
2141 Thurston Drive,
Suite 202
Ottawa, ON K1G 6C9
Telephone: (613) 737-4337
Fax: (613) 247-0540

Truss Plates, Trusses

Truss Plate Institute of Canada (TPIC)
c/o Jager Industries
21 Rodinea Road, Unit #1
Maple, ON L6A 1R3
Telephone: (905) 832-7070
Fax: (905) 832-2620

Canadian Wood Truss Association
1400 Blair Place, Suite 210
Ottawa, ON K1J 9B8
Telephone: (613) 747-5544
Fax: (613) 747-6264

Wood Products

Q-Web
540-979 de Bourgogne
Ste-Foy, QC G1W 2L4
Telephone: (418) 650-2424
Fax: (418) 650-9011

Canadian Lumbermen's Association (CLA)
(Association canadienne de l'industrie du bois)
27 Goulbourn Avenue
Ottawa, ON K1N 8C7
Telephone: (613) 233-6205
Fax: (613) 233-1929

Wood Products: Consumer Information, Codes & Standards, Wood Engineering

Canadian Wood Council
1400 Blair Place, Suite 210
Ottawa, ON K1J 9B8
Telephone: (613) 747-5544
Fax: (613) 747-6264

Photo Information

Page	Designer	Photographer	Location	Subject
5	Hancock Nicolson Tamaki Architects Inc.	Image West	Vancouver, BC	residence
6 *(top)*	Walter Francl Architect Inc.	Brad Lamoureux	Blaine, WA	residence
6 *(btm l)*	Zeidler Roberts Partnership/ Architects	Spalding Associates	Muskoka, ON	residence
6 *(btm r)*	Ken Cartier	Jim Hall, Hallmark Photo	Dewinton, AB	residence
7 *(top)*	Jenkins & Sturgess Architects	Ray VanNess	Calgary, AB	residence
7 *(btm)*	Paul Merrick Architects Ltd.	Danny Singer	West Vancouver, BC	residence
8 *(top)*	Dan S. Hanganu, Architect	John W. Webb	Mont-Tremblant, QC	condominiums
8 *(cen l)*	Baker McGarva Architecture	Susan Baker	Campbell River, BC	condominiums
9 *(top)*	Baker McGarva Architecture	Susan Baker	Campbell River, BC	condominiums
9 *(btm)*	Brian Bydwell, Jan Timmer	not known	Vancouver, BC	apartment
10 *(top, btm l)*	Dalla-Lana/Griffin Architects	Dalla-Lana/ Griffin Architects	Armstrong, BC	hospital
10 *(btm r)*	Schmidt Feldberg Croll Henderson	Y. Dubourdieu	Edmonton, AB	medical clinic
11 *(top)*	Schmidt Feldberg Croll Henderson	Y. Dubourdieu	Edmonton, AB	medical clinic
11 *(btm)*	Dalla-Lana/Griffin Architects	Dalla-Lana/ Griffin Architects	Armstrong, BC	hospital
12 *(top)*	not known	Robert Gallant	Kelowna, BC	restaurant
12 *(btm)*	Henry Hawthorn Architect Ltd.	Roger Brooks	Richmond, BC	boardwalk shops
13	TRA Architecture	Richard Cooke	Eugene, OR	passenger terminal
14 *(top)*	The Hulbert Group BC Ltd	Rick Etkin Photographs	Vancouver, BC	research offices
14 *(btm)*	Dalla-Lana/Griffin Architects	Scott Alpen	Vancouver, BC	film studio offices

Page	Designer	Photographer	Location	Subject
15 *(top)*	B+H Martin Consultants	Claude Gagnon	Timmins, ON	office
15 *(btm)*	Henry Hawthorne	Garry Otte	Vancouver, BC	office building
16 *(top)*	Dalla-Lana/Griffin Architects	Roger Brooks	Whistler, BC	school
16 *(cen l)*	Howard/Yano Architects	Destrube Photography	Courtenay, BC	college
16 *(cen r)*	Ala Kantti Woodman Architects Inc.	Mike Pinder Photography	Kemptville, ON	school
16 *(btm)*	George Robb, Architect	William Santillo	King City, ON	school
17 *(top)*	Koliger Schmidt architect•engineer	Koliger Schmidt architect•engineer	Kikino, AB	school
17 *(btm l)*	George Robb, Architect	William Santillo	King City, ON	school
17 *(btm r)*	Hughes Baldwin Architects	Bob Matheson & Roger Hughes	Saanich, BC	school gym
18 *(top)*	Ihor Stecura	Roman Stecura	Niagara Falls, ON	church
18 *(btm)*	Howard Funk Architect	Francis Peters	Winnipeg, MB	church
19 *(top r, btm)*	Howard Funk Architect	Francis Peters	Winnipeg, MB	church
20 *(top)*	B+H Martin Consultants	Claude Gagnon	Timmins, ON	lumber mill
20 *(btm)*	Culham Pedersen & Valentine Architects and Engineers	Malak	Calgary, AB	refrigeration plant
21 *(top)*	Western Archrib	Scott Alpen	Vancouver, BC	potash storage
21 *(btm)*	Kilborn Engineering	Malak	Saint John, NB	storage building
22 *(top)*	Cohos, Evamy Partners	Malak	Mount Allan, AB	ski lodge
22 *(btm)*	Les Architectes Reeves et Associés	Yves Lefebvre	Montréal, QC	beach pavillion
23 *(top)*	CJC Architects Inc	Malak	Canmore, AB	ski lodge
23 *(btm l)*	Barry Johns Architects	James Dow	Camrose, AB	high school
23 *(btm r)*	Lubor Trubka Architect	Peter Powles	Surrey, BC	arena

Index

Notes

Notes